Engineering Mechanics Statics

ENGINEERING MECHANICS Statics

D. K. Anand

P. F. Cunniff

University of Maryland
College Park

Houghton Mifflin Company / Boston

Atlanta / Dallas / Geneva, Illinois
Hopewell, New Jersey / Palo Alto

Library of Congress Catalog Card Number
Engineering Mechanics: Statics 72-6701
Engineering Mechanics: Dynamics 72-5646
Engineering Mechanics: Statics and Dynamics 72-11073

ISBN
Engineering Mechanics: Statics 0-395-14210-5
Engineering Mechanics: Dynamics 0-395-14209-1-X
Engineering Mechanics: Statics and Dynamics 0-395-14208-3

To our parents   Shanti Devi Anand   Della Josephine Cunniff
                  Anant Ram Anand   Martin Joseph Cunniff

Preface

This book is the first of a two-volume *Statics–Dynamics* set. Why should another such set be added to the many already available? We feel that the justification for these books lies in the pedagogy of the development of the subject matter. The basic format facilitates self study, and to help the student, each chapter has a summary of the important ideas as well as the important equations.

Chapter 1 reviews vectors and the fundamental laws useful for the study of statics. The concept of force and couple is introduced in Chapter 2, where we also consider the equilibrium of a particle. The equilibrium of rigid bodies is then covered in Chapter 3. Although two- as well as three-dimensional equilibrium is considered, stress is placed on the former, since the salient points can be grasped without introducing algebraic complexity. The equilibrium of structures and frames constitute Chapter 4. Here we have omitted a lengthy discussion of Maxwell's diagram, since it involves no new concept and is rarely used in practice.

Centroids and distributed loads are considered in Chapter 5. In section 5.2 a brief introduction to integration is included without any attempt at mathematical rigor. This section serves not only as a good review but also as an adequate introduction to integration for those who have not studied it yet. In our experience, students have found this section of considerable help. In this chapter we also include a brief discussion of the cable. Following up on the concept of the first moment, we introduce moments of area and mass in Chapter 6. Here we have deliberately suppressed a lengthy discussion of three-dimensional integration procedures. We have placed moments of area and mass earlier in this book to insure that the student is exposed to the concept of inertia before studying dynamics.

All of Chapter 7 is devoted to beam analysis. Friction is then treated in Chapter 8. We have not included fluid friction, since lack of time does not permit its inclusion in a statics course. The concept of virtual work is introduced in Chapter 9. We believe that it is important to include this chapter in *Statics* for two reasons. First, it provides an alternate method of deriving equations of static equilibrium, and second, it serves as a logical introduction to more advanced problems.

The material in this book has been used in our classes at the University of Maryland. To those students who used it and made many suggestions, we are very grateful. The final manuscript was reviewed by Professors J. Rossettos, S. Dharmarajan, and E. H. Ford, whom we gratefully acknowledge. The assistance of Mr. R. Root, who reviewed the entire manuscript and the problems, was most valuable. Special thanks are due to Mary Jane O'Neill, who patiently and expertly typed the manuscript.

Contents

Chapter 1
Basic
Concepts

An historical development of the subject of statics is traced from early civilization to the present day. Some definitions and laws fundamental to our study are presented, along with a review of vectors and vector algebra. The importance of units and dimension is included, as well as some recommended procedures for solving problems in engineering mechanics.

1.1 Introduction

Mechanics is the science that deals with both stationary and moving bodies under the action of forces. Theoretical mechanics is generally the concern of physicists and applied mathematicians; engineering mechanics is of interest to engineers. The study of mechanics is generally categorized into a study of the mechanics of fluids, the mechanics of bodies that deform, and the mechanics of rigid bodies. Here, we are concerned with the mechanics of rigid bodies.

The mechanics of rigid bodies may be considered to consist of two parts, statics and dynamics. Statics treats the equilibrium of stationary bodies under the influence of various kinds of forces. Dynamics, on the other hand, includes the motion of bodies and the forces that cause it. This volume is primarily concerned with the statics of rigid bodies, while dynamics will be explored in the next volume.

1.2 Historical Perspective

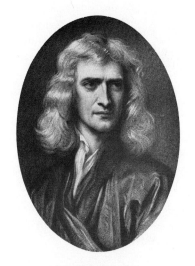

Sir Isaac Newton

Mechanics is among the oldest physical sciences. Interest in mechanical problems goes back to the time of Aristotle (384–322 B.C.). The lever fulcrum, as well as the theory of buoyancy, was explained by Archimedes (287–212 B.C.). After that there were few developments until, in the fifteenth century A.D., Leonardo da Vinci (1452–1519) continued Archimedes' work on levers and deduced the concept of moments as they apply to the equilibrium of bodies. Next, the laws of equilibrium and the parallelogram law were developed by Stevinus (1548–1620). Then Descartes (1596–1650) evolved the idea of virtual work, which is an extremely important concept in the formulation of advanced mechanical problems. Pascal (1623–1662), by means of the concept of virtual displacements, analytically established the direction of the propagation of stresses.

Despite the many important contributions made to mechanics before him, Newton's (1642–1727) three famous laws and his law of universal gravitation were perhaps the most important step in the progress of mechanics. Newton's work, based on geometry, was extended to rigid body systems by Euler (1707–1783), whose work was based on calculus. At about this time, much of the work in mechanics was reformulated by Lagrange (1736–1813), whose analytical approach was based on concepts of energy.

There are many other contributors whose works are notable. Varignon (1654–1722) related the moment of a force to its components. D'Alembert, Hamilton, Routh, and many more have made important contributions.

1.3 Fundamental Concepts

The concepts fundamental to a study of mechanics are those of space, time, inertia, and force.

Space By space we mean a geometric region in which physical events occur. It can have one, two, or three dimensions. Or, more than three dimensions can be conceptualized. Here we shall be concerned with, at most, three-dimensional space. Position in space is ascertained relative to some reference system. The basic reference system necessary for Newtonian mechanics is one that is considered fixed in space. Measurements relative to this system are considered as absolute.

Time Essentially a measure of the orderly succession of events occurring in space, time is considered as an absolute quantity. The unit of time is a *second,* which was originally related directly to the earth's rate of spin. Today, the standard of time is established by the frequency of oscillation of a cesium atom.

Inertia The ability of a body to resist a change in motion is called inertia.

Mass The mass of a body is a quantitative measure of its inertia.

Force A force is the action of one body on another. This action may exist due to contact between the bodies, which is called the push-pull effect; or this action may exist with the bodies apart, which is called the field-of-force effect.

Particle If the dimensions of a body are treated as negligible, the body is said to be a particle. Thus, the mass of a particle is concentrated at a point, and a particle is sometimes called a mass point.

Rigid Body A rigid body is characterized by the condition that any two points of the body remain at a fixed distance relative to each other for all time.

1.4 Some Fundamental Laws

The study of statics derives from several fundamental laws, the most important of which were expounded by Sir Isaac Newton in 1687.

Newton's Laws

I. Every particle remains at rest or continues to move in a straight line with a uniform motion if there is no unbalanced force acting upon it.

II. The time rate of change of the linear momentum of a particle is proportional to the unbalanced force acting upon it and occurs in the direction in which the force acts.

III. To every action there is an equal and opposite reaction. The mutual forces of two bodies acting upon each other are equal in magnitude and opposite in direction.

These laws have been verified experimentally over the years. It is important to realize that the first two laws hold for measurements made in a fixed reference frame. The problems of statics are primarily concerned with the first and third laws.

Newton also formulated the *law of gravitation* which governs the mutual attraction between two isolated bodies. This law is expressed mathematically as

$$F = G \frac{m_1 m_2}{r^2}$$

where

$F =$ mutual force of attraction between the two bodies

$G =$ universal gravitational constant

$m_1, m_2 =$ masses of the bodies

$r =$ distance between the centers of the bodies

The mutual forces between the two bodies obey Newton's third law so that they are equal in magnitude and opposite in direction along the line of centers joining the two bodies.

The Parallelogram Law

Two forces acting on a particle can be replaced by a resultant force which is the diagonal of a parallelogram that has sides equal to the two given forces.

The Principle of Transmissibility

If a force acting on a body at a given point is replaced by another force acting at a different point but having the same direction and line of action, then the equilibrium of the body is unchanged.

The next chapter will have more to say about the last two laws.

1.5 Vectors

Historically, much of the early work in statics was done via geometrical concepts. Later, many of the laws and equations were derived using calculus. In a modern study of statics it is desirable that we employ a symbology that is concise, simple, and complete. Such a symbology is to be found in vectors and vector mathematics.† When either a physical law or a mathematical operation is expressed in vector notation, it is independent of the coordinate axes. This property is quite important, especially in dynamics. In this section, we shall consider some basic fundamentals of vectors. We shall assume that the laws and mathematical operations are conducted in Euclidean space.

A *vector* is a variable that has two properties, magnitude and direction. These properties have no connection with any particular coordinate system. If a variable has magnitude but no direction, it is called a *scalar*. A vector shall be denoted by **V, A,** etc. having magnitude V, A, etc. Some sample vectors

†Originally introduced at the end of the nineteenth century by J. W. Gibbs and O. Heaviside.

are shown in Figure 1.1. The velocity of a car is an example of a vector since we must know the speed of the car as well as

Figure 1.1

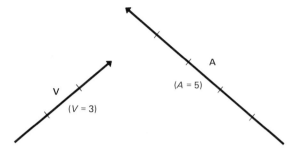

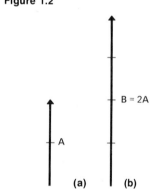

Figure 1.2

the direction in which it is proceeding. The force applied to a body is also a vector, as shown in Figure 1.2. Here a force is being applied at an angle θ to the horizontal.

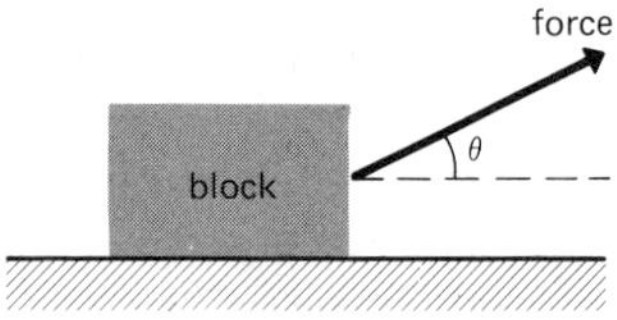

A vector **A** may be multiplied by a scalar without affecting its direction. Thus, if the vector **A** shown in Figure 1.3a is multiplied by 2, we obtain the vector **B** shown in Figure 1.3b whose magnitude is twice that of vector **A** and whose direction is the same as **A**. This suggests that we express a vector as consisting of a magnitude and a direction. This is most conveniently done by introducing a *unit vector* whose magnitude is unity and whose direction lies along the direction of the represented vector. Thus,

$$\mathbf{A} = A\mathbf{e}_A \qquad (1.1)$$

Figure 1.3

is a vector of magnitude A in the direction of unit vector $\mathbf{e}_A$. The symbol **e** will therefore be used for unit vectors along with an appropriate subscript. Thus, the vectors in Figure 1.1 are represented by unit vectors as shown in Figure 1.4. Unit

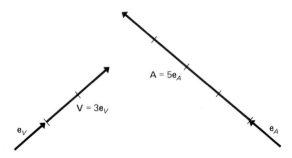

Figure 1.4

vectors associated with cartesian coordinates X, Y, Z are

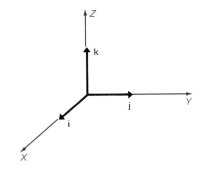

Figure 1.5

shown in Figure 1.5 by the conventional unit vectors **i**, **j**, **k**. A vector having a magnitude 5 in the X direction is written as **5i**. A vector having a magnitude of 6 in the Y direction is written as **6j**.

Vector Combination

Two vectors are defined to be equal if they have the same magnitude *and* the same direction. The sum of two vectors can be obtained by the parallelogram law or the triangle law of addition of vectors. This is shown in Figure 1.6. Since the

Figure 1.6

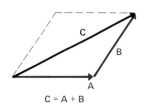

result is independent of the order of vector addition, we say that vector addition is *commutative*. The difference between two vectors can also be obtained by using the triangle law, as shown in Figure 1.7. Since vectors may be added or subtracted in any order, they are also *associative*.

If k is a scalar quantity, then

$$k(\mathbf{A} + \mathbf{B}) = k\mathbf{A} + k\mathbf{B}$$

and, therefore, multiplication by a scalar is *distributive*.

A vector can be broken down into several components. The particular components selected for solution of a problem are a matter of convenience. Consider the vector **V** shown in Figure 1.8a. When we construct a cartesian coordinate system whose origin coincides with the tail of this vector, the components of **V** appear as shown in Figure 1.8b. Conversely, if $\mathbf{V}_x$ and $\mathbf{V}_y$ are two component vectors, they can be added to yield **V** as shown in Figure 1.8c.

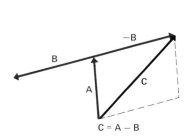

Figure 1.7

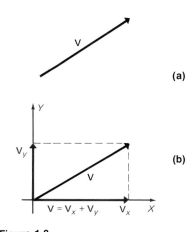

(a)

(b)

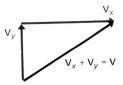

(c)

Figure 1.8

To add or subtract vectors, it is convenient to use the unit vector representation with a suitable coordinate system. For example, if

$$\mathbf{A} = A_x\mathbf{i} + A_y\mathbf{j} \quad \text{and} \quad \mathbf{B} = B_x\mathbf{i} + B_y\mathbf{j}$$

then

$$\mathbf{A} + \mathbf{B} = (A_x + B_x)\mathbf{i} + (A_y + B_y)\mathbf{j}$$

and

$$\mathbf{A} - \mathbf{B} = (A_x - B_x)\mathbf{i} + (A_y - B_y)\mathbf{j}$$

Scalar Product of Vectors

There are two types of vector products, a scalar or dot product and a vector or cross product. The *scalar product* of **A** and **B** is written as $\mathbf{A} \cdot \mathbf{B}$, and is defined as

$$\mathbf{A} \cdot \mathbf{B} \equiv AB \cos (\mathbf{A},\mathbf{B}) \tag{1.2}$$

where $(\mathbf{A},\mathbf{B})$ is the angle between the vectors **A** and **B**. If

$$\mathbf{A} \cdot \mathbf{B} = 0$$

and $A \neq 0$, $B \neq 0$, then **A** and **B** are orthogonal, i.e., the vectors are perpendicular to each other. If

$$\mathbf{A} \cdot \mathbf{B} = AB$$

then **A** and **B** are collinear and lie in the same direction.

The dot product can be used for obtaining the projection of a vector in a given direction. The projection of the vector **A** on the X axis shown in Figure 1.9 can be obtained by

$$\mathbf{A} \cdot \mathbf{i} = A \cos \theta$$

Similarly, the projection of vector **A** along the same direction as vector **B** in Figure 1.10 can be obtained as

$$\mathbf{A} \cdot \mathbf{e}_B = A \cos \beta$$

But the unit vector $\mathbf{e}_B$ is

$$\mathbf{e}_B = \frac{\mathbf{B}}{B}$$

so that the projection of **A** becomes

$$\frac{\mathbf{A} \cdot \mathbf{B}}{B}$$

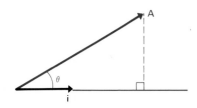

Figure 1.9

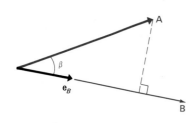

Figure 1.10

The scalar product is used to define the *direction cosines* of a vector. Consider a vector **A** in the cartesian system as shown in Figure 1.11.

Figure 1.11

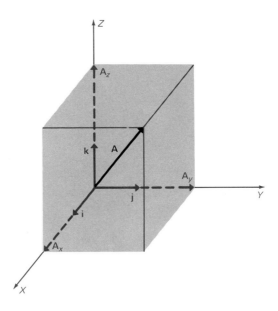

$$\mathbf{A} = A_x\mathbf{i} + A_y\mathbf{j} + A_z\mathbf{k} \qquad (1.3)$$

where **i**, **j**, **k** are unit vectors along the X, Y, Z axes, and A_x, A_y, A_z are components of **A** along the X, Y, Z axes. Let us form the scalar product of both sides with **i**. Thus,

$$\mathbf{A} \cdot \mathbf{i} = A_x(\mathbf{i} \cdot \mathbf{i}) + A_y(\mathbf{j} \cdot \mathbf{i}) + A_z(\mathbf{k} \cdot \mathbf{i})$$

$$= A_x$$

since $\mathbf{i} \cdot \mathbf{i}$ is unity and $\mathbf{j} \cdot \mathbf{i} = \mathbf{k} \cdot \mathbf{i} = 0$. Therefore, A_x is the dot product of **A** and **i**. But from the definition of a dot product,

$$\mathbf{A} \cdot \mathbf{i} = A_x = A \cos (\mathbf{A},\mathbf{i}) \qquad (1.4a)$$

where $(\mathbf{A},\mathbf{i})$ is the angle between **A** and **i**. Using the same process as above, we can obtain

$$\mathbf{A} \cdot \mathbf{j} = A_y = A \cos (\mathbf{A},\mathbf{j}) \qquad (1.4b)$$

$$\mathbf{A} \cdot \mathbf{k} = A_z = A \cos (\mathbf{A},\mathbf{k}) \qquad (1.4c)$$

Substituting equations (1.4) into equation (1.3), we obtain

$$\mathbf{A} = A \cos (\mathbf{A},\mathbf{i})\mathbf{i} + A \cos (\mathbf{A},\mathbf{j})\mathbf{j} + A \cos (\mathbf{A},\mathbf{k})\mathbf{k} \qquad (1.5)$$

However, we have established that

$$\mathbf{A} = A\mathbf{e}_A \qquad (1.1)$$

and when we substitute this into the left side of equation (1.5) and cancel the A, we obtain

$$\mathbf{e}_A = \cos(\mathbf{A},\mathbf{i})\mathbf{i} + \cos(\mathbf{A},\mathbf{j})\mathbf{j} + \cos(\mathbf{A},\mathbf{k})\mathbf{k} \qquad (1.6)$$

The three cosines are called the *direction cosines*. If we take the dot product of both sides with $\mathbf{e}_A$, then

$$\cos^2(\mathbf{A},\mathbf{i}) + \cos^2(\mathbf{A},\mathbf{j}) + \cos^2(\mathbf{A},\mathbf{k}) = 1$$

The direction cosines are

$$\cos(\mathbf{A},\mathbf{i}) = \frac{A_x}{A} \qquad (1.7a)$$

$$\cos(\mathbf{A},\mathbf{j}) = \frac{A_y}{A} \qquad (1.7b)$$

$$\cos(\mathbf{A},\mathbf{k}) = \frac{A_z}{A} \qquad (1.7c)$$

Here, A is the magnitude of $\mathbf{A}$. This can be obtained from the dot product of $\mathbf{A}$ with itself. Thus,

$$\mathbf{A} \cdot \mathbf{A} = A^2 = A_x^2 + A_y^2 + A_z^2$$

and the magnitude A becomes

$$A = \sqrt{A_x^2 + A_y^2 + A_z^2} \qquad (1.8)$$

The scalar product of two vectors $\mathbf{A}$ and $\mathbf{B}$ was written as

$$\mathbf{A} \cdot \mathbf{B} \equiv AB \cos(\mathbf{A},\mathbf{B}) \qquad (1.2)$$

However, if the vectors are written in cartesian coordinates,

$$\mathbf{A} = A_x\mathbf{i} + A_y\mathbf{j} + A_z\mathbf{k} \qquad \text{and} \qquad \mathbf{B} = B_x\mathbf{i} + B_y\mathbf{j} + B_z\mathbf{k}$$

so that the dot product becomes

$$\mathbf{A} \cdot \mathbf{B} = (A_x\mathbf{i} + A_y\mathbf{j} + A_z\mathbf{k}) \cdot (B_x\mathbf{i} + B_y\mathbf{j} + B_z\mathbf{k})$$
$$= A_xB_x + A_yB_y + A_zB_z$$

The angle between the vectors $\mathbf{A}$ and $\mathbf{B}$ can be obtained by equating this to equation (1.2) and solving for $\cos(\mathbf{A},\mathbf{B})$

$$\cos{(\mathbf{A},\mathbf{B})} = \frac{A_x B_x + A_y B_y + A_z B_z}{AB}$$

where A is the magnitude of **A** and B is the magnitude of **B**.

Example 1.5.1

A vector $\mathbf{A} = 2\mathbf{i} + 3\mathbf{j}$, and $\mathbf{B} = 3\mathbf{i} + \mathbf{j}$. What is the sum and difference of these two vectors (a) using components and (b) graphically?

(a)
$$\mathbf{A} - \mathbf{B} = (2\mathbf{i} + 3\mathbf{j}) - (3\mathbf{i} + \mathbf{j})$$

$$= -\mathbf{i} + 2\mathbf{j} \qquad \text{Answer}$$

$$\mathbf{A} + \mathbf{B} = (2\mathbf{i} + 3\mathbf{j}) + (3\mathbf{i} + \mathbf{j})$$

$$= 5\mathbf{i} + 4\mathbf{j} \qquad \text{Answer}$$

(b) The graphic solution is shown in Figure 1.12.

Figure 1.12

(a)

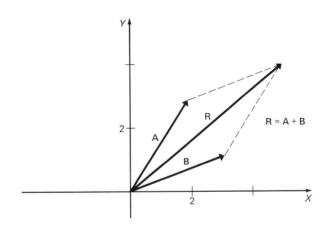

(b)

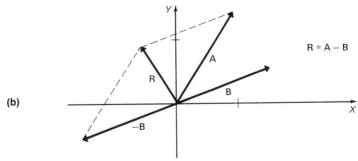

Example 1.5.2

A vector **A** is given by $\mathbf{A} = 4\mathbf{i} + 3\mathbf{j}$. Express this vector in terms of the unit vector $\mathbf{e}_A$ and its magnitude A.

The vector **A** can be expressed as $\mathbf{A} = A\mathbf{e}_A$ where its magnitude is

$$A = \sqrt{(4)^2 + (3)^2} = 5$$

Since

$$\mathbf{A} = 4\mathbf{i} + 3\mathbf{j} = 5\mathbf{e}_A$$

it follows that

$$\mathbf{e}_A = \frac{4\mathbf{i} + 3\mathbf{j}}{5} = 0.8\mathbf{i} + 0.6\mathbf{j}$$

and

$$\mathbf{A} = 5(0.8\mathbf{i} + 0.6\mathbf{j}) = 5\mathbf{e}_A \qquad \text{Answer}$$

Example 1.5.3

A vector **A** is given by $\mathbf{A} = 5\mathbf{i} + \mathbf{j} + 2\mathbf{k}$. (a) What is the magnitude of **A**? (b) What are the direction cosines of **A**? (c) What is the unit vector $\mathbf{e}_A$?

(a) From equation (1.8) we find that

$$A = \sqrt{5^2 + 1 + 2^2} = \sqrt{30} \qquad \text{Answer}$$

(b) We know from equations (1.4) and (1.7) that the direction cosines are

$$\cos(\mathbf{A}, \mathbf{i}) = \frac{\mathbf{A} \cdot \mathbf{i}}{A} = \frac{5}{\sqrt{30}}$$

$$\cos(\mathbf{A}, \mathbf{j}) = \frac{\mathbf{A} \cdot \mathbf{j}}{A} = \frac{1}{\sqrt{30}} \qquad \text{Answer}$$

$$\cos(\mathbf{A}, \mathbf{k}) = \frac{\mathbf{A} \cdot \mathbf{k}}{A} = \frac{2}{\sqrt{30}}$$

(c) The unit vector $\mathbf{e}_A$ is obtained by substituting these direction cosines into equation (1.6), thus

$$\mathbf{e}_A = \cos(\mathbf{A}, \mathbf{i})\mathbf{i} + \cos(\mathbf{A}, \mathbf{j})\mathbf{j} + \cos(\mathbf{A}, \mathbf{k})\mathbf{k} \qquad (1.6)$$

$$= \frac{1}{\sqrt{30}} (5\mathbf{i} + \mathbf{j} + 2\mathbf{k}) \qquad \text{Answer}$$

(*Note:* A unit vector $\mathbf{e}_A$ coincident with $\mathbf{A}$ can be obtained by dividing $\mathbf{A}$ by its own magnitude.)

Example 1.5.4

Obtain the projection of $\mathbf{A}$ on $\mathbf{B}$, if

$$\mathbf{A} = 2\mathbf{i} + 3\mathbf{j} \qquad \text{and} \qquad \mathbf{B} = 5\mathbf{i} + 2\mathbf{j} + \mathbf{k}$$

The projection of $\mathbf{A}$ on $\mathbf{B}$ is $A \cos (\mathbf{A},\mathbf{B})$. The dot product of $\mathbf{A}$ and $\mathbf{B}$ is

$$\mathbf{A} \cdot \mathbf{B} = AB \cos (\mathbf{A},\mathbf{B})$$

Therefore,

$$A \cos (\mathbf{A},\mathbf{B}) = \frac{\mathbf{A} \cdot \mathbf{B}}{B} = \frac{(2\mathbf{i} + 3\mathbf{j}) \cdot (5\mathbf{i} + 2\mathbf{j} + \mathbf{k})}{\sqrt{5^2 + 2^2 + 1}}$$

$$= \frac{16}{\sqrt{30}} \qquad \text{Answer}$$

Example 1.5.5

Obtain the angle between the vectors $\mathbf{A}$ and $\mathbf{B}$ given in example 1.5.1.

$$\mathbf{A} \cdot \mathbf{B} = AB \cos \theta$$

therefore,

$$\cos \theta = \frac{\mathbf{A} \cdot \mathbf{B}}{AB}$$

$$A = \sqrt{(2)^2 + (3)^2} = \sqrt{13} \qquad B = \sqrt{(3)^2 + (1)^2} = \sqrt{10}$$

$$\cos \theta = \frac{(2\mathbf{i} + 3\mathbf{j}) \cdot (3\mathbf{i} + \mathbf{j})}{\sqrt{13} \sqrt{10}} = \frac{6 + 3}{\sqrt{13} \sqrt{10}} = \frac{9}{\sqrt{13} \sqrt{10}} = 0.79$$

therefore,

$$\theta = 39.6° \qquad \text{Answer}$$

Cross Product of Vectors

Up till now we have treated only the scalar product of two vectors. Let us now consider the *vector* or *cross product* of two vectors, $\mathbf{A} \times \mathbf{B}$, which is defined as

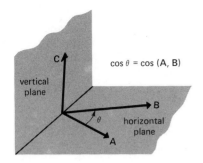

Figure 1.13

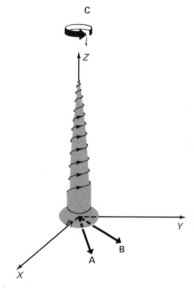

Figure 1.14

$$\mathbf{C} = \mathbf{A} \times \mathbf{B} \equiv AB \, |\sin (\mathbf{A,B})| \, \mathbf{e}_c \qquad (1.9)$$

where $\mathbf{e}_c$ is a unit vector perpendicular to the plane containing the vectors $\mathbf{A}$ and $\mathbf{B}$ as shown in Figure 1.13. The direction of $\mathbf{C}$ is obtained by the right-hand rule, i.e., if the vector $\mathbf{A}$ is rotated by the smallest angle that brings it into coincidence with $\mathbf{B}$, then the direction of $\mathbf{C}$ is that of an advancing right-hand screw which turns as the vector $\mathbf{A}$ shown in Figure 1.14. From the definition of cross product, if

$$\mathbf{A} \times \mathbf{B} = 0$$

and $A \neq 0$, $B \neq 0$, then $\mathbf{A}$ and $\mathbf{B}$ are collinear. If $\mathbf{A}$ and $\mathbf{B}$ are orthogonal, then

$$\mathbf{A} \times \mathbf{B} = AB\mathbf{e}_c$$

The cross product is not commutative. That is, in general, $\mathbf{A} \times \mathbf{B} \neq \mathbf{B} \times \mathbf{A}$ for, in accordance with the right-hand rule, $\mathbf{B} \times \mathbf{A} = -\mathbf{A} \times \mathbf{B}$.

Let us consider $\mathbf{A}$ and $\mathbf{B}$ in cartesian coordinates and form the cross product

$$\mathbf{A} \times \mathbf{B} = (A_x\mathbf{i} + A_y\mathbf{j} + A_z\mathbf{k}) \times (B_x\mathbf{i} + B_y\mathbf{j} + B_z\mathbf{k}) \quad (1.10)$$

It can be shown that the cross product is distributive, so that the above expression can be computed term by term. Recalling that $\mathbf{i}, \mathbf{j}, \mathbf{k}$ are unit vectors perpendicular to each other, we have the following relationships for the cross products of unit vectors $\mathbf{i}, \mathbf{j},$ and $\mathbf{k}$.

$$\mathbf{i} \times \mathbf{j} = \mathbf{k} = -\mathbf{j} \times \mathbf{i}$$
$$\mathbf{j} \times \mathbf{k} = \mathbf{i} = -\mathbf{k} \times \mathbf{j}$$
$$\mathbf{k} \times \mathbf{i} = \mathbf{j} = -\mathbf{i} \times \mathbf{k}$$
$$\mathbf{i} \times \mathbf{i} = \mathbf{j} \times \mathbf{j} = \mathbf{k} \times \mathbf{k} = 0$$

Using these relationships, equation (1.10) reduces to

$$\mathbf{A} \times \mathbf{B} = (A_yB_z - A_zB_y)\mathbf{i} + (A_zB_x - A_xB_z)\mathbf{j} + (A_xB_y - A_yB_x)\mathbf{k}$$

This can be compactly written as a *determinant*,

$$\mathbf{A} \times \mathbf{B} = \begin{vmatrix} \mathbf{i} & \mathbf{j} & \mathbf{k} \\ A_x & A_y & A_z \\ B_x & B_y & B_z \end{vmatrix}$$

Example 1.5.6

Obtain $\mathbf{A} \times \mathbf{B}$ for the vectors defined in example 1.5.4.

$$\mathbf{A} \times \mathbf{B} = \begin{vmatrix} \mathbf{i} & \mathbf{j} & \mathbf{k} \\ 2 & 3 & 0 \\ 5 & 2 & 1 \end{vmatrix}$$

$$= 3\mathbf{i} - 2\mathbf{j} - 11\mathbf{k} \qquad \text{Answer}$$

Example 1.5.7

Find $\mathbf{w} \times \mathbf{r}$ if $\mathbf{w} = 3\mathbf{k}$ and $\mathbf{r} = 2\mathbf{i} + \mathbf{j}$.

$$\mathbf{w} \times \mathbf{r} = 3\mathbf{k} \times (2\mathbf{i} + \mathbf{j})$$

$$= 3\mathbf{k} \times 2\mathbf{i} + 3\mathbf{k} \times \mathbf{j}$$

$$= 6\mathbf{j} - 3\mathbf{i} \qquad \text{Answer}$$

1.6 Dimensions and Units

When we measure the length of a string, we may choose to record its length in centimeters, inches, or feet. The concept of length is called a *dimension*, the terms centimeters, inches, and feet are called *units*. Similarly, the concept of time is a dimension and the units with which we record it may be seconds, minutes, hours, etc.

Three dimensions are essential to Newtonian mechanics. It has been agreed that length and time are fundamental to all systems and that mass or force may be selected as convenient. In other words, if the dimension of mass is selected as the third fundamental dimension, then the dimension of force is found from Newton's second law. Such a system, in which mass, length, and time are the fundamental dimensions, is called an *absolute system*. If force is selected as the third dimension, we have a *gravitational system* composed of force, length, and time. This text uses the gravitational system, and Table 1.1 lists the common quantities we will encounter, along with their associated units and dimensions. Note that the unit of radian is dimensionless.

Table 1.1
Gravitational Units and Dimensions

Quantity	Gravitational Units	Dimensions
Length	ft	L
Time	sec	T
Force	lb	F
Mass	lb-sec²/ft = slug	FT^2L^{-1}
Linear velocity	ft/sec	LT^{-1}
Linear acceleration	ft/sec²	LT^{-2}
Work	ft-lb	FL
Energy	ft-lb	FL
Power	ft-lb/sec	FLT^{-1}
Moment	lb-ft	FL
Moment of area	ft⁴	L^4
Moment of inertia	lb-ft-sec²	FLT^2

1.7 Problem Solving

In solving problems in statics, it is necessary to obtain a quantitative description of the forces acting on an engineering structure. The relationships between these forces are established from the requirements of equilibrium and can be stated in mathematical form. The mathematical equations can be solved assuming that the number of unknowns and the number of equations are the same. In general, the difficulty is not in the mathematics but in the thought process entailed in the quantitative description of the forces, i.e., in obtaining the model.

Obtaining the model is actually formulating the problem. It requires thinking in terms of a physical situation and then translating the situation into a mathematical expression. A neat sketch of the structure and all forces acting on it *must* be drawn. This sketch is called the *free-body diagram*.

Often it is necessary that approximations be made in formulating the problem. For example, small distances, angles, or forces may be neglected in favor of large distances, angles, or forces. If a force is acting on a very small area, it may be approximated as a force acting at a point. The formulation of a problem includes stating what data is given and what results are desired.

Once the problem has been formulated, the fundamental laws are used to derive the relationships between the various unknowns. In statics, application of these laws yields equations of equilibrium. These equations are solved and the answers are checked for units and computational error. This can be done by substituting the answers back into the equations to see if the equations are satisfied.

We can now summarize the following *musts* in solving a problem.

1. Formulate the problem. This includes
   Free-body diagram
   Necessary approximations
   Given data
   Results desired
2. Write the mathematical equations and solve for the unknowns.
3. Check the answers for units and errors made in computations.

The necessity for adherence to this procedure cannot be overemphasized. Such an orderly approach toward problem solving not only yields correct and quick results, it is what makes engineers unique as problem solvers.

In conclusion, we must say a few words about the accuracy of problem solutions. This accuracy depends upon the accuracy of the given data and the manner of computations. The accuracy of the computations need not be greater than the accuracy of the data. For example, if the weight of cargo to be carried by a truck is known to be 20,000 lb to within 25 lb, then the relative error is

$$\frac{25}{20,000} \times 100 = 0.125\%$$

Since the accuracy of the data is 0.125 percent, the accuracy of the computations should be within 0.125 percent.

In general, the answers obtained by the use of a slide rule are of sufficient accuracy for most engineering problems. Computations for problems in this textbook are based on slide-rule accuracy.

1.8 Summary

A The important *ideas*:

1. Our study of statics is concerned with the equilibrium, without motion, of rigid bodies under the influence of various kinds of forces.

2. The study of statics is based on Newtonian mechanics and is conducted via a vector approach.

B The important *equations*:

Vector: $\mathbf{A} = A\,\mathbf{e}_A$ (1.1)

Cartesian components: $\mathbf{A} = A_x\mathbf{i} + A_y\mathbf{j} + A_z\mathbf{k}$ (1.3)

Direction cosines: $\mathbf{e}_A = \cos(\mathbf{A},\mathbf{i})\mathbf{i} + \cos(\mathbf{A},\mathbf{j})\mathbf{j} + \cos(\mathbf{A},\mathbf{k})\mathbf{k}$ (1.6)

Scalar product: $\mathbf{A} \cdot \mathbf{B} = AB\cos(\mathbf{A},\mathbf{B})$ (1.2)

Vector product: $\mathbf{A} \times \mathbf{B} = AB\,|\sin(\mathbf{A},\mathbf{B})|\,\mathbf{e}_c$ (1.9)

1.9 Problems

1.9.1 Write an essay on the scientific achievements of any one of the great men who made a notable contribution to statics.

1.9.2 Define a vector. Give several examples of a vector quantity.

1.9.3 Vector **A** in the *XY* plane has a magnitude of 8 and makes a 60° angle with the positive *X* axis. Express this vector by its components.

1.9.4 If $\mathbf{A} = 5\mathbf{i} + 8\mathbf{j}$ and $\mathbf{B} = 6\mathbf{i} - 8\mathbf{j} + 2\mathbf{k}$, find $\mathbf{A} + \mathbf{B}$ and $\mathbf{A} - \mathbf{B}$.

1.9.5 Obtain $\mathbf{A} + 2\mathbf{B}$ and $3\mathbf{A} - \mathbf{B}$ for the vectors **A** and **B** given in problem 1.9.4.

1.9.6 Show that $\mathbf{A} \cdot \mathbf{B} = \mathbf{B} \cdot \mathbf{A}$.

1.9.7 A vector is given by $\mathbf{V} = 8.3\mathbf{i} + 2.5\mathbf{j} + 5\mathbf{k}$. What are its direction cosines?

1.9.8 What is the projection of vector $\mathbf{V}_1 = 5\mathbf{i} + 3.3\mathbf{k}$ on the vector $\mathbf{V}_2 = 3.3\mathbf{i} + 5\mathbf{k}$?

1.9.9 Obtain the angle between the vector $\mathbf{A} = \mathbf{i} + 3\mathbf{j} + 2\mathbf{k}$ and the vector $\mathbf{B} = 3\mathbf{j} + \mathbf{k}$.

1.9.10 If $\mathbf{C} = 10\mathbf{i} + 4\mathbf{j}$ and $\mathbf{D} = 4\mathbf{i} - 10\mathbf{j}$, find $\mathbf{C} \cdot \mathbf{D}$.

1.9.11 If $\mathbf{V}_1 = 2\mathbf{i} + 3\mathbf{k}$ and $\mathbf{V}_2 = -4\mathbf{k}$, find $\mathbf{V}_1 \cdot \mathbf{V}_2$.

1.9.12 Obtain a unit vector that gives the direction of the tip of $\mathbf{B}$ relative to the tip of $\mathbf{A}$, if $\mathbf{A} = 3\mathbf{i} + \mathbf{j}$ and $\mathbf{B} = \mathbf{i} + 2\mathbf{j} + 3\mathbf{k}$.

1.9.13 Using the dot product show that, if $\mathbf{C} = \mathbf{A} - \mathbf{B}$, then

$$C^2 = A^2 + B^2 - 2AB \cos (\mathbf{A},\mathbf{B}).$$

1.9.14 If $\mathbf{A} = 5\mathbf{i} + 5\mathbf{j} + \mathbf{k}$ and $\mathbf{B} = 2\mathbf{i} + 4\mathbf{k}$, find $\mathbf{A} \times \mathbf{B}$.

1.9.15 If $\mathbf{V}_1 = 2\mathbf{i} + \mathbf{j} + \mathbf{k}$ and $\mathbf{V}_2 = \mathbf{j} + 2\mathbf{k}$, find $\mathbf{V}_1 \times \mathbf{V}_2$.

1.9.16 Using $\mathbf{A} = A_1\mathbf{i} + A_2\mathbf{j}$ and $\mathbf{B} = B_1\mathbf{i} + B_2\mathbf{j}$, show that $\mathbf{A} \times \mathbf{B} = -\mathbf{B} \times \mathbf{A}$.

1.9.17 Using the definition of a cross product show that

$$\frac{\sin (\mathbf{A},\mathbf{C})}{B} = \frac{\sin (\mathbf{A},\mathbf{B})}{C}.$$

Let $\mathbf{A}$, $\mathbf{B}$, and $\mathbf{C}$ be the sides of a triangle where $\mathbf{C} = \mathbf{A} + \mathbf{B}$.

1.9.18 A missile is to be fired with velocity $\mathbf{V}_1$ so that it is headed in the direction shown in Figure 1.15. However, it misfires so that its velocity is $\mathbf{V}_2$. Obtain the magnitude and direction of the velocity difference $\mathbf{V}_2 - \mathbf{V}_1$. Let $\mathbf{V}_1 = 5\mathbf{i} + 3\mathbf{j}$ and $\mathbf{V}_2 = 4.9\mathbf{i} + 2.8\mathbf{j} + 0.5\mathbf{k}$.

1.9.19 If $\mathbf{w} = \mathbf{j} - \mathbf{k}$ and $\mathbf{r} = \mathbf{i} + 2\mathbf{j}$, find $\mathbf{w} \times \mathbf{r}$.

1.9.20 What is the magnitude of the vector obtained by crossing $\mathbf{r} = \mathbf{i} + 2\mathbf{j} + 3\mathbf{k}$ with $\mathbf{w} = 6\mathbf{k}$?

1.9.21 Three vectors are given by $\mathbf{A}_1 = 5\mathbf{i} + 2\mathbf{j}$, $\mathbf{A}_2 = 3\mathbf{i} + \mathbf{k}$, and $\mathbf{A}_3 = 8\mathbf{j}$. What are (a) the magnitude and (b) the direction cosines of the sum of these three vectors?

1.9.22 Using $\mathbf{A} = A_1\mathbf{i} + A_2\mathbf{j} + A_3\mathbf{k}$ and $\mathbf{B} = B_1\mathbf{i} + B_2\mathbf{j} + B_3\mathbf{k}$, show that $\mathbf{A} \cdot (\mathbf{B} \times \mathbf{A})$ is zero.

1.9.23 A line passes through the points $(1,8,3)$ and $(2,1,5)$. What are the direction cosines of this line?

1.9.24 A vector $\mathbf{A} = 5\mathbf{i} + \mathbf{j} + Z\mathbf{k}$ is crossed into $\mathbf{B} = 2\mathbf{i} + 3\mathbf{j}$ to obtain $-6\mathbf{i} + 4\mathbf{j} + 13\mathbf{k}$. What must be the value of Z?

1.9.25 A triangle ABC is defined by the points $A(3,0,0)$, $B(0,6,0)$, and $C(0,0,9)$. Obtain a unit vector perpendicular to the triangle surface ABC.

1.9.26 A vector going through the origin is given by $\mathbf{V} = 5\mathbf{i} + 3\mathbf{j} + 4\mathbf{k}$. What angle does it make with the plane of the triangle given by problem 1.9.25?

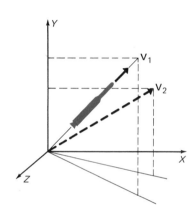

Figure 1.15

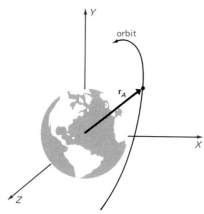

Figure 1.16

1.9.27 The position of a satellite in Figure 1.16 is given by

$$\mathbf{r}_A = (5\mathbf{i} + 3\mathbf{j} + 4.55\mathbf{k})R.$$

What is the magnitude of $\mathbf{r}_A$? Obtain a unit vector $\mathbf{e}_r$ coincident with $\mathbf{r}_A$.

1.9.28 Two cars in radio contact are shown in Figure 1.17. Their position is measured from a fixed point O and is given by

$$\mathbf{r}_B = 10(\cos \pi t\, \mathbf{i} + \sin \pi t\, \mathbf{j})$$

$$\mathbf{r}_A = 10 \cos 3\, \pi t\, \mathbf{i} + 10(2 + \sin 3\, \pi t)\mathbf{j}$$

What is the location of car A relative to B at $t = 1$ sec?

1.9.29 An airplane is flying at a velocity of V ft/sec horizontally, as shown in Figure 1.18. Express this in terms of the unit vectors $\mathbf{i}$ and $\mathbf{j}$.

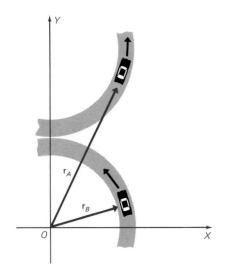

Figure 1.17

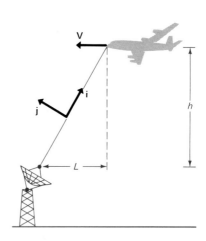

Figure 1.18

1.9.30 The velocity of the aircraft shown in Figure 1.19 consists of two parts, $\mathbf{V}_r$ and $\mathbf{V}_\theta$. Obtain the resultant velocity using cartesian coordinates.

1.9.31 A belt drive used to transport luggage is shown in Figure 1.20. Express the position of the luggage A as a vector quantity.

1.9.32 A pulley arrangement used to hoist a weight is shown in Figure 1.21. Express the vectors $\mathbf{MW}$ and $\mathbf{AB}$ as a magnitude and unit vector. Each pulley has a radius of 1 ft.

Figure 1.19

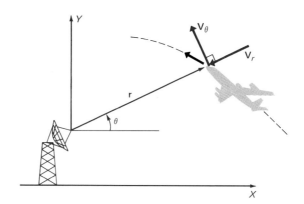

Figure 1.20

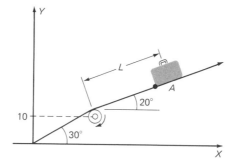

Figure 1.21

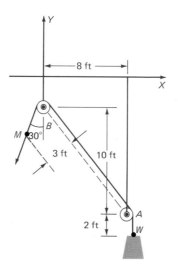

Chapter 2
Force and Couple

A force is defined and represented as a vector quantity. We show how a force is resolved into components, and how several forces are combined to form a resultant force. The resultant of many forces applied to a particle must be zero for equilibrium of the particle. The moment of a force and a couple, or pure moment, are introduced. It is shown how one resultant force and one resultant couple may replace several forces and couples applied to a body.

2.1 Introduction

An engineering structure is subjected to various kinds of forces. A careful examination of these forces is therefore an important part of statics. In this chapter we will be concerned with forces and moments and how several forces can be combined into a resultant force and a resultant moment. The material here and in the next chapter is fundamental to obtaining the understanding necessary for problem solving not only in statics, but in dynamics as well. It is, therefore, essential that this material be mastered.

2.2 Resolution of Forces

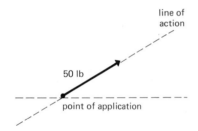

Figure 2.1

A force has been characterized as the action of one body on another. A force is a *vector* quantity, i.e., it has *magnitude* and *direction*. As it is applied to a body or a structure it is also characterized by its *point of application*. The magnitude of a force is given by a certain number of units. In engineering, the units of force are the pound (lb); the kilopound (kip), which is 1000 lb; or the ton which is two kips. The direction of a force is defined by its *line of action* and its sense is given by an arrow, as shown in Figure 2.1.

Since forces are vectors, they can be combined using the rules of vector combination discussed in the last chapter. When force $\mathbf{F}_1$ and force $\mathbf{F}_2$ are combined, we obtain the *resultant* of the two forces. The resultant formed by adding two vectors can be obtained graphically by using the parallelogram rule as shown in Figure 2.2a. In vector notation,

$$\mathbf{R} = \mathbf{F}_1 + \mathbf{F}_2$$

The resultant formed by the difference of these two vectors is shown graphically in Figure 2.2b, and is given by

$$\mathbf{R} = \mathbf{F}_1 - \mathbf{F}_2$$

Vectors $\mathbf{F}_1$ and $\mathbf{F}_2$ may also be added, as shown in Figure 2.3a, where the resultant is obtained by arranging the vectors in a *tip-to-tail* fashion, and then joining the tail of $\mathbf{F}_1$ to the tip of $\mathbf{F}_2$. The order of combining is not important, as seen in Figure 2.3b. The difference of two vectors obtained by this

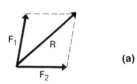

(a)

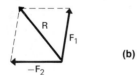

(b)

Figure 2.2

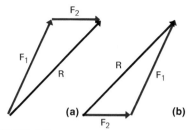

Figure 2.3

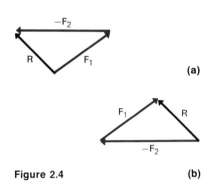

Figure 2.4

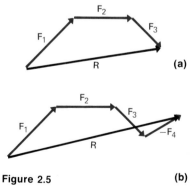

Figure 2.5

Figure 2.6 (a)

method is shown in Figure 2.4.

By following the tip-to-tail method, a resultant can be obtained for the combination of several vectors in the same plane. Vectors F_1, F_2, and F_3 are added in this fashion in Figure 2.5a. Another example, the resultant of

$$F_1 + F_2 + F_3 - F_4$$

is shown in Figure 2.5b. The method of combining several vectors in a tip-to-tail fashion to obtain a resultant is known as the *polygon rule* for vector addition. Notice that these graphical procedures can be easily carried out if all the forces are in the same plane.

From the foregoing discussion we can state that the resultant vector **R** is the sum of n forces,

$$R = \sum_{i=1}^{n} F_i \qquad (2.1)$$

If $n = 2$, we can use the parallelogram or triangle rule. If n is larger than 2, then we make use of the polygon rule. The sum in equation (2.1) is often referred to as a vector sum. A vector sum differs from the algebraic sum of scalar quantities, which involves only magnitudes.

Example 2.2.1

A steamer is pulled by two tugboats as shown in Figure 2.6a. Obtain the resultant force applied to the steamer: (a) using the parallelogram rule and (b) using the triangle rule. Assume that $F_1 = 1.5$ kips and $F_2 = 2$ kips.

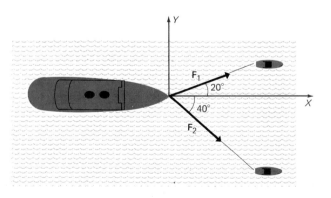

(a) By the parallelogram rule, the resultant force is $\mathbf{R}=\mathbf{F}_1+\mathbf{F}_2$. The resultant is 3 kips at a $-14.5°$ angle to the horizontal, as seen in Figure 2.6b.

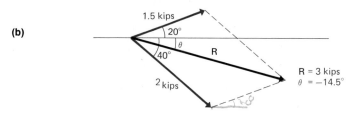

(b)

(b) Since the order of addition is not important, the resultant $\mathbf{R}$ can be obtained by the triangle rule in two ways (see Figures 2.6c and 2.6d). The resultant in both of these graphical solutions is the same as that obtained by the parallelogram rule.

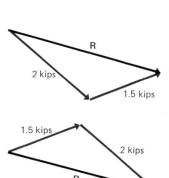

(c)

(d)

Figure 2.6

Example 2.2.2

A truck is towed using three ropes as shown in Figure 2.7a. What is the resultant of the three tensional forces?

The resultant can be obtained by the polygon rule as shown in Figure 2.7b. Since $\mathbf{R}=\mathbf{F}_1+\mathbf{F}_2+\mathbf{F}_3$, the resultant is 4.17 kips and makes a $-6.5°$ angle with the horizontal.

Figure 2.7

(a)

(b)

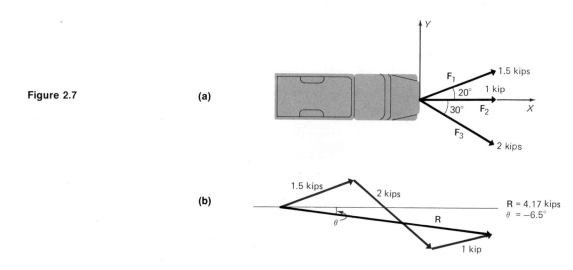

Two-Dimensional Force Components

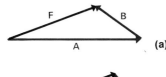

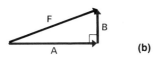

Figure 2.8

A resultant force is the sum of several forces. Conversely, force may be *resolved* into several *components*. The force **F** is resolved into two different sets of **A** and **B** components in Figures 2.8a and 2.8b. Clearly, the choice of the particular components is limitless. In engineering, a force is often resolved into rectangular or cartesian components. When a force expressed in rectangular coordinates has two components, we speak of the force as being *planar*.

A force represented in the cartesian system is shown in Figure 2.9. The force **F** has two components. The component $\mathbf{F}_x$ is the force in the X direction and $\mathbf{F}_y$ is in the Y direction, so that

$$\mathbf{F} = \mathbf{F}_x + \mathbf{F}_y \tag{2.2}$$

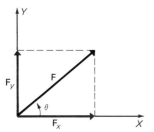

Figure 2.9

The components $\mathbf{F}_x$ and $\mathbf{F}_y$ are called *vector components*. When a force is expressed in this way, it is convenient to use the unit vector notation,

$$\mathbf{F}_x = F_x \mathbf{i} \qquad \mathbf{F}_y = F_y \mathbf{j}$$

The vectors **i** and **j** are unit vectors coincident with the X and Y axes as shown in Figure 2.10a. The force **F** can now be written as

$$\mathbf{F} = F_x \mathbf{i} + F_y \mathbf{j} \tag{2.3}$$

We also notice that since F_x and F_y are projections on the X and Y axes they can be expressed as

$$F_x = F \cos \theta \qquad F_y = F \sin \theta$$

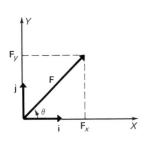

Figure 2.10 (a)

The components F_x and F_y are known as *scalar* components of the force vector **F**. Notice that F_x is simply the dot product between **F** and the unit vector **i**.

If the scalar components F_x and F_y are known, we may compute the magnitude and direction of the resultant force **F** using the following notation:

$$F = \sqrt{F_x^2 + F_y^2} \tag{2.4a}$$

$$\theta = \tan^{-1} \frac{F_y}{F_x} \tag{2.4b}$$

Note that a positive θ is counterclockwise measured off the X axis.

We have shown how several forces can be combined graphically with the parallelogram rule, the triangle rule, or the polygon rule. It is, of course, possible to combine forces by combining their components. For example, let us add **A** and **B** by adding their components. We have

$$\mathbf{A} = A_x\mathbf{i} + A_y\mathbf{j} \qquad \mathbf{B} = B_x\mathbf{i} + B_y\mathbf{j}$$

and, since the resultant is vector **R**,

$$\mathbf{R} = \mathbf{A} + \mathbf{B}$$

We substitute for **A** and **B** to obtain

$$\mathbf{R} = (A_x + B_x)\mathbf{i} + (A_y + B_y)\mathbf{j}$$

We may now think of the resultant as having two components, as shown in Figure 2.10b.

$$\mathbf{R} = R_x\mathbf{i} + R_y\mathbf{j}$$

where

$$R_x = A_x + B_x \qquad R_y = A_y + B_y$$

The magnitude and direction of **R** can be written as

$$R = \sqrt{R_x^2 + R_y^2}$$

$$\theta = \tan^{-1}\frac{R_y}{R_x}$$

The components of the resultant of several forces are, therefore, obtained by algebraically adding the corresponding scalar components of the individual forces. We can write the components of a resultant as

$$R_x = \Sigma F_x \qquad R_y = \Sigma F_y$$

A force can also be characterized by specifying its magnitude and two of the points through which it passes. Consider a force **F** whose line of action passes through two points, $P(x_1, y_1)$ and $Q(x_2, y_2)$ as shown in Figure 2.11. The force **F** can be written as

$$\mathbf{F} = F\mathbf{e}_F \tag{2.5}$$

where $\mathbf{e}_F$ is the unit vector shown in the figure. The vector **PQ** has the same direction as the force **F**, so that

$$\mathbf{PQ} = D\mathbf{e}_F$$

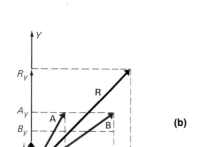

(b)

Figure 2.10

where D is the distance (or magnitude) between P and Q. From Figure 2.11 we can write

$$\mathbf{PQ} = (x_2 - x_1)\mathbf{i} + (y_2 - y_1)\mathbf{j} = D\mathbf{e}_F$$

If

$$D_x = x_2 - x_1 \quad \text{and} \quad D_y = y_2 - y_1$$

then

$$\mathbf{PQ} = D_x\mathbf{i} + D_y\mathbf{j} = D\mathbf{e}_F$$

where

$$D = \sqrt{D_x{}^2 + D_y{}^2}$$

We can now obtain the unit vector $\mathbf{e}_F$ thus:

$$\mathbf{e}_F = \frac{D_x}{D}\mathbf{i} + \frac{D_y}{D}\mathbf{j} \tag{2.6}$$

Substituting equation (2.6) into equation (2.5), we have

$$\mathbf{F} = F\left(\frac{D_x}{D}\mathbf{i} + \frac{D_y}{D}\mathbf{j}\right)$$

However, the vector $\mathbf{F}$ can be written as

$$\mathbf{F} = F_x\mathbf{i} + F_y\mathbf{j}$$

so that by comparison,

$$F_x = F\frac{D_x}{D} \qquad F_y = F\frac{D_y}{D}$$

The terms D_x/D and D_y/D are the direction cosines, i.e.,

$$\cos\theta_x = \frac{D_x}{D} \qquad \cos\theta_y = \frac{D_y}{D} \tag{2.7}$$

where θ_x is the angle between the vector $\mathbf{F}$ and the X axis, and θ_y is the angle between the vector $\mathbf{F}$ and the Y axis. Then,

$$\mathbf{F} = F(\cos\theta_x\,\mathbf{i} + \cos\theta_y\,\mathbf{j}) \tag{2.8}$$

From equation (2.7) we may derive an additional useful relationship. If we solve both equations in (2.7) for $1/D$ and equate them, we have

$$\frac{1}{D} = \frac{\cos\theta_x}{D_x} = \frac{\cos\theta_y}{D_y} \tag{2.9}$$

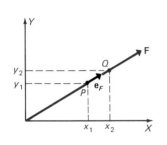

Figure 2.11

Remember that D_x and D_y are the distances along the X and Y axes between P and Q, whereas D is the straight-line distance between P and Q.

Example 2.2.3

A 1000-lb weight is lifted by a crane as shown in Figure 2.12. What are the components of the weight along the X and Y axes?

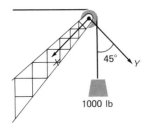

$$\mathbf{w} = w_x\mathbf{i} + w_y\mathbf{j}$$

$$w_x = w \cos 45° = 707 \text{ lb}$$

$$w_y = w \sin 45° = 707 \text{ lb}$$

$$\mathbf{w} = 707(\mathbf{i} + \mathbf{j}) \qquad \text{Answer}$$

where $\mathbf{i}$ and $\mathbf{j}$ are unit vectors in the X and Y directions.

Figure 2.12

Example 2.2.4

Obtain the resultant force for the truck being towed by three ropes as shown in Figure 2.7 (page 26).

$$\mathbf{R} = \mathbf{F}_1 + \mathbf{F}_2 + \mathbf{F}_3$$

$$\mathbf{F}_1 = 1.5(\cos 20° \, \mathbf{i} + \sin 20° \, \mathbf{j})$$

$$\mathbf{F}_2 = 1 \, \mathbf{i}$$

$$\mathbf{F}_3 = 2(\cos 30° \, \mathbf{i} - \sin 30° \, \mathbf{j})$$

Substituting, we obtain

$$\mathbf{R} = (1.5 \cos 20° + 1 + 2 \cos 30°)\mathbf{i} + (1.5 \sin 20° - 2 \sin 30°)\mathbf{j}$$

$$= 4.14\mathbf{i} - 0.49\mathbf{j}$$

$$R = 4.16 \text{ kips} \qquad \text{Answer}$$

$$\theta = -6.75°$$

which compare with the answers obtained in example 2.2.2.

Example 2.2.5

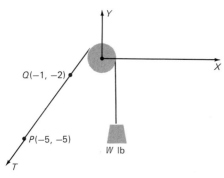

Figure 2.13

The tension T in the rope shown in Figure 2.13 supports the weight w. The rope is known to pass through $P(-5,-5)$ and $Q(-1,-2)$. If the tension is directed along the rope, express the tension as a vector quantity using a unit vector.

Let the unit vector and the force vector be written as

$$\mathbf{e}_T = \cos \theta_x \, \mathbf{i} + \cos \theta_y \, \mathbf{j} \qquad \mathbf{T} = T \mathbf{e}_T$$

The distances are

$$D_x = -5 + 1 = -4$$
$$D_y = -5 + 2 = -3$$
$$D = \sqrt{4^2 + 3^2} = 5$$

Therefore, from

$$\cos \theta_x = \frac{D_x}{D} \qquad \cos \theta_y = \frac{D_y}{D} \qquad (2.7)$$

$$\cos \theta_x = -\tfrac{4}{5} = -0.8 \qquad \cos \theta_y = -\tfrac{3}{5} = -0.6$$

so that the unit and force vectors become

$$\mathbf{e}_T = -0.8\mathbf{i} - 0.6\mathbf{j} \qquad \text{and} \qquad \mathbf{T} = T(-0.8\mathbf{i} - 0.6\mathbf{j})$$

Answer

Three-Dimensional Force Components

It is often necessary to consider a force in three dimensions. A force represented in three dimensions is sometimes referred to as a *space* force. In combining space forces, graphical rules can be used in principle but are difficult to implement since three-dimensional drawings are required. It is therefore customary to represent a space force by its components in three-dimensional space and then to combine the components algebraically.

A force **F** in space can be represented as

$$\mathbf{F} = F_x \mathbf{i} + F_y \mathbf{j} + F_z \mathbf{k}$$

where **i**, **j**, **k** are unit vectors as shown in Figure 2.14. The scalar components can be written as

$$F_x = \mathbf{F} \cdot \mathbf{i} \qquad F_y = \mathbf{F} \cdot \mathbf{j} \qquad F_z = \mathbf{F} \cdot \mathbf{k}$$

Evaluating these dot products, we obtain

$$F_x = F \cos \theta_x \qquad F_y = F \cos \theta_y \qquad F_z = F \cos \theta_z$$

Here, $\cos \theta_x$, $\cos \theta_y$, and $\cos \theta_z$ are the direction cosines. Solving for F in each case and equating, we obtain

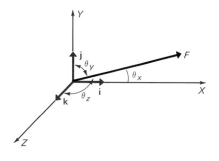

Figure 2.14

$$\frac{F_x}{\cos \theta_x} = \frac{F_y}{\cos \theta_y} = \frac{F_z}{\cos \theta_z}$$

If we have the scalar components of a vector, then its magnitude is given by

$$F = \sqrt{F_x^2 + F_y^2 + F_z^2}$$

and the direction cosines are

$$\cos \theta_x = \frac{F_x}{F} \qquad \cos \theta_y = \frac{F_y}{F} \qquad \cos \theta_z = \frac{F_z}{F}$$

If we have n forces represented in three-dimensional space, the resultant is obtained by summing the components:

$$\mathbf{R} = \sum_{i=1}^{n} \mathbf{F}_i$$

$$= R_x \mathbf{i} + R_y \mathbf{j} + R_z \mathbf{k}$$

and

$$R_x = \sum F_x \qquad R_y = \sum F_y \qquad R_z = \sum F_z$$

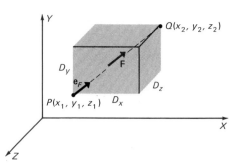

Figure 2.15

As in the two-dimensional case, a force can also be characterized by specifying its magnitude and two points in space through which the line of action must pass. Consider the force **F** whose line of action passes through P and Q as shown in Figure 2.15. Then,

$$\mathbf{F} = F \mathbf{e}_F$$

where

$$\mathbf{e}_F = \cos \theta_x \mathbf{i} + \cos \theta_y \mathbf{j} + \cos \theta_z \mathbf{k}$$

The direction cosines are defined as in equation (2.7), so that

$$\cos \theta_x = \frac{D_x}{D} \qquad \cos \theta_y = \frac{D_y}{D} \qquad \cos \theta_z = \frac{D_z}{D} \qquad (2.10)$$

We can solve for $1/D$ in equation (2.10) and obtain

$$\frac{1}{D} = \frac{\cos \theta_x}{D_x} = \frac{\cos \theta_y}{D_y} = \frac{\cos \theta_z}{D_z}$$

In this equation the distance between P and Q is

$$D = \sqrt{D_x^2 + D_y^2 + D_z^2}$$

where

$$D_x = x_2 - x_1 \qquad D_y = y_2 - y_1 \qquad D_z = z_2 - z_1$$

Example 2.2.6

A rope tied to an anchor supports a weight as shown in Figure 2.16. Find the components of the tension T of the rope along the X, Y, Z axes if the rope passes through the points $P(0,0,0)$ and $Q(8,5,2)$.

The tension in the rope is, from equation (2.5),

$$\mathbf{T} = T\mathbf{e}_T$$

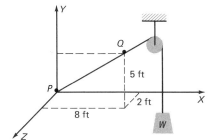

Figure 2.16

where

$$\mathbf{e}_T = \cos\theta_x\,\mathbf{i} + \cos\theta_y\,\mathbf{j} + \cos\theta_z\,\mathbf{k}$$

From Figure 2.16,

$$D_x = 8 \qquad D_y = 5 \qquad D_z = 2$$

Now we obtain the distance between P and Q,

$$D = \sqrt{8^2 + 5^2 + 2^2} = \sqrt{64 + 25 + 4} = \sqrt{93} = 9.64$$

The direction cosines become

$$\cos\theta_x = \frac{8}{9.64} = 0.829$$

$$\cos\theta_y = \frac{5}{9.64} = 0.518$$

$$\cos\theta_z = \frac{2}{9.64} = 0.207$$

$$\mathbf{T} = T(0.829\mathbf{i} + 0.518\mathbf{j} + 0.207\mathbf{k}) \qquad \text{Answer}$$

Example 2.2.7

A steamer is being pulled by two tugs as shown in Figure 2.17. The origin of the coordinate system is at the steamer. Tug 1 pulls with a force of $\mathbf{F}_1$ and tug 2 with a force of $\mathbf{F}_2$ as shown. What is the resultant force on the steamer? The magnitude of both $\mathbf{F}_1$ and $\mathbf{F}_2$ is 10 kips.

Force $\mathbf{F}_1$ is

$$\mathbf{F}_1 = F_1\mathbf{e}_1$$

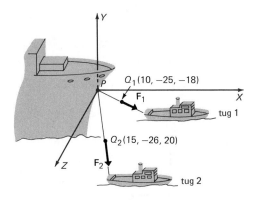

Figure 2.17

where

$$\mathbf{e}_1 = \cos \theta_{x1} \, \mathbf{i} + \cos \theta_{y1} \, \mathbf{j} + \cos \theta_{z1} \, \mathbf{k}$$

and $\cos \theta_{x1}$, $\cos \theta_{y1}$, $\cos \theta_{z1}$ are direction cosines of $\mathbf{PQ}_1$. The distances are

$$D_{x1} = 10 \qquad D_{y1} = -25 \qquad D_{z1} = -18$$

and

$$D = \sqrt{10^2 + 25^2 + 18^2} = 32.4$$

Therefore,

$$\cos \theta_{x1} = 0.308 \qquad \cos \theta_{y1} = -0.771 \qquad \cos \theta_{z1} = -0.555$$

so that

$$\mathbf{F}_1 = 10(0.308\mathbf{i} - 0.771\mathbf{j} - 0.555\mathbf{k})$$
$$= 3.08\mathbf{i} - 7.71\mathbf{j} - 5.55\mathbf{k}$$

Similarly,

$$\mathbf{F}_2 = F_2 \mathbf{e}_2$$
$$\mathbf{e}_2 = \cos \theta_{x2} \, \mathbf{i} + \cos \theta_{y2} \, \mathbf{j} + \cos \theta_{z2} \, \mathbf{k}$$

where $\cos \theta_{x2}$, $\cos \theta_{y2}$, $\cos \theta_{z2}$ are direction cosines of $\mathbf{PQ}_2$. The distances are

$$D_x = 15 \qquad D_y = -26 \qquad D_z = 20$$

and

$$D = 36.1$$

so that the direction cosines become

$$\cos \theta_{x2} = 0.415 \qquad \cos \theta_{y2} = -0.720 \qquad \cos \theta_{z2} = 0.555$$

and the force $\mathbf{F}_2$ can be written as

$$\mathbf{F}_2 = 10(0.415\mathbf{i} - 0.720\mathbf{j} + 0.555\mathbf{k})$$
$$= 4.15\mathbf{i} - 7.20\mathbf{j} + 5.55\mathbf{k}$$

The resultant force $\mathbf{R}$ is obtained from

$$\mathbf{R} = \mathbf{F}_1 + \mathbf{F}_2 = R_x\mathbf{i} + R_y\mathbf{j} + R_z\mathbf{k}$$

where

$$R_x = \Sigma F_x = 3.08 + 4.15 = 7.23$$
$$R_y = \Sigma F_y = -7.71 - 7.20 = -14.91$$
$$R_z = \Sigma F_z = -5.55 + 5.55 = 0$$

Substituting, we obtain

$$\mathbf{R} = 7.23\mathbf{i} - 14.91\mathbf{j} \text{ kips} \qquad \text{Answer}$$

Problems

Figure 2.18

2.2.1 Determine graphically the resultant force on the hook shown in Figure 2.18.

2.2.2 What is the resultant force on the structure of Figure 2.19? Use a graphical method.

2.2.3 Obtain graphically the resultant force on the rod *AB* shown in Figure 2.20.

2.2.4 The hook shown in Figure 2.21 is connected to three cables. What is the resultant force on the hook? Use a graphical method.

2.2.5 A barge is pulled by two ropes as shown in Figure 2.22. The tension in the two ropes is 200 lb. Graphically obtain the resultant force applied on the barge.

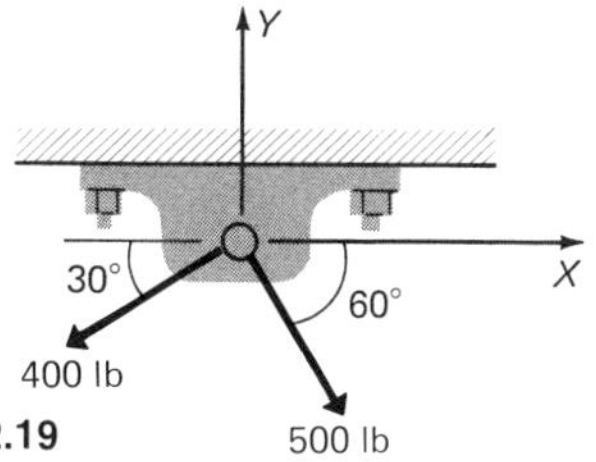

Figure 2.19

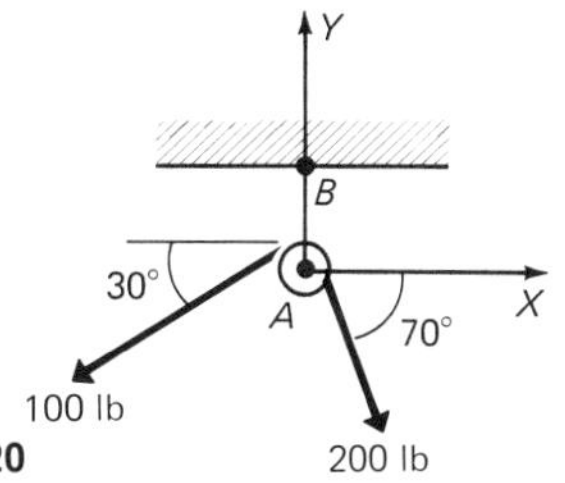

Figure 2.20

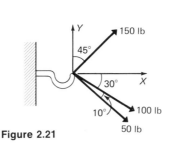

Figure 2.21

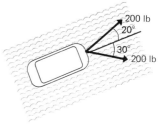

Figure 2.22

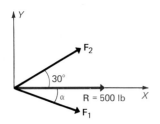

Figure 2.23

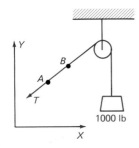

Figure 2.24

2.2.6 Using Figure 2.18, obtain the magnitude and direction of the resultant force by adding the components.

2.2.7 Using Figure 2.19, obtain the magnitude and direction of the resultant force by adding the components.

2.2.8 Using Figure 2.20, obtain the magnitude and direction of the resultant force by adding the components.

2.2.9 Using Figure 2.21, obtain the magnitude and direction of the resultant force by adding the components.

2.2.10 Obtain the angle α and the magnitude of $\mathbf{F}_1$ in Figure 2.23 if $|\mathbf{F}_2| = 100$ lb and $\mathbf{R} = \mathbf{F}_1 + \mathbf{F}_2$. Use (a) the parallelogram law and (b) the triangle law.

2.2.11 Solve problem 2.2.10 by writing the components of the forces.

2.2.12 The tension in a rope used to support a 1000-lb weight is T and is directed along the rope as shown in Figure 2.24. If the rope passes through $A(5,2)$ and $B(8,3)$, express the tension force as a vector quantity.

2.2.13 A force $\mathbf{F}_1$ is given by $\mathbf{F}_1 = 8\mathbf{i} + 9\mathbf{j}$. What is the projection of this force on a line whose direction is given by the unit vector $\boldsymbol{\lambda} = 0.8\mathbf{i} + 0.6\mathbf{j}$?

2.2.14 Obtain the resultant of the concurrent forces shown in Figure 2.25 using the polygon rule.

2.2.15 Obtain the magnitude and unit vector of the resultant force of problem 2.2.14 by summing the components of the four concurrent forces.

2.2.16 What are the direction cosines of the force $\mathbf{F}$ given by $\mathbf{F} = 1000\mathbf{i} + 600\mathbf{j} + 565\mathbf{k}$?

2.2.17 A 1000-lb force is applied to a truck as shown in Figure 2.26. Resolve this force in the XYZ direction.

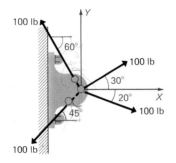

Figure 2.25

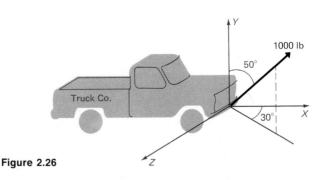

Figure 2.26

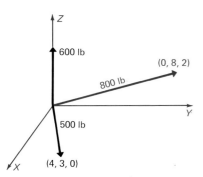

Figure 2.27

2.2.18 A force of 500 lb goes through points $A(5,6,2)$ and $B(2,1,3)$. Represent the force as a vector quantity.

2.2.19 Supply the magnitude and direction cosines of the resultant force obtained by

$$R = F_1 + F_2 - F_3$$

where

$$F_1 = 100i + 200j + 50k$$

$$F_2 = 50i - 10j + 10k$$

$$F_3 = 20i + 60j - 400k$$

2.2.20 Supply the magnitude and direction cosines of the resultant force obtained by adding the three forces shown in Figure 2.27.

2.3 Equilibrium of a Particle ────────────────────

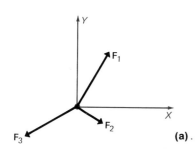

(a)

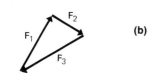

(b)

Figure 2.28

From Newton's first law we know that a particle will remain at rest if the resultant force is zero. This condition of no motion and, therefore, zero resultant force, is called a *condition of equilibrium.*

If a particle is subjected to forces F_1, F_2, and F_3, the sum of these forces must be zero for equilibrium. (This is shown in Figure 2.28a.) *If the forces applied to a particle at equilibrium are combined by the polygon rule, the resultant force is zero* (see Figure 2.28b). If the resultant force is zero, all the components of the resultant force must be zero. Therefore, for equilibrium,

$$R_x = \Sigma F_x = 0 \qquad R_y = \Sigma F_y = 0$$

provided the force is a planar force represented in the XY plane. If, however, there are forces which have components along the Z axis as well, then there is a third equation to be satisfied, i.e.,

$$R_z = \Sigma F_z = 0$$

The requirement that, for equilibrium, the resultant force be zero can be compactly written as

$$R = \Sigma F = 0 \qquad (2.11)$$

where

$$\Sigma F = (\Sigma F_x)i + (\Sigma F_y)j + (\Sigma F_z)k$$

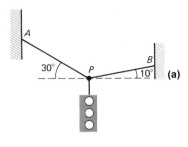

(a)

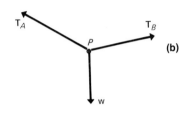

(b)

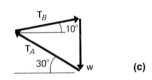

(c)

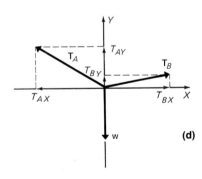

(d)

Figure 2.29

This vector equation is actually equivalent to three scalar equations, namely, $\Sigma F_x = 0$, $\Sigma F_y = 0$, and $\Sigma F_z = 0$, obtained by setting the coefficient of each independent unit vector equation equal to zero. The equations obtained by setting the resultant force to zero are called *equations of equilibrium*. For the equilibrium of a particle in three dimensions, there are three equations of equilibrium. These equations are most easily satisfied by a drawing of the particle showing all forces acting on it. When we thus isolate a particle from some physical situation and diagrammatically show all the forces acting on it, we have obtained a *free-body diagram*. A sketch showing the physical situation is called a *space diagram*.

Consider a traffic light suspended as shown in Figure 2.29a, and assume that the weight of the light is w lb. If we consider a particle at P, then the free-body diagram shown in Figure 2.29b may be drawn. Note that a particle at P is subjected to the weight of the light and the tension of the two cables. The particle is to be in equilibrium. Therefore, the resultant force must be zero. The three forces may be combined to obtain the force triangle shown in Figure 2.29c, so that the tensions $\mathbf{T}_A$ and $\mathbf{T}_B$ can be found. The values obtained for $\mathbf{T}_A$ and $\mathbf{T}_B$ are necessary for equilibrium. Notice that we are able to solve for two unknown forces.

As an alternate method for the computation of the unknown forces, we can use the components of the forces. The resultant force is

$$R = w + T_A + T_B$$

The components are

$$(R_x\mathbf{i} + R_y\mathbf{j}) = -w\mathbf{j} + (T_{Ax}\mathbf{i} + T_{Ay}\mathbf{j}) + (T_{Bx}\mathbf{i} + T_{By}\mathbf{j})$$

This yields two scalar equations:

the i equation is $\qquad R_x = T_{Bx} + T_{Ax}$

the j equation is $\qquad R_y = T_{By} + T_{Ay} - w$

We see from Figure 2.29d that

$$T_{Ax} = \mathbf{T}_A \cdot \mathbf{i} = -T_A \cos 30°$$

$$T_{Ay} = \mathbf{T}_A \cdot \mathbf{j} = T_A \cos 60°$$

$$T_{Bx} = \mathbf{T}_B \cdot \mathbf{i} = T_B \cos 10°$$

$$T_{By} = \mathbf{T}_B \cdot \mathbf{j} = T_B \cos 80°$$

and we know that, for equilibrium,

$$R_x = 0 \qquad R_y = 0$$

so that the *i* and *j* equilibrium equations become

$$T_B \cos 10° - T_A \cos 30° = 0 \qquad T_B \cos 80° + T_A \cos 60° = w$$

The solution of these two equations yields an answer identical to that obtained by the force triangle.

Example 2.3.1

A man weighing 150 lb is walking a tightrope as shown in Figure 2.30a. What is the tension in the rope at the instant shown?

Figure 2.30   **(a)**

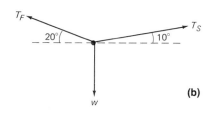

(b)

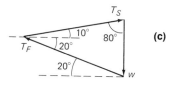

(c)

First we construct a free-body diagram of a particle at point *P* where the man is standing. The three forces acting at point *P* are the weight *w*, a tensile force T_S in *PS*, and a tensile force T_F in *PF* as shown in Figure 2.30b. These tensions may be obtained from the force triangle shown in Figure 2.30c. From the geometry we get

$$\frac{T_S}{\sin 70°} = \frac{T_F}{\sin 80°} = \frac{w}{\sin 30°}$$

therefore

$$T_S = \frac{w \sin 70°}{\sin 30°} = \frac{150(0.94)}{0.5} = 282 \text{ lb}$$

Answer

$$T_F = \frac{w \sin 80°}{\sin 30°} = \frac{150(0.985)}{0.5} = 295 \text{ lb}$$

As an alternate method, the two equations of equilibrium can be used, i.e.,

$$T_S \cos 10° - T_F \cos 20° = R_x = 0$$

$$T_S \sin 10° + T_F \sin 20° - w = R_y = 0$$

or

$$T_S \cos 10° - T_F \cos 20° = 0$$
$$T_S \sin 10° + T_F \sin 20° = w$$

Solving the first of these for T_F and substituting into the second, we obtain

$$T_S \sin 10° + \left(T_S \frac{\cos 10°}{\cos 20°} \cdot \sin 20° \right) = w$$

$$T_S(\sin 10° \cos 20° + \cos 10° \sin 20°) = w \cos 20°$$

From trigonometry, we know that

$$\sin 10° \cos 20° + \cos 10° \sin 20° = \sin (10° + 20°) = \sin 30°$$

so that the last equation becomes

$$T_S \sin 30° = w \cos 20° = w \sin 70°$$

and therefore

$$T_S = \frac{w \sin 70°}{\sin 30°} = 282 \text{ lb} \qquad \text{Answer}$$

which is identical to the result obtained geometrically from the force triangle. It is left as an exercise to show that $T_F = 295$ lb.

Example 2.3.2

A block weighing 100 lb is suspended by three ropes lying in the XY plane as shown in Figure 2.31a. It is known that the tension in rope C is 20 lb. What is the tension in ropes A and B for equilibrium?

A free-body diagram for the particle at P is shown in Figure 2.31b. The equilibrium equations are

$$\Sigma F_x = -T_A \cos 30° + T_B \sin 50° + 20 \cos 10° = 0$$
$$\Sigma F_y = T_A \sin 30° + T_B \cos 50° + 20 \sin 10° = 100$$

Substituting for the sines and cosines, we obtain

$$-0.866T_A + 0.766T_B = -19.7$$
$$0.5T_A + 0.643T_B = 96.5$$

When the first equation is solved for T_B and substituted into the second equation, we get

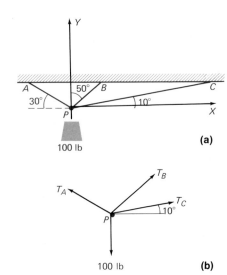

Figure 2.31

$$0.5T_A + 0.643 \left(-\frac{19.7}{0.766} + \frac{0.866}{0.766} T_A \right) = 96.5$$

$$1.227 T_A = 113$$

$$T_A = 92.2 \text{ lb}$$
Answer

Substituting this into the first equation gives

$$-79.8 + 0.766 T_B = -19.7$$

$$0.766 T_B = 60.1$$

$$T_B = 78.5 \text{ lb} \qquad \text{Answer}$$

Example 2.3.3

A chandelier weighing 200 lb is suspended by three chains as shown in Figure 2.32a. Find the equations of equilibrium relating the three tensions.

A free-body diagram of the particle at P is first drawn, as in Figure 2.32b. Before the equations of equilibrium are written, each force is written as a vector quantity. Thus,

$$\mathbf{w} = -200\mathbf{j}$$

and

$$\mathbf{T}_A = T_A \mathbf{e}_A \qquad \mathbf{T}_B = T_B \mathbf{e}_B \qquad \mathbf{T}_C = T_C \mathbf{e}_C$$

Then, since

$$\mathbf{e}_A = -\frac{20}{D_A}\mathbf{i} + \frac{10}{D_A}\mathbf{j} \qquad\qquad D_A = \sqrt{400 + 100} = 22.4$$

$$\mathbf{e}_B = -\frac{20}{D_B}\mathbf{i} + \frac{10}{D_B}\mathbf{j} - \frac{5}{D_B}\mathbf{k} \qquad D_B = \sqrt{400 + 100 + 25} = 22.8$$

$$\mathbf{e}_C = \frac{20}{D_C}\mathbf{i} + \frac{10}{D_C}\mathbf{j} + \frac{5}{D_C}\mathbf{k} \qquad D_C = \sqrt{400 + 100 + 25} = 22.8$$

we find that

$$\mathbf{e}_A = -0.894\mathbf{i} + 0.447\mathbf{j}$$

$$\mathbf{e}_B = -0.873\mathbf{i} + 0.436\mathbf{j} - 0.218\mathbf{k}$$

$$\mathbf{e}_C = 0.873\mathbf{i} + 0.436\mathbf{j} + 0.218\mathbf{k}$$

The necessary condition for equilibrium is

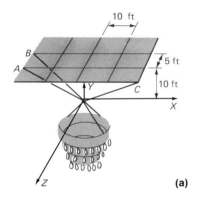

(a)

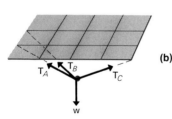

(b)

Figure 2.32

$$\mathbf{R} = \mathbf{w} + \mathbf{T}_A + \mathbf{T}_B + \mathbf{T}_C = 0$$

Substituting the above into this equation gives us

$$-200\mathbf{j} + T_A(-0.894\mathbf{i} + 0.447\mathbf{j}) + T_B(-0.873\mathbf{i} + 0.436\mathbf{j} - 0.218\mathbf{k})$$
$$+ T_C(0.873\mathbf{i} + 0.436\mathbf{j} + 0.218\mathbf{k}) = 0$$

from which we separate the components and write three equations,

for **i**: $0.894T_A + 0.873T_B - 0.873T_C = 0$

for **j**: $0.447T_A + 0.436T_B + 0.436T_C = 200$

for **k**: $-0.218T_B + 0.218T_C = 0$

Answer

Since there are three unknowns and three equations we may easily solve for the tensions T_A, T_B, and T_C.

Problems

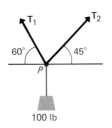

Figure 2.33

100 lb

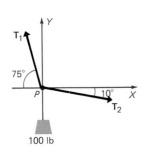

100 lb

Figure 2.34

2.3.1 Graphically obtain T_1 and T_2 so that the particle P in Figure 2.33 is at equilibrium.

2.3.2 Graphically obtain T_1 and T_2 so that the particle P in Figure 2.34 is at equilibrium.

2.3.3 Considering the equilibrium of the particle at C, obtain graphically the tension in cables AC and BC in Figure 2.35.

2.3.4 Considering the equilibrium of the particle at C, obtain graphically the tension in cables AC and BC in Figure 2.36.

2.3.5 Write the equations of equilibrium and obtain the tension to maintain equilibrium for the system of Figure 2.33.

2.3.6 Write the equations of equilibrium and obtain the tension to maintain equilibrium for the system of Figure 2.34.

2.3.7 Write the equations of equilibrium and obtain the tension to maintain equilibrium for the system of Figure 2.35.

2.3.8 Write the equations of equilibrium and obtain the tension to maintain equilibrium for the system of Figure 2.36.

2.3.9 A particle is subjected to two forces given by $\mathbf{F}_1 = 8\mathbf{i} + 6\mathbf{j}$ and $\mathbf{F}_2 = 9\mathbf{i} + 15\mathbf{j}$. What additional force must be applied in order to have the particle at equilibrium?

2.3.10 A spring is stretched by a 150-lb force as shown in Figure 2.37. What is the tension in AB and BC?

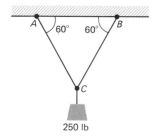

Figure 2.35

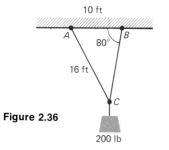

Figure 2.36

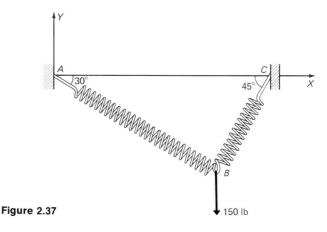

Figure 2.37

2.3.11 Write the equations of equilibrium for the particle at P in terms of x and h as shown in Figure 2.38.

2.3.12 For the configuration of Figure 2.39, determine the value of θ for equilibrium.

2.3.13 A particle is subjected to four forces as shown in Figure 2.40. Determine the magnitude of the forces F_1 and F_2 necessary for the particle to be in equilibrium.

2.3.14 A crane is used to raise a 500-lb weight, as shown in Figure 2.41. Determine the reaction at point A.

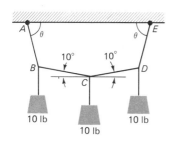

Figure 2.38

Figure 2.39

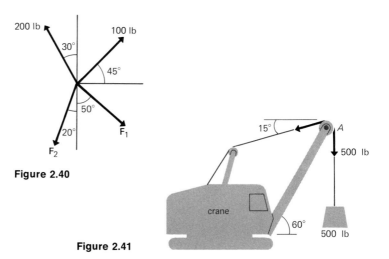

Figure 2.40

Figure 2.41

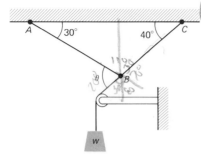

Figure 2.42

Figure 2.43

2.3.15 The maximum tension in ropes AB and BC can be 500 lb (Figure 2.42). What is the maximum value of w to insure equilibrium?

2.3.16 A crane is used to pick up a bundle of logs weighing 5000 lb, as shown in Figure 2.43. A man pulls to prevent any swaying. For the instant shown, what is the tension in the two cables, AB and BC?

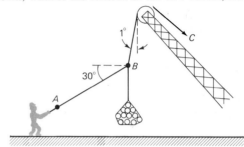

2.3.17 A particle is subjected to two forces $\mathbf{F}_1$ and $\mathbf{F}_2$ given by $\mathbf{F}_1 = 5\mathbf{i} + 6\mathbf{j} + 2\mathbf{k}$ and $\mathbf{F}_2 = \mathbf{i} + 3\mathbf{j} - \mathbf{k}$, where the magnitude is in kips. (a) What is the magnitude and (b) what are the direction cosines of the third force necessary for equilibrium?

2.3.18 A 1000-lb weight is supported by three cables as shown in Figure 2.44. Determine the tension in each cable.

2.3.19 Determine the forces in the three members PA, PB, PC shown in Figure 2.45.

2.3.20 A traffic light weighing 200 lb is suspended as shown in Figure 2.46. Determine the tension in cables AB, AC, and AD.

2.3.21 A 240-lb weight is suspended as shown in Figure 2.47. The ring has a 3-ft diameter and the point D is 4 ft below the center of the ring. Determine the magnitude of the tension in each wire.

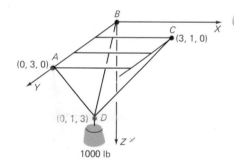

Figure 2.44

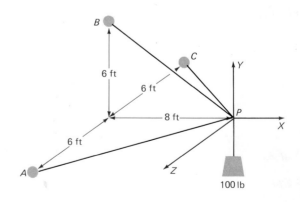

Figure 2.45

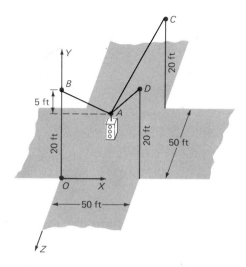

Figure 2.46

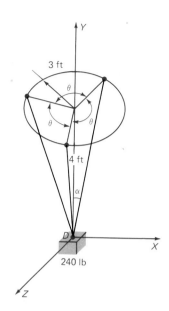

Figure 2.47

2.4 Moment of a Force

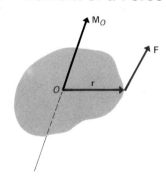

Figure 2.48

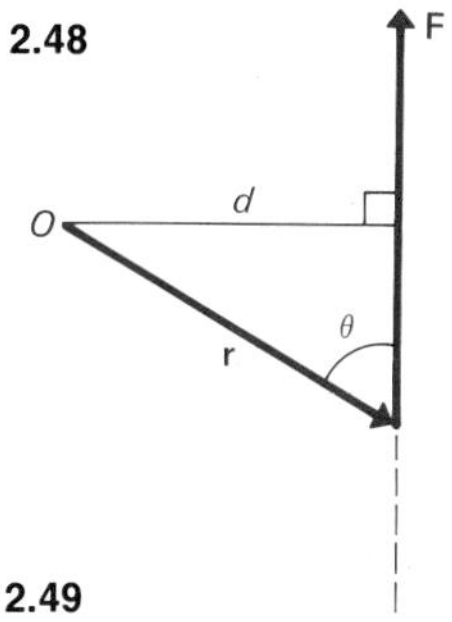

Figure 2.49

A force applied to a body creates a tendency for the body to translate. The tendency to rotate, on the other hand, is created by a *moment* or *torque*. The moment of force **F** about a point O, shown in Figure 2.48, is defined as

$$\mathbf{M}_O = \mathbf{r} \times \mathbf{F} \tag{2.12}$$

The moment $\mathbf{M}_O$ is a vector whose line of action is perpendicular to **r** as well as **F**. The direction of $\mathbf{M}_O$ is obtained by the right-hand rule as applied to the cross product. The line of action of $\mathbf{M}_O$ is the axis about which the body tends to rotate.

If **F** makes an angle θ with the position vector **r** as shown in Figure 2.49, then the magnitude of the moment becomes

$$M_O = (r \sin \theta)F = Fd \tag{2.13}$$

where d is the perpendicular distance between the line of action of **F** and the point O. This leads to an important observation. The moment $\mathbf{M}_O$ depends upon **r** as well as upon the magnitude and direction of the force **F**, but not on its point of application. Therefore, if we know only $\mathbf{M}_O$, we obviously can say nothing about the point of application of the force **F** that produced it. Also, from the transmissibility principle, we know that two forces are equivalent provided they have the same magnitude, direction, and line of action. We may now expand this to say that two forces are equivalent if, in addition, they produce the same moment about any given point.

Components of a Moment

Consider a force in the XY plane, that is,

$$\mathbf{F} = F_x\mathbf{i} + F_y\mathbf{j}$$

and a position vector

$$\mathbf{r} = x\mathbf{i} + y\mathbf{j}$$

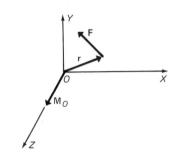

Figure 2.50

as shown in Figure 2.50. The moment about O due to this force is

$$\mathbf{M}_O = \mathbf{r} \times \mathbf{F} \qquad (2.12)$$

Recall from Chapter 1 that a vector product can be written in matrix form, so that

$$\mathbf{M}_O = \mathbf{r} \times \mathbf{F} = \begin{vmatrix} \mathbf{i} & \mathbf{j} & \mathbf{k} \\ x & y & 0 \\ F_x & F_y & 0 \end{vmatrix}$$

$$= (xF_y - yF_x)\mathbf{k}$$

The moment vector due to a force in the XY plane is directed along the Z axis.

If the force is three dimensional, so that

$$\mathbf{F} = F_x\mathbf{i} + F_y\mathbf{j} + F_z\mathbf{k} \qquad \text{and} \qquad \mathbf{r} = x\mathbf{i} + y\mathbf{j} + z\mathbf{k}$$

then the moment becomes

$$\mathbf{M}_O = \mathbf{r} \times \mathbf{F} = \begin{vmatrix} \mathbf{i} & \mathbf{j} & \mathbf{k} \\ x & y & z \\ F_x & F_y & F_z \end{vmatrix}$$

$$= (yF_z - zF_y)\mathbf{i} + (zF_x - xF_z)\mathbf{j} + (xF_y - yF_x)\mathbf{k}$$

Here, the moment has three components and may be written as

$$\mathbf{M}_O = M_x\mathbf{i} + M_y\mathbf{j} + M_z\mathbf{k}$$

where

$$M_x = yF_z - zF_y \qquad M_y = zF_x - xF_z \qquad M_z = xF_y - yF_x$$

The magnitude of the moment is given by

$$M_O = \sqrt{M_x^2 + M_y^2 + M_z^2}$$

and the direction cosines are

$$\frac{1}{M_O} = \frac{\cos\theta_x}{M_x} = \frac{\cos\theta_y}{M_y} = \frac{\cos\theta_z}{M_z}$$

Moment Due to Several Forces

If several forces are applied to a point P as shown in Figure 2.51, the moment caused by these forces is

$$M_O = r \times (F_1 + F_2 + \cdots + F_n)$$

Since vector products are distributive, this can be written as

$$M_O = r \times (F_1 + F_2 + \cdots + F_n)$$
$$= (r \times F_1) + (r \times F_2) + \cdots + (r \times F_n)$$

This equation states that the moment due to several concurrent forces is equal to the sum of the moments caused by individual forces. This observation is often referred to as *Varignon's Theorem,* after the French mathematician Varignon (1654–1722) who first deduced it.

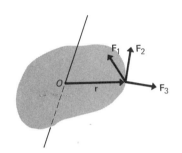

Figure 2.51

Example 2.4.1

Compute the moment about O due to force $\mathbf{F}$ of magnitude 100 lb applied at point A to the structural member shown in Figure 2.52.

We first represent the force as a vector,

$$\mathbf{F} = 100(0.707\mathbf{i} - 0.707\mathbf{j})$$

The position vector $\mathbf{r} = \mathbf{OA}$ is

$$\mathbf{r} = 6\mathbf{i} + 8\mathbf{j}$$

The moment about O is

$$\mathbf{M}_O = \mathbf{r} \times \mathbf{F} = \begin{vmatrix} \mathbf{i} & \mathbf{j} & \mathbf{k} \\ 6 & 8 & 0 \\ 70.7 & -70.7 & 0 \end{vmatrix}$$

$$= -70.7(14)\mathbf{k} = -990\mathbf{k} \quad \text{lb-in. Answer}$$

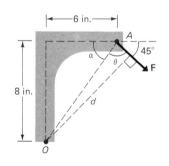

Figure 2.52

An alternate method is to direct the moment vector into and perpendicular to the plane of the paper, since the force is in the XY plane. From equation (2.13), the magnitude M_O is

$$M_O = Fd$$

where d is the perpendicular distance from O to the line of action of the force.

$$d = |\mathbf{OA}| \sin \theta \qquad |\mathbf{OA}| = \sqrt{8^2 + 6^2} = 10$$

$$\alpha = 53.1 \qquad \theta = 180 - 45 - 53.1 = 81.9$$

therefore

$$d = 10 \sin 81.9° = 10(0.990) = 9.90$$

The moment about point O is thus found to be

$$M_O = (9.90)(100)$$

$$\mathbf{M}_O = 990 \text{ lb-in.} \qquad \text{Answer}$$

which is the answer obtained with the first method. Notice that $\curvearrowright$ represents the clockwise (CW) direction and is the direction in which the body tends to rotate. From the right-hand rule, a screw tending to rotate this way advances in the $-\mathbf{k}$ direction. Therefore $\curvearrowright$ and $-\mathbf{k}$ are equivalent, vectorially speaking.

Example 2.4.2

A transmitting antenna is secured by guy wires as shown in Figure 2.53a. The tensile forces in the wire as shown in Figure 2.53b are $T_1 = 150$ lb and $T_2 = 200$ lb. What is the moment due to these forces about point O?

$$\mathbf{M}_O = \mathbf{r}_1 \times \mathbf{T}_1 + \mathbf{r}_2 \times \mathbf{T}_2 \qquad (2.14)$$

The position vectors and tensions are

$$\mathbf{r}_1 = 30\mathbf{j} \qquad \mathbf{T}_1 = 150(0.5\mathbf{i} - 0.866\mathbf{j})$$

$$\mathbf{r}_2 = 20\mathbf{j} \qquad \mathbf{T}_2 = 200(-0.707\mathbf{i} - 0.707\mathbf{j})$$

The two moments become

$$\mathbf{r}_1 \times \mathbf{T}_1 = \begin{vmatrix} \mathbf{i} & \mathbf{j} & \mathbf{k} \\ 0 & 30 & 0 \\ 75 & -130 & 0 \end{vmatrix} = -2250\mathbf{k} \quad \text{lb-ft}$$

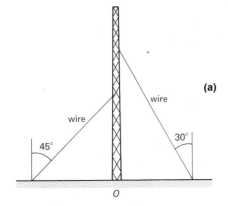

(a)

Figure 2.53

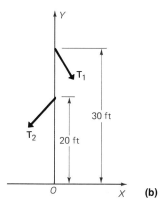

$$\mathbf{r}_2 \times \mathbf{T}_2 = \begin{vmatrix} \mathbf{i} & \mathbf{j} & \mathbf{k} \\ 0 & 20 & 0 \\ -141.4 & -141.4 & 0 \end{vmatrix} = 2828\mathbf{k} \quad \text{lb-ft}$$

Substitution of these values into equation (2.14) gives

$$\mathbf{M}_O = -2250\mathbf{k} + 2828\mathbf{k} = 578\mathbf{k} \quad \text{lb-ft} \quad \text{Answer}$$

Example 2.4.3

Two cables are used to support a rod on which a sign is hung, as shown in Figure 2.54a. The tension in each cable is 500 lb. The sign weighs 100 lb. What is the resultant moment about O?

The resultant moment about O consists of three moments caused by $\mathbf{w}$, $\mathbf{T}_R$, and $\mathbf{T}_L$. Referring to Figure 2.54b, we see that these forces are

$$\mathbf{w} = -1000\mathbf{j}$$

and

$$\mathbf{T}_R = 500\left(-\frac{5}{D_1}\mathbf{i} + \frac{8}{D_1}\mathbf{j} + \frac{2}{D_1}\mathbf{k}\right) \quad D_1 = \sqrt{5^2 + 8^2 + 2^2} = 9.64$$

$$\mathbf{T}_L = 500\left(-\frac{5}{D_2}\mathbf{i} + \frac{8}{D_2}\mathbf{j} - \frac{2}{D_2}\mathbf{k}\right) \quad D_2 = 9.64$$

so that

$$\mathbf{T}_R = 500(-0.518\mathbf{i} + 0.829\mathbf{j} + 0.207\mathbf{k})$$

$$\mathbf{T}_L = 500(-0.518\mathbf{i} + 0.829\mathbf{j} - 0.207\mathbf{k})$$

The three moments can now be computed.

1. Since $\mathbf{r} = 9\mathbf{i}$ and $\mathbf{w} = -1000\mathbf{j}$,

$$\mathbf{r} \times \mathbf{w} = -9000\mathbf{k} \quad \text{lb-ft}$$

2. Since $\mathbf{r}_R = 5\mathbf{i}$ and, from above,

$$\mathbf{T}_R = -259\mathbf{i} + 414\mathbf{j} + 104\mathbf{k},$$

$$\mathbf{r}_R \times \mathbf{T}_R = \begin{vmatrix} \mathbf{i} & \mathbf{j} & \mathbf{k} \\ 5 & 0 & 0 \\ -259 & 414 & 104 \end{vmatrix} = -520\mathbf{j} + 2070\mathbf{k} \quad \text{lb-ft}$$

3. And, since $\mathbf{r}_L = 5\mathbf{i}$ and, from above,

$$\mathbf{T}_L = -259\mathbf{i} + 414\mathbf{j} - 104\mathbf{k},$$

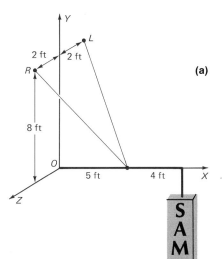

(a)

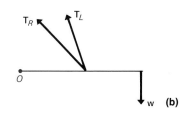

(b)

Figure 2.54

$$\mathbf{r}_L \times \mathbf{T}_L = \begin{vmatrix} \mathbf{i} & \mathbf{j} & \mathbf{k} \\ 5 & 0 & 0 \\ -259 & 414 & -104 \end{vmatrix} = 520\mathbf{j} + 2070\mathbf{k} \qquad \text{lb-ft}$$

The total moment about O therefore becomes

$$\mathbf{M}_O = (\mathbf{r} \times \mathbf{w}) + (\mathbf{r}_R \times \mathbf{T}_R) + (\mathbf{r}_L \times \mathbf{T}_L)$$

$$= -9000\mathbf{k} + (-520\mathbf{j} + 2070\mathbf{k}) + (520\mathbf{j} + 2070\mathbf{k})$$

$$= -4860\mathbf{k} \qquad \text{lb-ft} \qquad\qquad \text{Answer}$$

2.5 Moment of a Couple

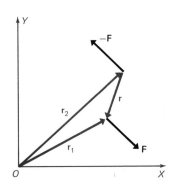

Figure 2.55

When two forces $\mathbf{F}$ and $-\mathbf{F}$ are equal in magnitude, parallel in their lines of action, but opposite in direction, they form what is known as a couple. Obviously, here the sum of $\mathbf{F}$ and $-\mathbf{F}$ is zero. But the sum of the moments of these two forces about O is not zero, as seen in Figure 2.55.

$$\mathbf{M}_O = \mathbf{r}_1 \times \mathbf{F} + \mathbf{r}_2 \times (-\mathbf{F}) = \mathbf{r}_1 \times \mathbf{F} - \mathbf{r}_2 \times \mathbf{F} = (\mathbf{r}_1 - \mathbf{r}_2) \times \mathbf{F} = \mathbf{M}$$

If we set

$$\mathbf{r} = \mathbf{r}_1 - \mathbf{r}_2$$

then

$$\mathbf{M} = \mathbf{M}_O = \mathbf{r} \times \mathbf{F} \qquad\qquad (2.12)$$

where $\mathbf{r}$ is the vector joining the points of application of the two forces. Notice that it is not important where the point O is since the final answer does not depend on it. The vector $\mathbf{M}$ is called the *moment of a couple,* sometimes referred to as a *pure moment.* It is a *free vector* and can be applied at every point, perpendicular to the plane of its contributing forces.

We can make an important observation here. A moment of a couple, or a couple as we call it for short, can be applied to a body about any point as long as the direction of the couple is fixed. The sum of forces that give rise to this couple is zero. However, when a moment is caused by one applied force, the resultant of the forces is not zero. For this reason, a couple is sometimes referred to as a *pure moment.* Several examples of couples and their moments are given in Figure 2.56.

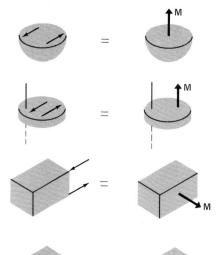

Figure 2.56

If the line of action of **F** makes an angle θ with **r** as shown in Figure 2.57, then the magnitude of **M**, the moment of the couple, becomes

$$M = F(r \sin \theta) = Fd$$

that is, the moment of the couple is the product of the force F and the perpendicular distance *between* the lines of action of the two equal but opposite forces **F**, $-$**F**. The direction of this couple is perpendicular to the plane containing the two forces.

Since the moment of a couple is a vector, the moments of more than one couple can be combined using the rules already developed. In general, the moment of a couple can have as many as three components and may be expressed by its components like any other vector considered so far.

Example 2.5.1

What is the moment of the couple when two 100-lb forces **F** that are parallel but opposite in direction are applied as shown in Figure 2.58?

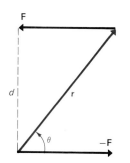

Figure 2.57

Figure 2.58

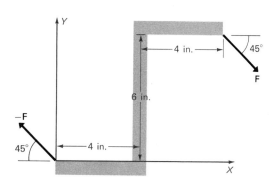

From equation (2.12) we have

$$\mathbf{M} = \mathbf{r} \times \mathbf{F}$$

where

$$\mathbf{r} = 8\mathbf{i} + 6\mathbf{j}$$

$$\mathbf{F} = 100(0.707\mathbf{i} - 0.707\mathbf{j})$$

Substituting, we get

$$\mathbf{M} = \begin{vmatrix} \mathbf{i} & \mathbf{j} & \mathbf{k} \\ 8 & 6 & 0 \\ 70.7 & -70.7 & 0 \end{vmatrix} = -14(70.7)\mathbf{k}$$

$$= -990\mathbf{k} \quad \text{lb-in.} \qquad \text{Answer}$$

Problems

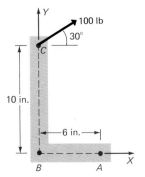

Figure 2.59

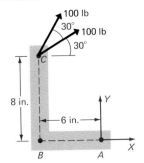

Figure 2.60

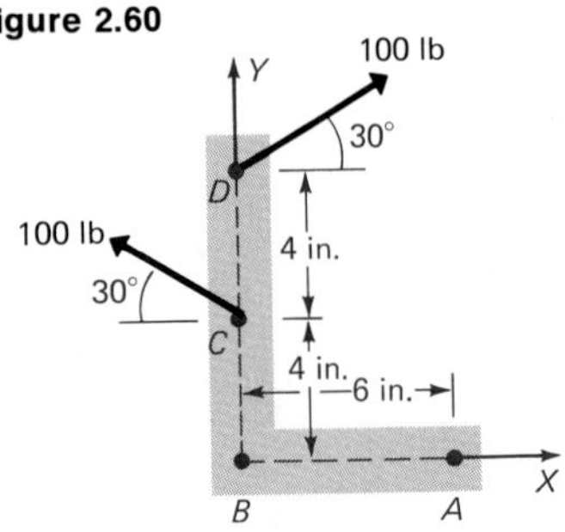

2.5.1 Determine the moment about points *A* and *B* in Figure 2.59.

2.5.2 Determine the moment about points *A* and *B* in Figure 2.60.

2.5.3 Determine the moment about points *A* and *B* in Figure 2.61.

2.5.4 Determine the moment about points *A* and *B* in Figure 2.62.

2.5.5 Determine the moment about points *A* and *B* in Figure 2.63.

2.5.6 Determine the moment about point *A* in Figure 2.64.

2.5.7 What is the moment about *A* and *B* due to the applied load in problem 2.3.4 on page 42?

2.5.8 Compute the moment about point *O* for the system shown in Figure 2.65.

2.5.9 A force $\mathbf{F} = 50\mathbf{i} + 60\mathbf{j}$ lb is applied at a point whose position vector from *O* is given by $\mathbf{r} = \mathbf{i} + 4\mathbf{j}$ ft. What is the resulting moment about the point *O*?

2.5.10 Determine the moment about *A* due to the 250-lb applied force as shown in Figure 2.66.

2.5.11 What moment does the 20-lb force create about *A* in Figure 2.67?

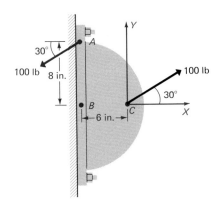

Figure 2.61

Figure 2.62

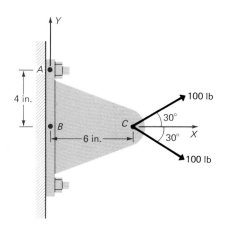

Figure 2.63

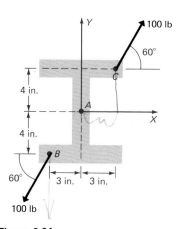

Figure 2.64

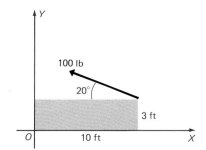

Figure 2.65

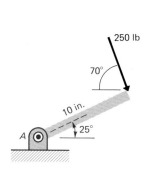

Figure 2.66

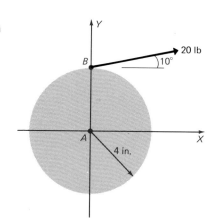

Figure 2.67

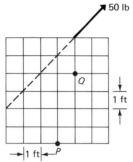
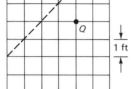

Figure 2.68

2.5.12 Calculate the moment of the 50-lb force about point P of the plate shown in Figure 2.68.

2.5.13 What is the resultant moment about point P of the plate shown in Figure 2.69?

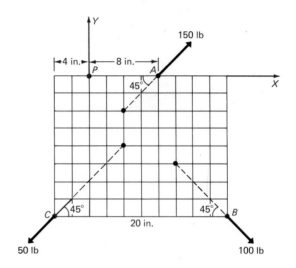

Figure 2.69

2.5.14 A bolt is to be tightened as shown in Figure 2.70. Determine the moment applied about point A.

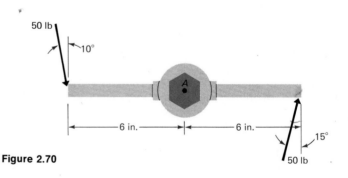

Figure 2.70

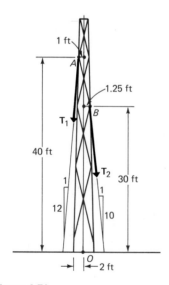

Figure 2.71

2.5.15 An antenna is supported in two dimensions as shown in Figure 2.71. If $T_1 = 200$ lb and $T_2 = 150$ lb, what is the resulting moment about point O?

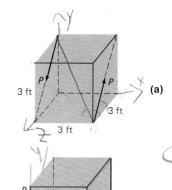

(a)

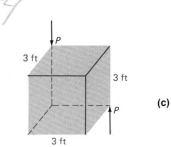

(b)

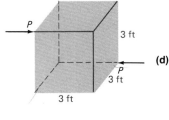

(c)

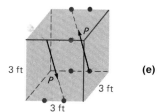

(d)

(e)

Figure 2.72

2.5.16 Determine the couple applied to the bracket shown in Figure 2.62.

2.5.17 Determine the couple applied to the I beam shown in Figure 2.64.

2.5.18 A bolt is to be tightened as shown in Figure 2.70. What is (a) the net force and (b) the moment acting on the bolt?

2.5.19 Obtain the resultant couple in each of the configurations shown in Figure 2.72 if $P = 10$ lb.

2.5.20 Obtain the resultant couple in the structure shown in Figure 2.61.

2.5.21 Obtain the magnitude of the moment of the 50-lb force about point A shown in Figure 2.73.

2.5.22 Obtain the moment about point A due to the 100-lb force shown in Figure 2.74. Express the answer (a) in the form of a magnitude and (b) as direction cosines.

Figure 2.73

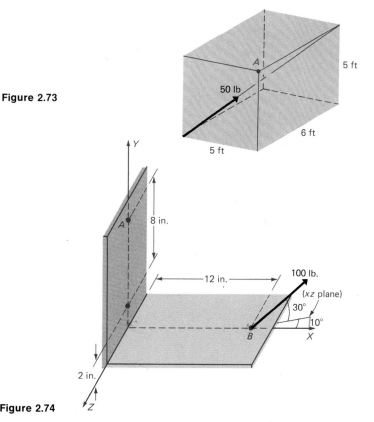

Figure 2.74

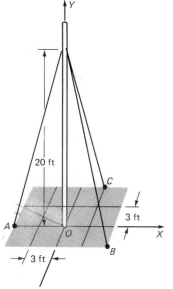

Figure 2.75

Figure 2.76

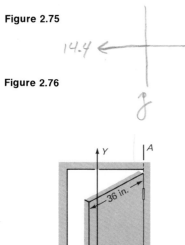

Figure 2.77

2.5.23 A force $\mathbf{F} = 8\mathbf{i} + 5\mathbf{j} + 3\mathbf{k}$ kips is applied at a point whose position vector from O is given by $\mathbf{r} = 3\mathbf{i} + 2\mathbf{j} + \mathbf{k}$ where distances are measured in feet. What is the resulting moment about O?

2.5.24 A flagpole is supported as shown in Figure 2.75. If the tension in each rope is 50 lb, what is the resulting moment about O? Give the answer (a) as a magnitude and (b) in terms of unit vectors.

2.5.25 Compute the moment about point O due to the tensile force in the cable BA supporting the traffic light of problem 2.3.20 on p. 44.

2.5.26 What is the magnitude of the projection of the couple $994\mathbf{k}$ lb-ft on a line passing through the points $A(1,2,3)$ and $B(-1,-2,-3)$?

2.5.27 Compute the magnitude and direction cosines of the couple produced by $\mathbf{F}$ and $-\mathbf{F}$ where $\mathbf{F} = 5\mathbf{i} + 4\mathbf{j} + \mathbf{k}$ lb. The position vector from the point of application of $-\mathbf{F}$ to $\mathbf{F}$ is given by $\mathbf{r} = 3\mathbf{i} + \mathbf{j} + 2\mathbf{k}$ ft.

2.5.28 Two ropes are tied as shown in Figure 2.76. What is the resulting couple on the plate?

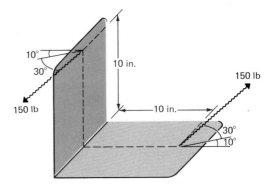

2.5.29 A door is opened by applying a 20-lb force to the handle as shown in Figure 2.77. What is the resulting moment about the axis AA?

2.6 Forces, Moments, and Couples

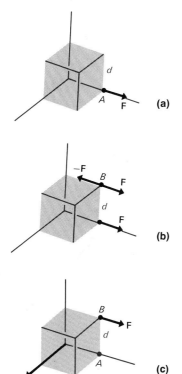

Figure 2.78

We have been dealing with forces, moments, and couples on an individual basis. Actually, however, it often happens that several forces, moments, and couples are simultaneously applied to an engineering structure. It is, therefore, desirable that we be able to combine them in a systematic way to obtain simpler but equivalent systems.

Consider the force **F** applied to the cube at point A shown in Figure 2.78a. We wish to move the force to a different point but retain the *same* system. We select a second point, B, and apply forces **F** and −**F** as shown in Figure 2.78b. Notice that since $\mathbf{F} + (-\mathbf{F}) = 0$ we have not really done anything to produce an unbalance in the system. We notice that **F** applied at A and −**F** applied at B constitute a couple in the Z direction and have magnitude Fd. We therefore remove **F** at A and −**F** at B and replace them by a couple to obtain the equivalent system shown in Figure 2.78c. Recall that the point of application of the couple vector **M** is arbitrary.

As another case in point, consider the system in Figure 2.79a, where $\mathbf{F}_1$ and $\mathbf{F}_2$ are in the XY plane and $\mathbf{M}_3$ is a couple. We first place $\mathbf{F}_1$ and −$\mathbf{F}_1$ at point A as shown in Figure 2.79b. If $\mathbf{F}_1$ and −$\mathbf{F}_1$ are considered as constituting a couple $\mathbf{M}_1$, where

$$\mathbf{M}_1 = \mathbf{r}_1 \times \mathbf{F}_1$$

then Figure 2.79c is an equivalent system. Next, we place $\mathbf{F}_2$ and −$\mathbf{F}_2$ at A as shown in Figure 2.79d, and define a couple $\mathbf{M}_2$ so that

$$\mathbf{M}_2 = \mathbf{r}_2 \times \mathbf{F}_2$$

and obtain the system shown in Figure 2.79e. Finally, by adding the couples and forces, i.e.,

$$\mathbf{M} = \mathbf{M}_1 + \mathbf{M}_2 + \mathbf{M}_3$$

$$\mathbf{F} = \mathbf{F}_1 + \mathbf{F}_2$$

we obtain the system shown in Figure 2.79f. Thus, we have reduced a *system* of forces and couples to one resultant force and one resultant couple. It is important to recognize that in this general situation the resulting magnitude of the couple depends upon the location of point A.

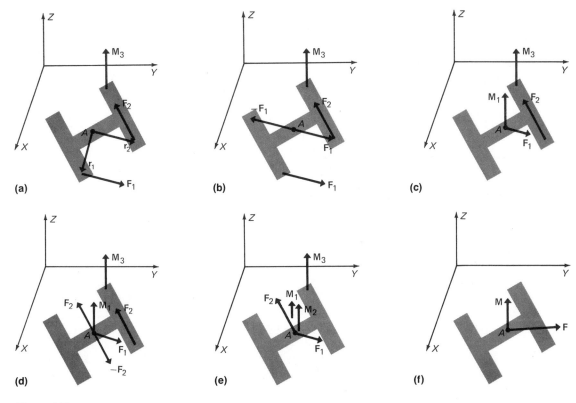

(a) **(b)** **(c)**

(d) **(e)** **(f)**

Figure 2.79

We can represent the previous observations compactly using the system illustrated in Figure 2.80. The resultant force and moment are given by

$$\mathbf{R} = \Sigma\mathbf{F}$$

$$\mathbf{M} = \Sigma(\mathbf{r} \times \mathbf{F})$$

Notice that if all the forces went through A, then the resulting moment is zero. Such a system of forces in which all forces pass through the same point is called a *concurrent system* of

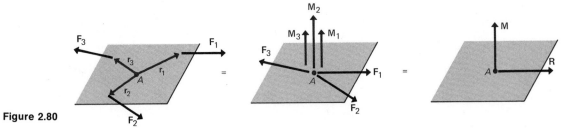

Figure 2.80

forces.

If **R** and **M** are mutually perpendicular, it is possible to replace the system by an equivalent system having a single force **R** applied at a different point. In general, this can be done when the forces are (a) concurrent, (b) in one plane, or (c) parallel. Although forces in a particular case other than these three situations may be reducible to an equivalent system of one force, this does not happen too often and is not intuitively obvious. We restrict our discussion, therefore, to these three cases.

Concurrent forces arise when all the forces applied to a body pass through the same point as shown in Figure 2.81. Clearly we may obtain the resultant by directly adding. Thus,

$$\mathbf{R} = \Sigma\mathbf{F}$$

where **R** is applied at *O*. We now have an equivalent system with one resultant force. This is perhaps the most intuitive and trivial case.

Next we consider the case of coplanar forces as shown in Figure 2.82a. It is clear from the discussion above that these forces can be easily replaced by one force and one couple as shown in Figure 2.82b. By shifting the force to a new point we can reduce the system to one force only (see Figure 2.82c). The distance from *O* to *A* is

$$d = \frac{M_O}{R}$$

For the more general case shown in Figure 2.83a, we can obtain the equivalent system shown in Figure 2.83b, where the resultant force **R** is introduced at a point defined by

$$\mathbf{r} = x\mathbf{i} + y\mathbf{j}$$

so that

$$M_O = |\mathbf{r} \times \mathbf{R}|$$
$$= |xR_y - yR_x|$$

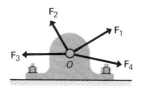

Figure 2.81

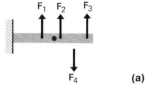

(a)

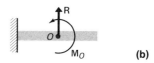

(b)

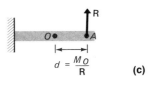

Figure 2.82

(c)

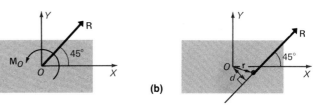

Figure 2.83

(a)

(b)

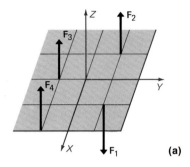

(a)

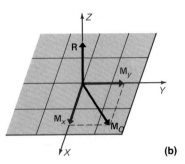

(b)

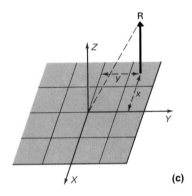

(c)

Figure 2.84

Notice that we are able to obtain the line of action and not a specific point.

Finally, we consider the case of parallel forces shown in Figure 2.84a. The forces, since they are in the vertical plane, give rise to moments about the X and Y axes. The resultant moment vector will, therefore, be in the XY plane, as shown in Figure 2.84b. The final equivalent system is shown in Figure 2.84c. The resultant force $\mathbf{R}$ is located at the coordinate point (x,y) so as to produce the same moments about the X and Y axes. Thus,

$$\mathbf{M} = \mathbf{r} \times \mathbf{R} \qquad \text{or} \qquad M_x\mathbf{i} + M_y\mathbf{j} = yR\mathbf{i} - xR\mathbf{j}$$

so that

$$x = -\frac{M_y}{R} \qquad y = \frac{M_x}{R}$$

The system shown in Figure 2.84c, where only one resultant force $\mathbf{R}$ is applied, is therefore equivalent to that shown in Figure 2.84a.

The condition in which a resultant force vector $\mathbf{R}$ and a couple vector $\mathbf{M}$ have the same line of action is known as a *wrench*. When the directions of $\mathbf{R}$ and $\mathbf{M}$ are the same, the wrench is positive and if they are opposite the wrench is negative. The *pitch* of a wrench (PW) is defined as

$$PW = \frac{\text{projection of the couple vector on the axis parallel to the resultant force axis}}{\text{resultant force}}$$

or

$$PW = \frac{\mathbf{M} \cdot \boldsymbol{\lambda}}{R} \qquad (2.15)$$

where

$$\boldsymbol{\lambda} = \frac{\mathbf{R}}{R}$$

Example 2.6.1

A beam is subjected to two forces as shown in Figure 2.85a. Reduce the system to only one force and one couple.

The 150-lb force is moved to A and a couple M is added as shown in Figure 2.85b, thus,

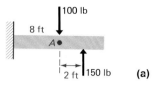

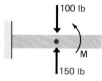

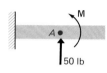

Figure 2.85

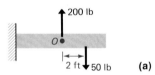

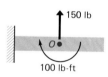

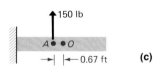

Figure 2.86

$$M = 2(150)$$

$$\mathbf{M} = 300 \; \rangle \; \text{lb-ft} \qquad\qquad \text{Answer}$$

The resultant force and couple are shown in Figure 2.85c.

$$F = 100 - 150$$

$$\mathbf{F} = -50 \qquad \downarrow \text{lb} \qquad\qquad \text{Answer}$$

Example 2.6.2

Reduce the loading shown in Figure 2.86a to a system of one force only.

We move the 50-lb force to point O and introduce a couple of $100 \; \rfloor$ lb-ft as shown in Figure 2.86b.

Assume that point A is the point where there is no couple and one resultant force. We move the 150-lb force to A and introduce a couple $150d$ lb-ft. The resultant couple must be zero. Therefore,

$$150d = 100$$

$$d = 0.67 \text{ ft} \qquad\qquad \text{Answer}$$

Example 2.6.3

Reduce the force-couple system in Figure 2.87 to one force and one couple. It is known that $\mathbf{M}_3 = 100\mathbf{i} + 400\mathbf{j} + 300\mathbf{k}$, $\mathbf{F}_1 = -100\mathbf{i} + 100\mathbf{j} - 50\mathbf{k}$, and $\mathbf{F}_2 = -100\mathbf{j}$. Compute the value of PW.

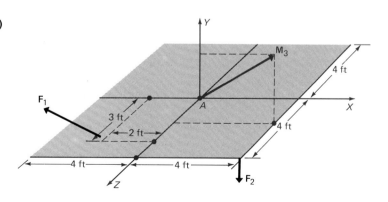

Figure 2.87

With reference to the point A, the resultant force is

$$\mathbf{R} = (-100\mathbf{i} + 100\mathbf{j} - 50\mathbf{k}) + (-100\mathbf{j})$$

$$= -100\mathbf{i} - 50\mathbf{k} \qquad\qquad \text{Answer}$$

and the couples to be added are:

For $\mathbf{F}_1$:　　$\mathbf{M}_1 = \mathbf{r}_1 \times \mathbf{F}_1$

$$= (-2\mathbf{i} + 3\mathbf{k}) \times (-100\mathbf{i} + 100\mathbf{j} - 50\mathbf{k})$$

$$= -300\mathbf{i} - 400\mathbf{j} - 200\mathbf{k}$$

For $\mathbf{F}_2$:　　$\mathbf{M}_2 = \mathbf{r}_2 \times \mathbf{F}_2$

$$= (4\mathbf{i} + 4\mathbf{k}) \times (-100\mathbf{j})$$

$$= 400\mathbf{i} - 400\mathbf{k}$$

The resultant moment therefore becomes

$$\mathbf{M} = (100\mathbf{i} + 400\mathbf{j} + 300\mathbf{k}) + (-300\mathbf{i} - 400\mathbf{j} - 200\mathbf{k})$$
$$+ (400\mathbf{i} - 400\mathbf{k})$$

$$= 200\mathbf{i} - 300\mathbf{k} \qquad\qquad \text{Answer}$$

In order to compute PW, we obtain $\boldsymbol{\lambda}$, where

$$\boldsymbol{\lambda} = \frac{\mathbf{R}}{R} \qquad R = \sqrt{100^2 + 50^2} = \sqrt{12500} = 111.8$$

so that

$$\boldsymbol{\lambda} = -\frac{100}{111.8}\mathbf{i} - \frac{50}{111.8}\mathbf{k} = -0.894\mathbf{i} - 0.447\mathbf{k}$$

and therefore

$$PW = \frac{\mathbf{M} \cdot \boldsymbol{\lambda}}{R} = \frac{(200\mathbf{i} - 600\mathbf{k}) \cdot (-0.894\mathbf{i} - 0.447\mathbf{k})}{111.8}$$

$$= \frac{-178.9 + 268}{111.8}$$

$$= 0.80 \text{ ft} \qquad\qquad \text{Answer}$$

Example 2.6.4

Reduce the system of Figure 2.88a to an equivalent system of one force.

The couple is written as

$$\mathbf{M} = 100(\sin 30° \, \mathbf{i} + \cos 30° \, \mathbf{j})$$

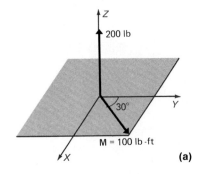

Figure 2.88

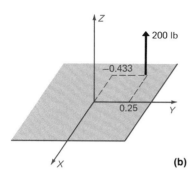

(b)

$$= 50\mathbf{i} + 86.6\mathbf{j}$$

We move the 200-lb force to a point whose coordinates are (x,y) so that

$$(x\mathbf{i} + y\mathbf{j}) \times 200\mathbf{k} = 50\mathbf{i} + 86.6\mathbf{j} = 200y\mathbf{i} - 200x\mathbf{j}$$

Solving for the coordinates x and y, we obtain

$$x = -\frac{86.6}{200} \qquad y = \frac{50}{200}$$

$$= -0.433 \text{ ft} \qquad = 0.25 \text{ ft} \qquad \text{Answer}$$

Problems

2.6.1 Reduce the force applied to the bracket shown in Figure 2.59 (p. 52) to an equivalent system of a force and moment applied at A.

2.6.2 Reduce the forces applied to the bracket shown in Figure 2.60 (p. 52) to an equivalent system of a force and moment applied at A.

2.6.3 Reduce the forces applied to the bracket shown in Figure 2.61 (p. 52) to an equivalent system of a force and moment applied at A.

2.6.4 Reduce the forces applied to the bracket shown in Figure 2.62 (p. 52) to an equivalent system of a force and moment applied at A.

2.6.5 Reduce the forces applied to the bracket shown in Figure 2.63 (p. 53) to an equivalent system of a force and moment applied at A.

2.6.6 Reduce the forces applied to the bracket shown in Figure 2.64 (p. 53) to an equivalent system of a force and moment applied at A.

2.6.7 Replace the force applied to the plate in Figure 2.68 (p. 54) by an equivalent system of a force and moment applied at Q.

2.6.8 Replace the forces applied to the plate in Figure 2.69 (p. 54) by an equivalent system of a force and moment applied at P.

2.6.9 The four forces shown in Figure 2.89 are to be replaced by one force and a moment about A. What is the magnitude of (a) the force and (b) the moment?

2.6.10 Determine the resultant force and moment applied at A to replace the forces and moments shown in Figure 2.90. Assume $\mathbf{M}$ is $50 \curvearrowright$ lb-in.

2.6.11 Reduce the system of problem 2.6.10 to one resultant force. Assume that the moment applied at B is $10 \curvearrowright$ lb-in. (a) What is this resultant force? (b) Where must it be applied?

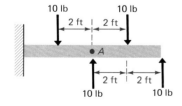

Figure 2.89

Figure 2.90

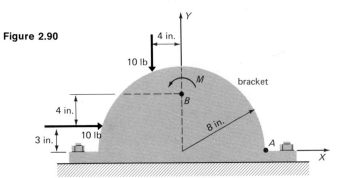

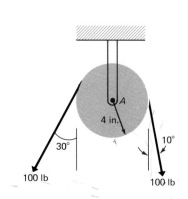

Figure 2.91

2.6.12 Obtain the equivalent force-couple system at A for the pulley shown in Figure 2.91.

2.6.13 Obtain the equivalent force-couple system at A for the gear shown in Figure 2.92.

2.6.14 A roof is loaded as shown in Figure 2.93. What is the equivalent force-couple system at A?

2.6.15 Obtain the equivalent force-couple system at A for the system shown in Figure 2.94.

2.6.16 Obtain the equivalent force-couple system at A for the system shown in Figure 2.95.

2.6.17 Obtain the equivalent force-couple system at A for the system shown in Figure 2.96.

2.6.18 What is the resultant force and couple at A for the system shown in Figure 2.97?

2.6.19 Determine the magnitude of the resultant force shown in Figure 2.98. Where is its point of application?

2.6.20 The wrench shown in Figure 2.99 must be replaced by two forces. One force must go through A and the other must be in the XY plane. Obtain these forces.

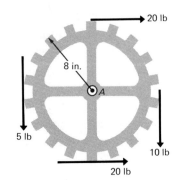

Figure 2.92

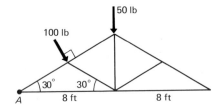

Figure 2.93

Figure 2.94

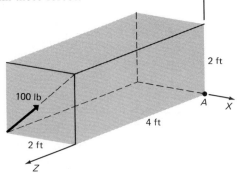

Figure 2.95

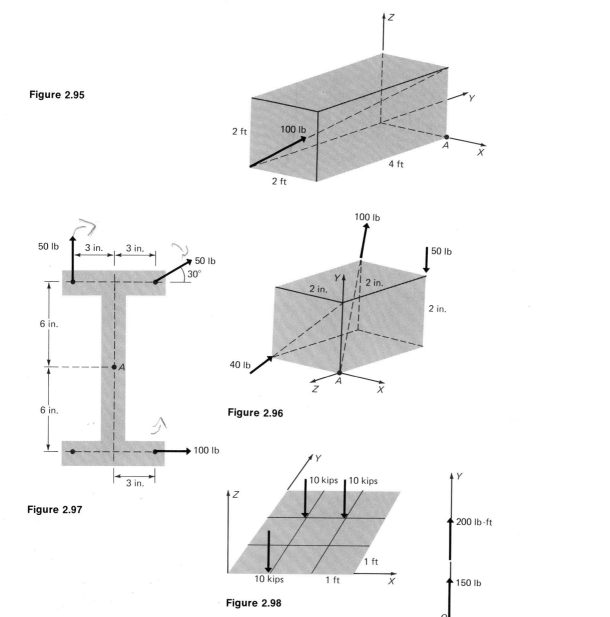

Figure 2.96

Figure 2.97

Figure 2.98

Figure 2.99

2.7 Summary

A The important *ideas*:

1. A force is a vector quantity. It has magnitude, direction, and point of application.

2. For a particle to be in equilibrium, the resultant of all forces applied to the particle must be zero.

3. Whereas a force creates a tendency for a body to translate, the moment of a force creates a tendency for the body to rotate about the line of action of the moment.

4. A moment of a couple is a pure moment.

B The important *equations*:

Resultant force: $\mathbf{R} = \Sigma\mathbf{F}$ (2.1)

Force components: $\mathbf{F} = F_x\mathbf{i} + F_y\mathbf{j}$ (2.3)

$\mathbf{F} = F(\cos\theta_x\,\mathbf{i} + \cos\theta_y\,\mathbf{j})$ (2.8)

$$\frac{1}{D} = \frac{\cos\theta_x}{D_x} = \frac{\cos\theta_y}{D_y}$$ (2.9)

Equilibrium of a particle: $\mathbf{R} = \Sigma\mathbf{F} = 0$ (2.11)

Moment of force: $\mathbf{M}_O = \mathbf{r} \times \mathbf{F}$ (2.12)

Pitch of wrench $(PW) = \dfrac{\mathbf{M}\cdot\boldsymbol{\lambda}}{R}$ (2.15)

$$\boldsymbol{\lambda} = \frac{\mathbf{R}}{R}$$

Chapter 3
Rigid Body Equilibrium

The free-body diagram of a rigid body in equilibrium must show the externally applied forces and moments as well as the reactions at the supports. The resultant force and moment obtained from the free-body diagram must be zero for the rigid body to be in equilibrium.

3.1 Introduction

A particle is in equilibrium if the resultant force acting on it is equal to zero. Similarly, a rigid body is in equilibrium if (1) the resultant force is zero and (2) the resultant moment is zero.

Forces and moments can be *external* or *internal*. Forces that hold together a structure or rigid body are known as internal forces. We shall have more to say about these in the next chapter. The forces that are applied to a rigid body by another body or by the earth are external forces. Snow on the roof is an external force on the structure. The weight of a body is another case of an external force. Since we shall consider the equilibrium of the entire rigid body, our concern in this chapter is with external forces and the moments they produce.

External forces can be further divided into *reactive* forces and *applied* forces. Reaction forces are those that are contributed by a body's supports or connections. Applied forces are those that are directly applied to a body. The requirement that the resultant force and moment must be zero for equilibrium includes the reactive as well as the applied forces.

3.2 Free-Body Diagrams

A body is isolated from its supports and connections when a free-body diagram is drawn. This diagram shows all reactive forces, applied forces, and internal forces, as well as any moments acting on the body. Thus, when *all* the forces and moments are shown, the conditions of equilibrium are applied on the entire rigid body. If the equilibrium of the entire structure is considered, then the free-body diagram does not include internal forces. If a part of a structure is analyzed, then we include appropriate internal forces. This is considered in the next chapter. Here we consider the equilibrium of the entire body.

Consider the block shown in Figure 3.1a. The free-body diagram of the block under equilibrium is shown in Figure 3.1b. Essentially, we have removed the ground and replaced it with a reactive force N. Clearly, for equilibrium, we have $N = w$. As another example, consider the block on an incline shown in Figure 3.2a. Here, in order to draw the free-body diagram, we replace the inclined plane and its tread with two reactive forces N_1 and N_2. The free-body diagram in Figure 3.2b now

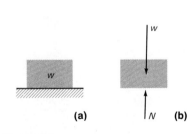

(a)   **(b)**

Figure 3.1

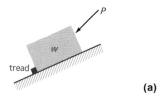

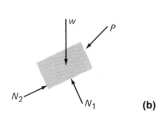

Figure 3.2

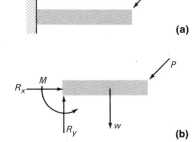

Figure 3.3

shows four forces applied to the block, w, P, N_1, and N_2. We note that N_1 and N_2 are unknowns. Since, as we shall see, in this case we can write two equations of equilibrium, we can solve for the two unknown forces.

In many situations, the removal of connections and supports gives rise not only to reactive forces but reactive moments as well. Consider, for example, the cantilever beam shown in Figure 3.3a, where a force of P is applied as shown. Now, when we remove the connections at the wall, we have not only the reactive forces R_x and R_y but a moment M as well, as seen in Figure 3.3b. Clearly, if no moment existed, the beam would rotate, which would violate conditions of equilibrium. We now see that there are three unknowns, R_x, R_y, and M. We can, however, write two equations for forces and one for moments. Since the number of equations and unknowns are equal, the unknowns can be found.

In general we can say that for equilibrium of a rigid body in three dimensions, the resultant force as well as the resultant moment must be zero, i.e.,

$$\Sigma \mathbf{F} = 0 \tag{3.1}$$

$$\Sigma \mathbf{M} = 0 \tag{3.2}$$

3.3 Equilibrium in Two Dimensions

If we restrict all forces to the XY plane, the problem of equilibrium is restricted to two dimensions. We have already established that when a force has components along the X and Y axes, the resulting moment is directed along the Z axis, and there are no components of moments along the X axis or the Y axis. Therefore, for equilibrium in two dimensions, we must satisfy the following equilibrium equations:

$$\Sigma F_x = 0 \qquad \Sigma F_y = 0 \qquad \Sigma M_z = 0 \tag{3.3}$$

Since all forces are restricted to a plane, the reaction forces of a two-dimensional structure must also be confined to a plane. These reaction forces as well as the reaction moments are to be included in the free-body diagram. In general, the reaction forces of supports and connections can be classified as shown in Table 3.1. A structure or body is often composed of several of these connections, which impose forces and moments on the constrained body or structure as soon as external forces or moments are applied to the body. Naturally, for equilibrium, the resultant of the applied forces and moments plus the forces and moments due to the constraints of supports and connections must be zero. For two-dimensional equilibrium, supports and connections can be grouped on the basis of their reaction forces.

One Reaction Force   Here, we have the first four examples in Table 3.1—smooth surfaces; rollers, rockers, and ball supports; sliding collar; and a spring and cable connection. In the first three examples, free motion can occur in one direction while a reaction force exists in another direction. The cable connection has one unknown since it only supports a tension force.

Two Reaction Forces   This group includes rough surfaces— where both a normal force and a tangential or frictional force exist—and the smooth pin connection which allows rotational motion but does not allow any translational motion. The reactive forces of this group are normally represented by their rectangular components in the vertical and horizontal directions.

Three Reaction Forces   This group is exemplified by a fixed or clamped support. Such a support is capable of withstanding two forces as well as a moment.

Once the reaction forces are known, we can draw the free-body diagram. If the reaction forces acting on a two-dimensional structure involve more than three unknowns, these forces are said to be *statically indeterminate,* which means that we have more unknown forces than available equations. When there are as many equations of equilibrium (i.e., equations of statics) as there are unknowns, the reaction forces are said to be *statically determinate,* and the structure is said to be *completely constrained.* If there are less unknowns than there are available equations of equilibrium, the structure is referred to as *partially constrained.*

Table 3.1

Support or Connection	Reaction Force	Unknowns
Smooth surface: Reaction force is normal to surface.		1
Roller, rocker, or ball support: Reaction force is normal.		1
Collar on a rod or pin in smooth slot: Reaction force is normal to rod or slot.		1
Spring or cable connection: Reaction is always a tension in direction of cable.		1
Rough surface: Reaction force is normal and tangential.		2
Smooth pin: Reaction force has unknown direction.		2
Fixed support: Reaction is of unknown force and moment.		3

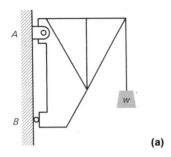

(a)

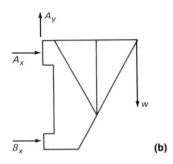

(b)

Figure 3.4

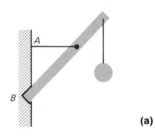

(a)

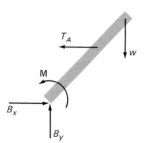

(b)

Figure 3.5

Consider the structure shown in Figure 3.4a. The upper support is a smooth pin while the lower support is a roller. The free-body diagram is drawn in Figure 3.4b, where the weight of the body is assumed to be negligible. We notice that there are three unknowns, A_x, A_y, and B_x. Since we can write three equations, the system is statically determinate and the structure is completely constrained. The three unknowns are found by writing the equilibrium equations,

$$\Sigma F_x = 0 \qquad \Sigma F_y = 0 \qquad \Sigma M_z = 0 \qquad (3.3)$$

The moment can be taken about any point since the entire rigid body is under equilibrium. However, since all moment equations are equivalent, *only one independent moment equation exists*. The specific point selected about which the moment is taken is a matter of convenience. The point which leads to the least amount of complexity is generally chosen. In this case, taking the moment about point A yields B_x immediately.

As another example, consider the structure shown in Figure 3.5a. The free-body diagram is shown in Figure 3.5b. We notice that there are four unknowns; and since we can only obtain three equations of equilibrium, this system is statically indeterminate. If the fixed support were replaced by a smooth pin connection, the number of unknowns would become three and the system would become determinate.

As another example, consider the bridge structure shown in Figure 3.6a. The free-body diagram is shown in Figure 3.6b. We observe that there are two unknown reactions although we have three equilibrium equations to satisfy. This is a *partially constrained* structure.

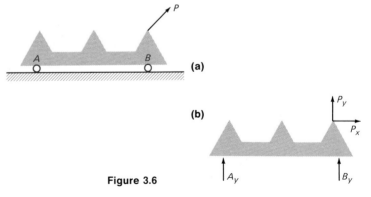

(a)

(b)

Figure 3.6

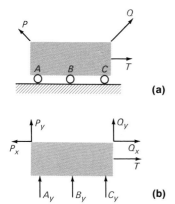

Figure 3.7

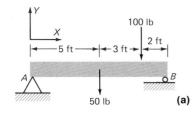

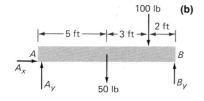

Figure 3.8

Although it appears that when the number of unknowns and equations are the same, the reaction forces are determinate, this is not true if a body is *improperly constrained*. This is demonstrated by the example shown in Figure 3.7a. The roller support gives rise to one reaction at each wheel as shown in the free-body diagram of Figure 3.7b. When we write the equations of equilibrium, we find that summing the horizontal forces does not include our unknown forces at all. We are, therefore, left with two equations that relate three unknowns. Clearly, the three-roller support has led to a statically indeterminate situation. This kind of a situation should be avoided in designing stationary structures.

Example 3.3.1

A force of 100 lb is applied to a beam as shown in Figure 3.8a. The beam weighs 50 lb. What are the reactions at A and B?

The necessary free-body diagram is shown in Figure 3.8b. Summing the forces in the horizontal direction we obtain

$$\Sigma F_x = 0 \qquad \text{and therefore} \qquad A_x = 0 \quad \text{Answer}$$

Now taking the moments about A and setting the sum equal to zero for equilibrium, i.e.,

$$\Sigma M_A = 0$$

we obtain

$$-5(50) - 8(100) + 10B_y = 0$$

$$B_y = 105 \text{ lb} \qquad \text{Answer}$$

The second reaction at A may be found by summing the forces in the vertical direction.

$$\Sigma F_y = 0 = A_y + B_y - 50 - 100$$

therefore,

$$A_y = 45 \text{ lb} \qquad \text{Answer}$$

Since the signs of the reactive forces are positive, the assumed directions of these forces as seen in the free-body diagram are correct.

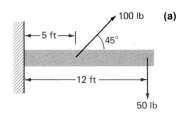

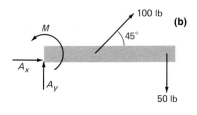

Figure 3.9

Example 3.3.2

Two forces are applied to a cantilever beam as shown in Figure 3.9a. Obtain the reactions at the support.

The free-body diagram is shown in Figure 3.9b. We note that there are two reaction forces A_x, A_y and one reaction moment M. This moment is often called a *clamping moment*.

The clamping moment may be obtained by summing the moments about A,

$$\Sigma M_A = 0 = M + (0.707)(100)(5) - 12(50)$$

therefore,

$$M = 246 \text{ lb-ft} \qquad \text{Answer}$$

Summing the forces in the X direction, we find that

$$\Sigma F_x = 0 = A_x + (0.707)(100)$$

therefore,

$$A_x = -70.7 \text{ lb} \qquad \text{Answer}$$

Note that the reaction at A in the X direction is *opposite* to that originally assumed.

Finally, we obtain A_y by summing forces in the Y direction.

$$\Sigma F_y = 0 = A_y + (0.707)(100) - 50$$

therefore,

$$A_y = -20.7 \text{ lb} \qquad \text{Answer}$$

The reaction at A in the Y direction is also opposite to that assumed.

Example 3.3.3

A car is hoisted by a jack as shown in Figure 3.10a. The weight of the car is w lb. (a) Obtain the reactions at A and B as functions of a, b, c, w, and θ. (b) Obtain the reactions for $a = 6$ ft, $b = 8$ ft, $c = 2$ ft, $w = 2500$ lb, $\theta = 10°$. Assume that the only reaction at A is that which is normal to the ground. This is true since the wheel is free to rotate.

(a) We note from Figure 3.10b that summing the moments about B yields A_y immediately.

$$\Sigma M_B = 0 = w(b \cos \theta + \frac{c}{2} \sin \theta) + A_y \frac{c}{2} \sin \theta - A_y(a+b) \cos \theta$$

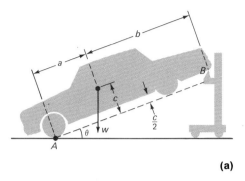

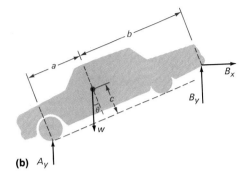

(a)

(b)

Figure 3.10

therefore,

$$A_y = \frac{w(2b \cos \theta + c \sin \theta)}{2(a + b) \cos \theta - c \sin \theta}$$ Answer

Summing the forces in the vertical direction, we have

$$\Sigma F_y = 0 = A_y + B_y - w$$

therefore,

$$B_y = w - \frac{(2b \cos \theta + c \sin \theta)w}{2(a + b) \cos \theta - c \sin \theta}$$

$$= \frac{2w(a \cos \theta - c \sin \theta)}{2(a + b) \cos \theta - c \sin \theta}$$ Answer

Finally, we obtain B_x by summing horizontal forces.

$$\Sigma F_x = 0$$

so that

$$B_x = 0$$ Answer

(b) For $a = 6$ ft, $b = 8$ ft, $c = 2$ ft, $w = 2500$ lb, and $\theta = 10°$, the reactions become

$$A_y = \frac{2500(2)(8)(0.985) + 2(0.174)}{2(14)(0.985) - 2(0.174)}$$

$$= 1479 \text{ lb}$$ Answer

$$B_y = 2500 - 1479$$

$$= 1021 \text{ lb}$$ Answer

$$B_x = 0$$ Answer

From the previous example we can make a very important observation about the reaction forces and moments. This is, the reaction forces and moments *depend* upon the magnitude and location of the applied loading. In the previous example the magnitude and location of *w* clearly dictated the magnitude of the reaction forces.

Problems

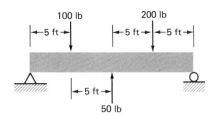

Figure 3.11

3.3.1 Neglecting the weight of the beam, obtain the reactions for the beam in Figure 3.11.

3.3.2 Neglecting the weight of the beam, obtain the reactions for the beam in Figure 3.12.

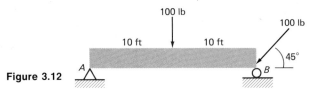

Figure 3.12

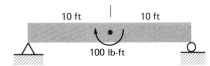

Figure 3.13

3.3.3 Neglecting the weight of the beam, obtain the reactions for the beam in Figure 3.13.

3.3.4 Neglecting the weight of the beam, obtain the reactions for the beam in Figure 3.14.

3.3.5 Neglecting the weight of the beam, obtain the reactions for the beam in Figure 3.15.

3.3.6 Neglecting the weight of the beam, obtain the reactions for the beam in Figure 3.16.

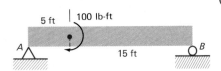

Figure 3.14

3.3.7 Determine the tension *T* necessary to hold the two weights in equilibrium on the inclined plane shown in Figure 3.17. Assume that the inclined surface is smooth.

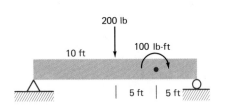

Figure 3.15

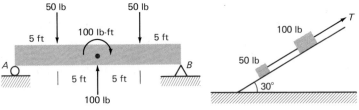

Figure 3.16

Figure 3.17

3.3.8 A car for carrying coal is resting on an inclined plane as shown in Figure 3.18. The weight of the car and coal is represented by the 500-lb force going through C. (a) Determine the tension T necessary to hold the car. (b) What is the reaction at the wheels? Let $\theta = 20°$ and $h = 1$ ft.

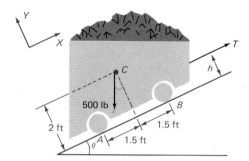

Figure 3.18

3.3.9 Determine (a) the tension T and (b) the reaction at the wheels for $\theta = 40°$ and $h = 2$ ft for problem 3.3.8.

3.3.10 Determine the tension T necessary to keep the weight shown in Figure 3.19 at equilibrium.

3.3.11 What is the tension T necessary to keep the weight at equilibrium in Figure 3.20?

3.3.12 A 500-lb weight is supported through three pulleys. What tension T will insure the equilibrium of the weight as shown in Figure 3.21?

3.3.13 Determine the (a) tension T and (b) the reaction at O as a function of θ and the applied force P for the jig shown in Figure 3.22.

Figure 3.19

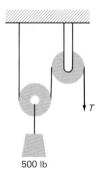

Figure 3.20

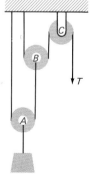

Figure 3.21   500 lb

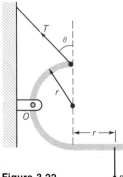

Figure 3.22

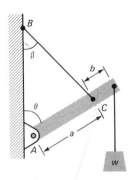

Figure 3.23

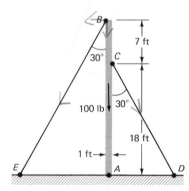

Figure 3.24

3.3.14 Calculate (a) the tension T and (b) the reaction at O for the jig shown in Figure 3.22 for $\theta = 10°$, $r = 6$ in., and $P = 100$ lb.

3.3.15 Derive expressions for the reactions at A and B for the loading shown in Figure 3.23.

3.3.16 Determine (a) the tension in the rope CB and (b) the reactions at A for the system shown in Figure 3.23. Let $\theta = 30°$, $\beta = 60°$, $a = 2$ ft, $b = 3$ ft, $w = 100$ lb.

3.3.17 A flagpole weighing 100 lb is supported as shown in Figure 3.24. It is known that the tension in cable BE is 75 lb and in CD it is 65 lb. Determine the reaction at A.

3.3.18 For the structure shown in Figure 3.25, what is the reaction at point A?

3.3.19 A 200-lb weight is supported by the structure shown in Figure 3.26. What is (a) the reaction at A and (b) the tension in the cable C?

3.3.20 If the connection at A in problem 3.3.19 were made into a rigid connection (such as shown in Figure 3.25), is it possible to obtain (a) the reaction and (b) the tension in problem 3.3.19?

3.3.21 Obtain (a) the reaction at A and (b) the tension in the cable for the structure in Figure 3.23 if $w = 100$ lb, $\theta = 90°$, $\beta = 45°$, $a = 6$ ft, and $b = 2$ ft.

3.3.22 A weight is supported as shown in Figure 3.27. Obtain (a) the tension in cable C and (b) the reactions at A.

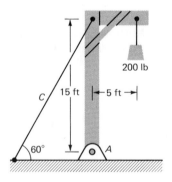

Figure 3.26

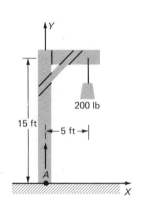

Figure 3.25

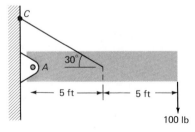

Figure 3.27

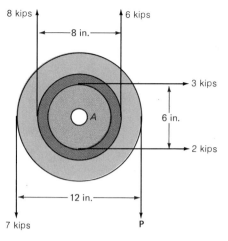

Figure 3.28

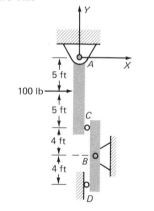

Figure 3.30

3.3.23 A stepped pulley, shown in Figure 3.28, is subjected to different tensions. What is the reaction at A if $P = 5$ kips? Assume that the pulley is not allowed to move.

3.3.24 What must P be in problem 3.3.23 if the resultant moment about A is to be zero?

3.3.25 A car-and-trailer system is shown in Figure 3.29. (a) What is the reaction at A? (b) What are the reactions at the three wheels? Assume that the point at A may be considered as a ball support. (*Hint:* Draw separate free-body diagrams for the car and the trailer.)

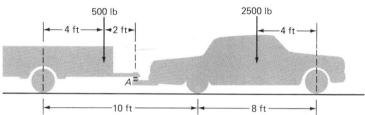

Figure 3.29

3.3.26 Obtain the reactions at A and B for the two-bar system shown in Figure 3.30.

3.3.27 Determine the reactions at A and B for the mechanism shown in Figure 3.31.

3.3.28 A pair of tongs are used to hold a steel ball as shown in Figure 3.32. If the applied force is 5 lb, what is the magnitude of the compressive forces acting on the steel ball?

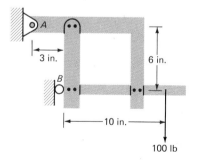

Figure 3.31

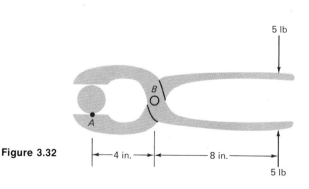

Figure 3.32

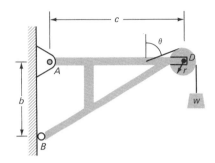

Figure 3.33

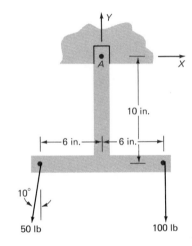

Figure 3.34

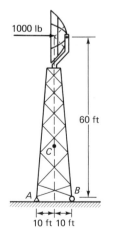

Figure 3.35

3.3.29 Obtain the reactions at *A* and *B* for the rigid structure shown in Figure 3.33.

3.3.30 Determine the reaction at *A* for the system shown in Figure 3.34.

3.3.31 An antenna 60 ft high, shown in Figure 3.35, has a horizontal force of 1000 lb applied due to wind pressure. What is the reaction at the supports *A* and *B*? Neglect the weight of the antenna.

3.3.32 If the antenna in problem 3.3.31 weighs 1500 lb and the weight acts down through *C* vertically, what is the reaction at the supports?

3.3.33 For the structure in Figure 3.33, obtain the reaction at *D*. Assume that $\theta = 60°$ and $w = 100$ lb.

3.3.34 Determine the reaction at the wheels of the mobile crane shown in Figure 3.36. Assume $w = 800$ lb.

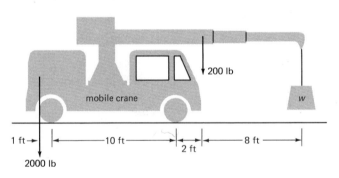

Figure 3.36

3.3.35 Derive an expression for the tension in the rope and the reaction at *A* for the crane shown in Figure 3.37. Calculate the answer for $w_1 = 0$, $w_2 = 1000$ lb, $a = 8$ ft, $b = 1$ ft, and $\theta = 30°$.

3.3.36 Repeat problem 3.3.35 assuming that the weight w_1 of the crane is not zero but 500 lb.

3.3.37 The crane shown in Figure 3.38 is used in a dockyard. The maximum weight w_1 is 20,000 lb. The weight w_2 is the weight of the crane boom and is shown at the midpoint of the boom. Determine (a) the reaction at *A* for the boom and (b) the tension in the cable *C*.

3.3.38 Obtain the reaction at *A* for the boom in Figure 3.38 but neglect the pulley diameter. What percentage error does this cause? Is such an assumption justified in engineering work?

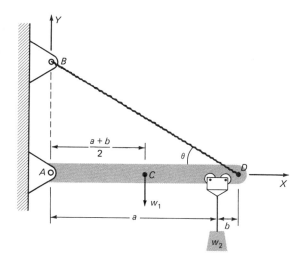

Figure 3.37

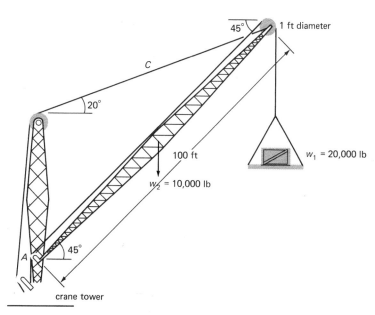

Figure 3.38

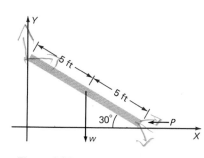

Figure 3.39

3.3.39 A uniform bar weighing 50 lb is to be supported in the equilibrium position shown in Figure 3.39. Determine the horizontal force needed to insure equilibrium. The floor and wall are to be considered smooth.

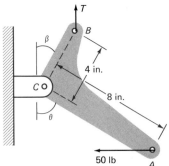

Figure 3.40

3.3.40 The bell crank shown in Figure 3.40 has a 50-lb force applied at A. Determine (a) the tension T and (b) the reaction at C. Assume $\theta = 30° = \beta$.

3.3.41 Determine (a) the tension T and (b) the reaction at C for problem 3.3.40, if $\theta = 20°$, $\beta = 40°$.

3.3.42 A rod of negligible weight has two unequal wheels at either end as shown in Figure 3.41. Determine the angle θ necessary for equilibrium.

3.3.43 Determine (a) the tension T and (b) the reaction at A necessary to keep the bar shown in Figure 3.42 in equilibrium. Let $\theta = 30°$.

3.3.44 Derive an expression relating the tension T and the reaction at A to the angle θ of problem 3.3.43.

3.3.45 A motor weighing 75 lb is mounted on a bracket as shown in Figure 3.43. The tensions in the belt are 100 lb and 150 lb when the motor is running. Determine the reaction at A and B when the motor is running.

3.3.46 A motor is mounted on a cantilever beam as shown in Figure 3.44. Determine the reactions at the clamped point A when $\theta = 45°$. Neglect the weight of the beam.

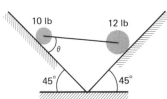

Figure 3.41

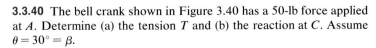

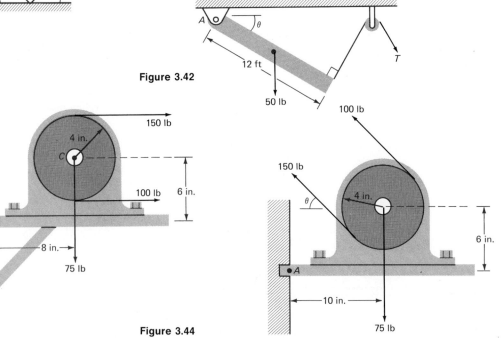

Figure 3.42

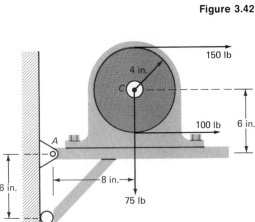

Figure 3.43

Figure 3.44

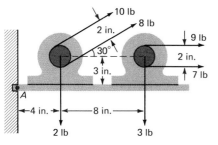

Figure 3.45

3.3.47 For problem 3.3.45, obtain the reactions at the shaft shown as point C if (a) the motor is running and (b) if the motor is not running but the tensions remain the same. (*Hint:* In the latter case there is a resisting moment at point C.)

3.3.48 Two small control motors are mounted on a cantilever beam as shown in Figure 3.45. Determine the reaction at A. Neglect the weight of the beam.

3.4 Equilibrium in Three Dimensions

The equilibrium of a three-dimensional rigid structure requires that the resultant forces and the resultant moments about the X, Y, and Z axes be equal to zero.

$$\Sigma F_x = 0 \qquad \Sigma F_y = 0 \qquad \Sigma F_z = 0 \qquad (3.4)$$

$$\Sigma M_x = 0 \qquad \Sigma M_y = 0 \qquad \Sigma M_z = 0 \qquad (3.5)$$

There are, therefore, six equations of equilibrium and we can solve for six unknowns. If there are more than six unknowns, the system is statically indeterminate. If we have six unknowns and can write six equations of equilibrium that relate these unknowns, the reactions are statically determinate and the structure is completely constrained. It is, of course, possible that there be less than six unknowns. For a system to be determinate, the number of distinct equations of equilibrium must equal the number of unknowns.

Supports and connections for a three-dimensional structure give rise to from one to as many as six reactions, as shown in Table 3.2. The number of unknown reactions at any joint can be determined by ascertaining which of the six (three translational and three rotational) motions are prevented. If a joint allows five motions while it constrains one motion, then there is only one reaction force. As with two-dimensional equilibrium, supports and connections can be grouped on the basis of their reaction forces for three-dimensional equilbrium (as shown in Table 3.2).

Table 3.2

Support or Connection		Reaction Force	Unknowns
	Ball or smooth-surface		1
	Cable or spring		1
	Roller		2
	Ball and socket		3
	Universal joint		4
	Pin and hinge		5
	Cantilever beam		6

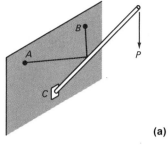

(a)

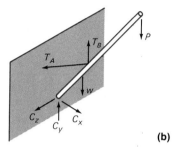

(b)

Figure 3.46

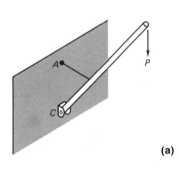

(a)

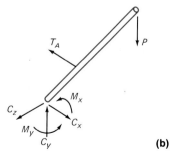

(b)

Figure 3.47

One Reaction Force Ball and smooth surface supports, cable and spring connections all contribute only one reaction force.

Two Reaction Forces A roller support has two reaction forces, one due to the earth, the other due to the fact that a roller prevents motion perpendicular to the direction of rolling provided friction exists between the roller and the supporting surface.

Three Reaction Forces This set of forces is supplied by a ball and socket joint, since it allows rotational freedom but constrains the three translational motions.

Four Reaction Forces Here, four possible motions must be constrained. A universal joint satisfies this criterion, since it resists all translational motion and one rotational motion around the axis of the joint.

Five Reaction Forces Both a hinge and a bracket are examples of devices that allow rotation only about their hinged axis.

Six Reaction Forces The combination of three forces and three moments contributed by a rigid connection does not permit any motion.

The equations of equilibrium in three dimensions may be obtained with facility provided we first draw a free-body diagram, as before. This diagram includes all the forces applied from outside the structure as well as the reactive forces supplied by the supports or connections from which it has been isolated. Consider the flagpole shown in Figure 3.46a, where the point C is a ball and socket joint. The free-body diagram is shown in Figure 3.46b. The reactions at C consist of three reactions, C_x, C_y, and C_z. The weight w of the pole is shown at the center of gravity of the pole. The cables connected at A and B can support tension only, so that they are replaced by two tensions, T_A and T_B as shown. Here we have five unknowns, C_x, C_y, C_z, T_A, and T_B. We shall see below, in example 3.4.1, that we can indeed obtain five distinct equations of equilibrium.

Let us reconsider the flagpole above, but instead of a ball and socket joint at C we now have a pin connection and there is only one cable, as shown in Figure 3.47a. The free-body diagram is shown in Figure 3.47b, where the reactions at the connection now include three forces and two couples. The total number of unknowns are now six, which is the maximum that may be solved in a three-dimensional structure.

Example 3.4.1

Obtain the reactions for the support at C and the tension in the cables connected at A and B for the sign shown in Figure 3.48a. The joint at C is a ball and socket and the sign weighs 200 lb. Neglect the weight of the pole.

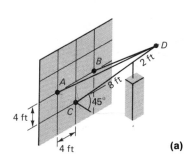

(a)

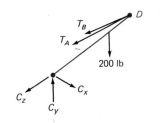

(b)

Figure 3.48

We first express the tensions and the weight of the sign as vector quantities. Referring to Figure 3.48b,

$$\mathbf{T}_A = T_A\left(-\frac{7.07}{D_A}\mathbf{i} - \frac{3.07}{D_A}\mathbf{j} + \frac{4}{D_A}\mathbf{k}\right)$$

$$D_A = \sqrt{(7.07)^2 + (3.07)^2 + (4)^2} = 8.68$$

$$\mathbf{T}_A = T_A(-0.815\mathbf{i} - 0.354\mathbf{j} + 0.461\mathbf{k})$$

$$\mathbf{T}_B = T_B(-0.815\mathbf{i} - 0.354\mathbf{j} - 0.461\mathbf{k})$$

$$\mathbf{w} = -200\mathbf{j}$$

The reactions at C are

$$\mathbf{C} = C_x\mathbf{i} + C_y\mathbf{j} + C_z\mathbf{k}$$

Summing the moments about C, we obtain

$$(5.66\mathbf{i} + 5.66\mathbf{j}) \times (-200\mathbf{j}) + (7.07\mathbf{i} + 7.07\mathbf{j}) \times \mathbf{T}_A \\ + (7.07\mathbf{i} + 7.07\mathbf{j}) \times \mathbf{T}_B = 0$$

Working out the algebra we obtain,

$$-1131\mathbf{k} + T_A(3.26\mathbf{i} - 3.26\mathbf{j} + 3.26\mathbf{k}) \\ + T_B(-3.26\mathbf{i} + 3.26\mathbf{j} + 3.26\mathbf{k}) = 0$$

Collecting terms gives us

$$3.26(T_A - T_B)\mathbf{i} + 3.26(T_B - T_A)\mathbf{j} \\ + (3.26T_A + 3.26T_B - 1131)\mathbf{k} = 0$$

This is a vector equation, so that

$$T_A - T_B = 0 \qquad T_B - T_A = 0 \qquad 3.26T_A + 3.26T_B - 1131 = 0$$

The first and second equations yield $T_A = T_B$. Substitution of this in the third equation results in

$$6.52T_A = 1131$$

therefore

$$T_A = T_B = 173.5 \text{ lb} \qquad \text{Answer}$$

We can obtain three additional equilibrium equations by summing the forces. That is, by substituting from above into

$$\mathbf{R} = \mathbf{C} + \mathbf{T}_A + \mathbf{T}_B + \mathbf{w} = 0$$

we obtain

$$(C_x\mathbf{i} + C_y\mathbf{j} + C_z\mathbf{k}) + 173.5(-0.815\mathbf{i} - 0.354\mathbf{j} + 0.461\mathbf{k})$$
$$+ 173.5(-0.815\mathbf{i} - 0.354\mathbf{j} - 0.461\mathbf{k}) - 200\mathbf{j} = 0$$

$$(C_x\mathbf{i} + C_y\mathbf{j} + C_z\mathbf{k}) + (-282\mathbf{i} - 122.8\mathbf{j}) - 200\mathbf{j} = 0$$

The three scalar equations thus become,

$$C_x - 282 = 0 \qquad C_y - 322.8 = 0 \qquad C_z = 0$$

The reactions are therefore

$$C_x = 282 \text{ lb} \qquad C_y = 322.8 \text{ lb} \qquad C_z = 0$$

Answer

Problems

3.4.1 The flagpole shown in Figure 3.49 has a ball and socket joint at C and is supported by two cables. Determine (a) the tensions T_1, T_2 and (b) the reactions at C.

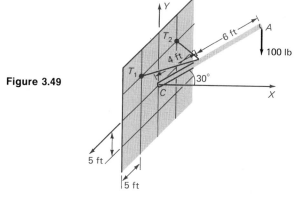

Figure 3.49

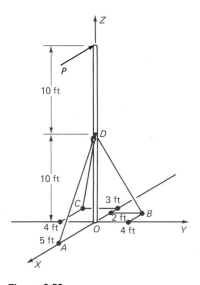

Figure 3.50

3.4.2 A 20-ft boom is held by a ball and socket joint at O and three cables as shown in Figure 3.50. Determine (a) the tension in the cables and (b) the reaction at O if a force P lb is applied as shown. Let $\mathbf{P} = (500\mathbf{i} + 100\mathbf{j} - 50\mathbf{k})$. Note that the cables DC and DA go over a pulley.

3.4.3 In problem 3.4.1, assume that an additional force of $\mathbf{P}$ lb acting at A is applied. (a) What are the tensions T_1 and T_2? (b) What is the reaction at C? Let $\mathbf{P} = 86.7\mathbf{i} + 50\mathbf{j}$.

3.4.4 A steel bracket is mounted, as shown in Figure 3.51, in order to support a 5-lb motor which develops a couple of $-50\mathbf{j}$ lb-in. Assuming that the bracket at A is bolted, determine the reaction at A.

Figure 3.51

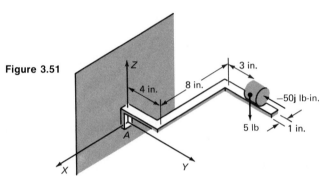

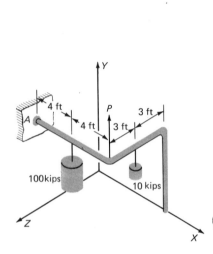

Figure 3.52

3.4.5 A rigid piece of pipe is bent as shown in Figure 3.52. A 100-kip and a 10-kip weight are hung, and a cable connected at a corner applies a tension $\mathbf{P} = 50\mathbf{j}$ kips. Determine the reaction at A assuming that it is a rigid connection. Neglect the weight of the pipe.

3.4.6 A steel bar is hinged to the wall and supported by a cable as shown in Figure 3.53. (a) What is the tension in the cable? (b) What is the reaction at A? Neglect the weight of the bar.

3.4.7 If the weight of the bar of problem 3.4.6 is represented as a 150-lb force directed vertically down through the point C, what is the tension of the cable?

Figure 3.53

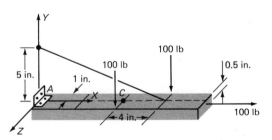

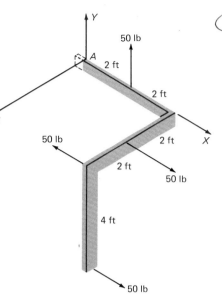

Figure 3.54

3.4.8 A cantilever beam is bent and subjected to four forces as shown in Figure 3.54. Neglecting the weight of the beam, determine the reaction at A.

3.4.9 A 250-lb sign is hung as shown in Figure 3.55. If the joint at O is a ball and socket, determine (a) the reaction at O and (b) the tension in cables AC and BC.

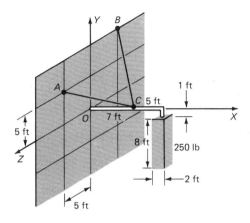

Figure 3.55

3.4.10 A 10-lb bracket is rigidly fixed to the wall as shown in Figure 3.56. Determine the reaction for the loading shown.

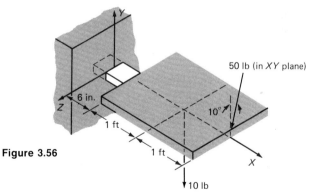

Figure 3.56

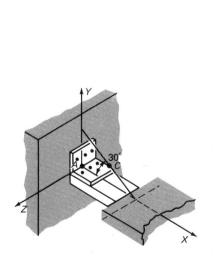

Figure 3.57

3.4.11 The bracket of problem 3.4.10 is hinged at A as shown in Figure 3.57, so that it may be hung flush with the wall when not in use. Determine (a) the reaction at A and (b) the tension in the cable. The loading is the same as for problem 3.4.10.

3.5 Summary

A   The important *ideas:*

1. A rigid body is in equilibrium if the resultant force is zero and the resultant moment is zero.

2. A free-body diagram must include the applied as well as the reactive forces and moments.

3. When the number of unknown reactions is equal to the number of equations of equilibrium, a structure is completely constrained, and the system is said to be statically determinate. If the number of unknowns are more than the equations of equilibrium, the system is statically indeterminate.

B   The important *equations:*

Equilibrium in two dimensions

$$\Sigma F_x = 0 \qquad \Sigma F_y = 0 \qquad \Sigma M_z = 0 \qquad (3.3)$$

Equilibrium in three dimensions

$$\Sigma F_x = 0 \qquad \Sigma F_y = 0 \qquad \Sigma F_z = 0 \qquad (3.4)$$

$$\Sigma M_x = 0 \qquad \Sigma M_y = 0 \qquad \Sigma M_z = 0 \qquad (3.5)$$

Chapter 4
Structures

A structure consists of a series of connected rigid bodies. The equilibrium of a structure requires that the resultant forces and moments acting on the entire structure, as well as any portion of the structure, be zero. Several methods are discussed for ascertaining conditions for the equilibrium of different types of structures and for obtaining the internal forces acting on structural members.

4.1 Introduction

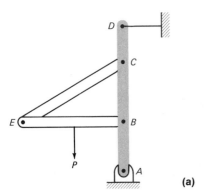

(a)

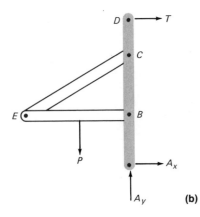

(b)

Figure 4.1

To this point, we have been concerned with analysis of the external—applied and reactive—forces acting on an isolated rigid body. But problems in engineering are concerned not only with single rigid bodies, but with structures that are formed by a series of connected rigid bodies. Examples of such structures can be observed in our everyday experiences—e.g., cranes, electric transmission and TV towers, bridges, roof trusses, and the like. These structures can be analyzed by means of the basic concepts of equilibrium developed in earlier chapters, whereby a free-body diagram of an isolated rigid body is used to obtain the equilibrium equations of statics in order to find the unknown reactive forces. However, a structure composed of several rigid bodies introduces a new concept— that of *internal* forces. Thus, when a separate free-body diagram is drawn of each member of the structure, the internal forces that hold the structure together are shown as reactive external forces at each member's connections.

Consider the structure illustrated in Figure 4.1a, which supports the external load P. Figure 4.1b shows the free-body diagram of the entire structure with the external load P and the reactive forces A_x, A_y, and T. From our earlier study of the equilibrium of rigid bodies, we can find these reactive forces. Having these forces, we now remove each member from the structure and draw the free-body diagrams as shown in Figure 4.1c. The forces at B, C, and E are internal forces. Note that these internal forces occur in equal and opposite pairs at each joint of the structure. This is a consequence of Newton's third law which states that every action has an equal and opposite reaction.

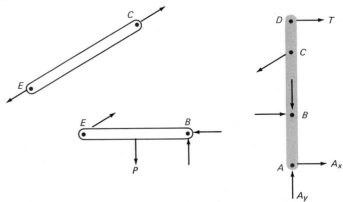

(c)

A system in which all the unknown forces acting in a structure can be obtained from the equations of statics is said to be *statically determinate*. If we are unable to determine all the forces, the system is said to be *statically indeterminate*. These latter structures require advanced techniques for their analysis and, consequently, are not treated here. However, it is important to keep in mind that when the number of equilibrium equations are less than the number of unknowns, we have an indeterminate situation.

In our analysis of structures, we will be concerned with trusses, frames, and machines. While the basic equilibrium equations hold for each of these structures, certain distinctions between them do exist and will be taken into account in what follows.

4.2 Equilibrium of Plane Trusses

A truss consists of a series of straight structural members connected to each other such that no member is continuous through a joint. The structural members can be bars, angles, or steel or timber beams, and the connection of each member may be accomplished by bolts, rivets, welds, etc. A truss that is designed to carry applied loads in a plane is a two-dimensional structure and is called a *plane* truss. An example of a plane truss is shown in Figure 4.2. This particular truss consists of seven distinct members joined at five joints by riveted gusset plates.

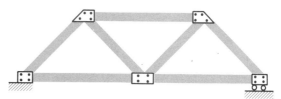

Figure 4.2

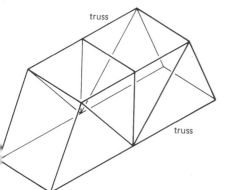

Figure 4.3

Trusses are used to carry heavy loads in many situations, generally for economic reasons. Bridges and roofs of buildings are two common applications of trusses. Figure 4.3 shows a sketch of a bridge which consists of two trusses and several

Figure 4.4

trusses

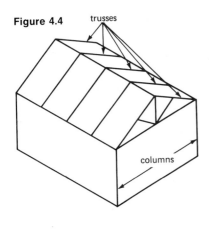

columns

other structural members. Figure 4.4 shows a sketch of a building with several roof trusses. It is not our intention to learn how to analyze and design these entire structures, but to indicate that the trusses we will be analyzing are, in reality, part of an overall structure, such as a bridge or a roof. Various types of bridge and roof trusses are shown in Figures 4.5 and 4.6.

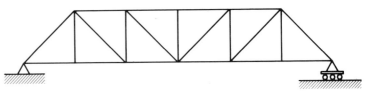

Pratt bridge truss

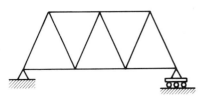

Warren bridge truss

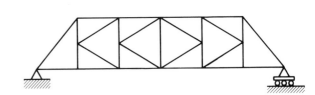

K bridge truss

Figure 4.5

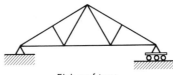

Fink roof truss

Pratt roof truss

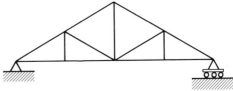

Howe roof truss

Figure 4.6

It can be seen from the last two figures that trusses may be formed by repeating a basic geometric pattern. A triangle is perhaps the most common pattern. In general, a *simple* truss is created by adding two new members to the joints of a triangle and thereby creating a new joint that is not in line with the other joints. Thus, in simple trusses, the addition of two members creates one new joint. Consequently, the total number of members M is given by

$$M = 2J - 3 \qquad (4.1)$$

where J is the number of joints.

In this chapter, we are interested in obtaining the magnitude and direction of the internal forces acting on each member of a truss. It is this information that enables a designer to select the sizes and shapes of the structural members forming a truss. Four assumptions are basic to the following analyses.

1. We are analyzing plane trusses only.
2. Smooth pins connect the members which form the truss.
3. All loads and reactions act at the joints.
4. The weight of each structural member is neglected.

Since the members are assumed to be pinned together, the resultant force acting at the end of a member consists only of a force. Furthermore, since each force is applied to each end of a member, it is called a *two-force member*. Plane trusses are composed of two-force members connected by smooth pins. In Figure 4.7, the member A is subjected to tensile forces, while member B is under compressive forces. Note that these forces must be equal in magnitude, opposite in direction, and collinear, in accord with Newton's third law. All external loads and reactive forces are applied to the truss at the joints. While we will neglect the weight of the structural members, in practice they are accounted for by distributing their magnitudes at the joints as additional applied loads.

For purposes of analysis the many pins and members in a truss must be labeled in an orderly fashion. Consider the Warren truss shown in Figure 4.8a. The pin joints are labeled $A, B, C, D,$ and E. The member joining pins A and B is referred to as AB. The force in this member is F_{AB}. When the number of pins becomes very large, each pin is assigned a number as shown in Figure 4.8b. The member joining pin 2 and 3 is 23 and the force in this member is $\mathbf{F}_{23}$. This latter method of labeling becomes very attractive for computer programming. In this text we shall use the alphabet system shown in Figure 4.8a.

With the above ideas in mind we may proceed to draw free-body diagrams for the truss and each of its components and to

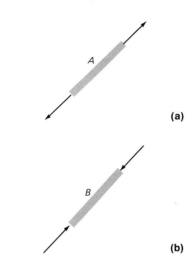

(a)

(b)

Figure 4.7

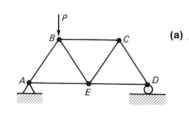

(a)

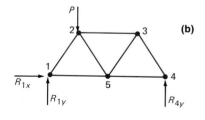

(b)

Figure 4.8

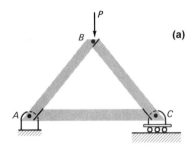

(a)

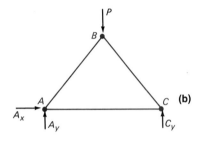

(b)

Figure 4.9

(c)

write the equilibrium equations. Consider the truss shown in Figure 4.9a. The free-body diagram of the entire truss is shown in Figure 4.9b, while the free-body diagrams for each member and each pin are shown in Figure 4.9c. We can solve for the forces acting at a pin by writing the sum of the forces in the X and Y directions and setting them equal to zero. This means that each pin is in equilibrium, which is true, since the entire truss is in static equilibrium. Since there are three pins in this example, i.e., $J = 3$ in equation (4.1), we have six equilibrium equations for six unknowns—three reactive forces and three internal forces.

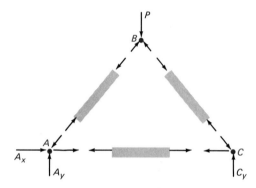

One approach to solution is to obtain the reactive forces first by writing the equilibrium equations of the entire truss using a free-body diagram as in Figure 4.9b. Having these reactive forces, we then proceed to calculate the internal forces. It should be noted that the equilibrium equations of the entire truss are not independent, but rather they are a subset of the $2J$ equations obtained by analyzing the pins.

The following sections introduce three common methods employed in analyzing trusses: (1) the method of joints, (2) the graphical method, and (3) the method of sections.

4.3 Method of Joints

The method of joints satisfies the conditions of equilibrium of forces at each pin. Since each member of the truss transmits a single force to its joints, the forces are concurrent at each pin. For static equilibrium of these forces, $\Sigma F_x = 0$ and $\Sigma F_y = 0$ must be satisfied. We therefore apply these equilibrium equations at each joint of the truss. In this way we are able to calculate all internal forces in the truss.

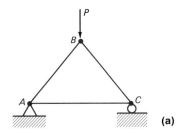

(a)

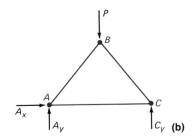

(b)

Figure 4.10

(c)

Before we consider examples, we need a method of ascertaining the direction of the internal force. When a force acts toward a pin, the member under consideration is in compression. When the force is directed away from the pin, the member is in tension. A force $\mathbf{F}_{AB}$ is written as $F_{AB}C$ for compression and $F_{AB}T$ for tension.

The steps in this procedure are as follows:

1. Label all pin joints. (See Figure 4.10a.)
2. Draw and label a free-body diagram of the entire frame and calculate the reaction forces using three equations of statics. (See Figure 4.10b.)
3. Draw a free-body diagram for each member and each pin as shown in Figure 4.10c. While it is often possible to predict the correct direction of the internal forces, there are many cases where it is necessary to assume their direction.

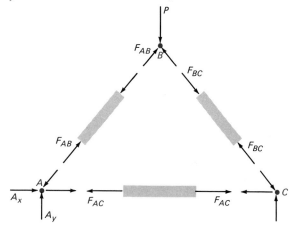

4. Apply the two equations of statics at each joint, namely,

$$\Sigma F_x = 0 \qquad \Sigma F_y = 0.$$

If a calculated internal force is negative, it means that the assumed direction of the force is incorrect. Note that it is not necessary to change the direction of the internal force. Continue to apply the equilibrium equations from joint to joint using the original free-body diagram.

In practice, step 2 is not necessary; we could begin with the pin that has a known external force and no more than two unknown internal forces. Once this joint is analyzed, the remaining joints are then analyzed. However, all four steps are generally the most convenient approach to a solution for all the internal and reactive forces.

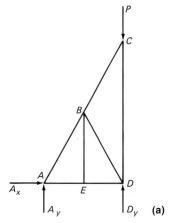

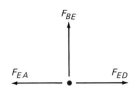

Joint E **(b)**

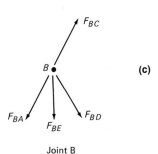

Joint B

Figure 4.11

Before we proceed with examples of the method of joints, let us consider the truss shown in Figure 4.11a. Having found the reactive forces, consider the free-body diagram of joint E shown in Figure 4.11b. Summing forces in the vertical direction yields $F_{BE} = 0$. Thus member BE does not carry a force and is called a *zero-force member*. If we consider joint B in Figure 4.11c, we see that $F_{BD} = 0$, so that member BD is also a zero-force member. The recognition that certain members of a truss are zero-force members facilitates the analysis by the method of joints.

Example 4.3.1

Using the method of joints, find the force in each member for the truss shown in Figure 4.12a.

Figure 4.12b shows the free-body diagram of the entire truss. The reactive forces are labeled $\mathbf{A}_x$, $\mathbf{A}_y$, and $\mathbf{D}_y$. Three equations of statics are applied to the entire structure to find these reactive forces.

Equilibrium of the entire truss:

$$\Sigma M_A = 0 \qquad 20D_y + 50(6) - 50(14) - 100(6) = 0$$

$$D_y = 50 \text{ lb} \qquad \mathbf{D}_y = 50\mathbf{j} \quad \text{lb}$$

$$\Sigma F_x = 0 \qquad -A_x + 50 = 0$$

$$A_x = 50 \text{ lb} \qquad \mathbf{A}_x = -50\mathbf{i} \quad \text{lb}$$

$$\Sigma F_y = 0 \qquad A_y + 50 - 50 - 100 = 0$$

$$A_y = 100 \text{ lb} \qquad \mathbf{A}_y = 100\mathbf{j} \quad \text{lb}$$

Figure 4.12

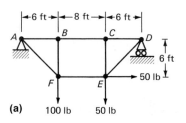

(a)

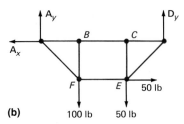

(b)

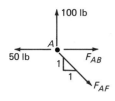

(c)

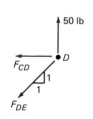

(d)

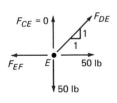

(e)

The free-body diagrams for the joints are also shown in Figure 4.12. The reactive forces just calculated are shown in the appropriate diagrams and the internal forces are all assumed tensile. Zero-force members are also labeled where appropriate. The equilibrium of the joints, starting with joint A, is

Joint A: $\quad \Sigma F_x = 0 \quad -50 + F_{AB} + 0.707 F_{AF} = 0$

$$\Sigma F_y = 0 \quad 100 - 0.707 F_{AF} = 0$$

$$F_{AF} = 141.1 \text{ lb } T$$

and, substituting the second of the above equations into the first, gives us

$$F_{AB} = -50 \text{ lb} = 50 \text{ lb } C$$

Joint B: $\quad \Sigma F_x = 0 \quad -F_{AB} + F_{BC} = -(-50) + F_{BC} = 0$

$$F_{BC} = -50 \text{ lb} = 50 \text{ lb } C$$

Joint C: $\quad \Sigma F_x = 0 \quad -F_{BC} + F_{CD} = -(-50) + F_{CD} = 0$

$$F_{CD} = -50 \text{ lb} = 50 \text{ lb } C$$

Joint D: $\quad \Sigma F_x = 0 \quad -F_{CD} - 0.707 F_{DE} = 50 - 0.707 F_{DE} = 0$

$$F_{DE} = 70.7 \text{ lb} T$$

As a check on our computations we use

$$\Sigma F_y = 0 \quad 50 - 0.707 F_{DE} = 0$$

$$50 - 50 = 0 \qquad \text{(Checks)}$$

Joint E: $\quad\quad\quad \Sigma F_x = 0 \quad -F_{EF} + 0.707 F_{DE} + 50 = 0$

$$F_{EF} = 100 \text{ lb } T$$

As a check we use

$$\Sigma F_y = 0 \quad 0.707 F_{DE} - 50 = 0$$

$$50 - 50 = 0 \qquad \text{(Checks)}$$

Joint F: This final joint also provides a check on the calculations since F_{AF} has already been calculated at joint A. Thus,

$$\Sigma F_x = 0 \quad -0.707 F_{AF} + F_{EF} = 0$$

$$-100 + 100 = 0 \qquad \text{(Checks)}$$

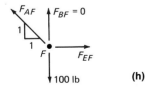

(f)

(g)

(h)

Example 4.3.2

Using the method of joints, find the force in each member for the truss shown in Figure 4.13a.

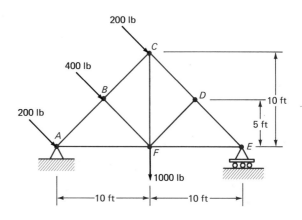

(a)

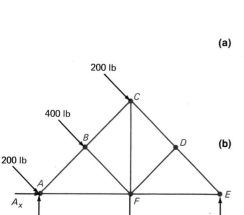

(b)

Figure 4.13

The free-body diagram of the entire truss is shown in Figure 4.13b.

Equilibrium of the entire truss:

$$\Sigma M_A = 0 \quad -400(7.07) - 200(14.14) + 20E_y - 1000(10) = 0$$

$$E_y = 783 \text{ lb} \qquad \mathbf{E}_y = 783\mathbf{j} \quad \text{lb}$$

$$\Sigma F_x = 0 \quad A_x + 0.707(200 + 400 + 200) = 0$$

$$A_x = -566 \text{ lb} \qquad \mathbf{A}_x = -566\mathbf{i} \quad \text{lb}$$

$$\Sigma F_y = 0 \quad A_y - 0.707(200 + 400 + 200) + 782.8 - 1000 = 0$$

$$A_y = 783 \text{ lb} \qquad \mathbf{A}_y = 783\mathbf{j} \quad \text{lb}$$

As a check of these calculations for the reactive forces, let us sum moments about some arbitrary joint, say joint F.

$$\Sigma M_F = 0 \quad -10A_y + 200(7.07) - 200(7.07) + 10E_y = 0$$

$$A_y = E_y \qquad \text{(Checks)}$$

The free-body diagrams for the joints shown in Figure 4.13 include the reactive forces just calculated. Zero-force member DF is also labeled.

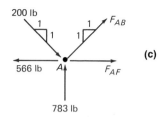

(c)

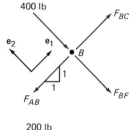

(d)

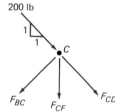

(e)

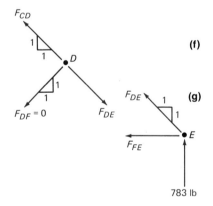

(f)

(g)

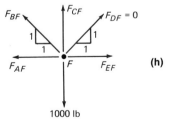

(h)

Joint A: $\Sigma F_y = 0$ $783 - 0.707(200) + 0.707 F_{AB} = 0$

$$F_{AB} = -907 \text{ lb} = 907 \text{ lb } C$$

$$\Sigma F_x = 0$$

$$-566 + 0.707(200) + 0.707 F_{AB} + F_{AF} = 0$$

$$-566 + 141.4 - 641 + F_{AF} = 0$$

$$F_{AF} = 1066 \text{ lb } T$$

Joint B: For convenience, vectors e_1 and e_2 as shown in Figure 4.13d are selected rather than the original xy coordinates. This simplifies the algebra.

$$\Sigma F_{e1} = 0 \quad -F_{AB} + F_{BC} = 0 \quad F_{BC} = F_{AB} = 907 \text{ lb } C$$

$$\Sigma F_{e2} = 0 \quad -400 - F_{BF} = 0 \quad F_{BF} = 400 \text{ lb } C$$

Joint C: $\Sigma F_x = 0$

$$-0.707 F_{BC} + 0.707(200) + 0.707 F_{CD} = 0$$

$$F_{CD} = -1107 \text{ lb} = 1107 \text{ lb } C$$

Joint D: $F_{DE} = F_{CD} = 1107 \text{ lb } C$

Joint E: $\Sigma F_x = 0$ $-F_{FE} - 0.707 F_{DE} = 0$

$$F_{FE} = -0.707 F_{DE} = 783 \text{ lb } T$$

Summing forces in the y direction adds nothing new in our calculations for internal forces. However, it does provide a valuable check on our calculations.

$$\Sigma F_y = 0 \quad 783 + 0.707 F_{DE} = 783 + 0.707(-1107) = 0$$

$$783 - 783 = 0 \quad \quad \text{(Checks)}$$

Joint F: The equilibrium equations at joint F also provide a check on our calculations.

$$\Sigma F_x = 0 \quad -F_{AF} - 0.707 F_{BF} + F_{FE} = 0$$

$$-1066 - 0.707(-400) + 783 = 0$$

$$-1066 + 283 + 783 = 0 \quad \text{(Checks)}$$

Problems

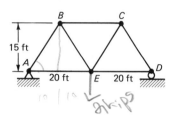

Figure 4.14

4.3.1 Calculate the reactive forces for the truss shown in Figure 4.14.

4.3.2 Calculate the reactive forces for the truss shown in Figure 4.15.

4.3.3 Obtain the forces at joints *A* and *E* for the truss shown in Figure 4.14.

4.3.4 Obtain the forces at joints *E* and *D* for the truss shown in Figure 4.15.

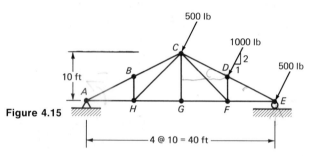

Figure 4.15

4.3.5 Use the method of joints to obtain the forces in members *BF* and *BC* of the truss shown in Figure 4.16.

4.3.6 Use the method of joints to obtain the forces at joints *D* and *E* for the truss shown in Figure 4.17.

4.3.7 Use the method of joints to obtain the forces in all the members of the truss shown in Figure 4.18.

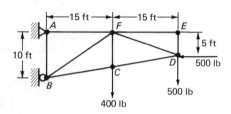

Figure 4.16

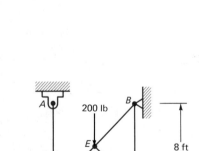

Figure 4.17

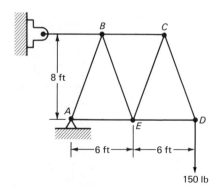

Figure 4.18

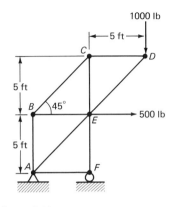

Figure 4.19

4.3.8 Use the method of joints to obtain the forces in all members of the truss shown in Figure 4.19.

4.3.9 Obtain the forces at joint A and D in the truss of Figure 4.20.

4.3.10 Find the force in member BC for the truss shown in Figure 4.21.

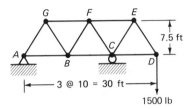

Figure 4.20

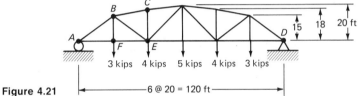

Figure 4.21

4.3.11 Obtain the forces in members AE, AD, DB, and CB in the truss of Figure 4.22.

4.3.12 Find the force in member CE for the truss shown in Figure 4.23.

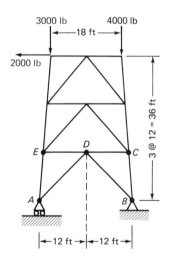

Figure 4.22

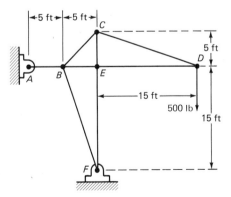

Figure 4.23

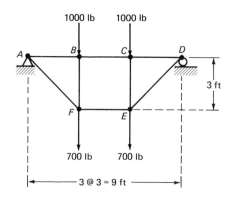

1000 lb   1000 lb

700 lb   700 lb

3 ft

3 @ 3 = 9 ft

Figure 4.24

4.3.13 Find the forces in all the members of the truss shown in Figure 4.24.

4.3.14 Find the forces in the cross bar CG for the truss shown in Figure 4.25.

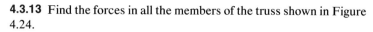

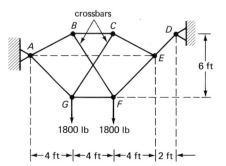

crossbars

1800 lb   1800 lb

6 ft

Figure 4.25 |←4 ft→|←4 ft→|←4 ft→|2 ft|←

4.3.15 Obtain the forces in all the members of the truss shown in Figure 4.26.

4.3.16 Find the forces in members AC and AD for the structure shown in Figure 4.27.

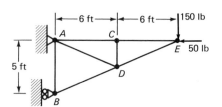

←6 ft→|←6 ft→|150 lb

5 ft

E 50 lb

Figure 4.26

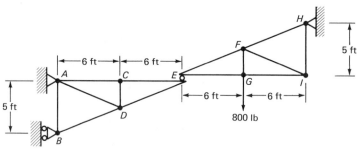

←6 ft→|←6 ft→|

5 ft

←6 ft→|←6 ft→|

800 lb

5 ft

Figure 4.27

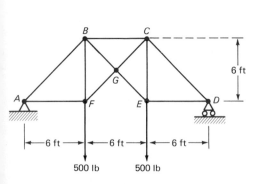

6 ft

←6 ft→|←6 ft→|←6 ft→|

500 lb   500 lb

Figure 4.28

4.3.17 Obtain the forces in all the members of the truss shown in Figure 4.28.

4.3.18 Find the forces in all the members for the truss shown in Figure 4.15.

4.4 Graphical Method

The following graphical method for analyzing trusses is the graphical equivalent of the method of joints. Since the equations of equilibrium are satisfied at each joint and the forces are concurrent at each joint, a force polygon can be drawn at each joint. We start the solution by finding the reactive forces using the equilibrium equations and then begin the graphical solution starting with a joint which has no more than two unknown internal forces. When the force polygons for each joint have been obtained, they can be combined into a single diagram called the *Maxwell diagram.*

The graphical method affords a quick procedure for obtaining the internal forces in the truss members and provides an independent check on other solutions used. However, it has the disadvantage of being cumbersome when a large-scale drawing is required.

Example 4.4.1

Use the graphical method to find all internal forces for the truss shown in Figure 4.29a.

First, from the free-body diagram of the truss, shown in Figure 4.29b, determine the equilibrium of the entire truss.

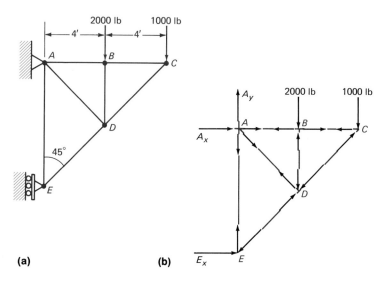

Figure 4.29　　　　　　　　**(a)**　　　　　　　　**(b)**

Figure 4.29

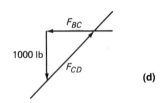

(c)

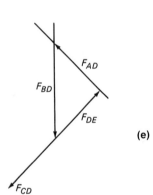

(d)

(e)

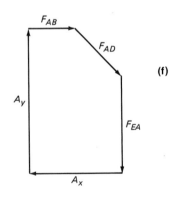

(f)

$$\Sigma M_A = 0 \qquad -2000(4) - 1000(8) + E_x(8) = 0$$

$$E_x = 2000 \text{ lb} \qquad \mathbf{E}_x = 2000\mathbf{i} \qquad \text{lb}$$

$$\Sigma F_x = 0 \qquad -A_x + E_x = 0$$

$$A_x = E_x = 2000 \text{ lb} \qquad \mathbf{A}_x = -2000\mathbf{i} \qquad \text{lb}$$

$$\Sigma F_y = 0 \qquad A_y - 2000 - 1000 = 0$$

$$A_y = 3000 \text{ lb} \qquad \mathbf{A}_y = 3000\mathbf{j} \qquad \text{lb}$$

We begin the graphical analysis by selecting a joint which has only two unknowns. In this example we have a choice between joints C and E. Let us begin with joint E. At joint E there are three forces in equilibrium; of these, we know the magnitude and direction of the force $\mathbf{E}_x$ and the lines of direction for the other two forces $\mathbf{F}_{EA}$ and $\mathbf{F}_{ED}$. Referring to Figure 4.29c, lay off force $\mathbf{E}_x$ to scale. From the tip of $\mathbf{E}_x$, lay off a vertical line along which $\mathbf{F}_{EA}$ lies. At the tail of $\mathbf{E}_x$, lay off a line 45° off the vertical; along this line $\mathbf{F}_{ED}$ must lie. The two lines intersect to close the force polygon. The force $\mathbf{F}_{EA}$ acts away from the joint E while $\mathbf{F}_{ED}$ acts toward the joint E as shown in Figure 4.29c. Thus, member EA is in tension while member ED is in compression. Having the directions of the forces acting at joint E, it is useful to show these directions on Figure 4.29b for future use.

Figure 4.29d shows the force polygon for joint C. We begin by laying off the applied force which is 1000 lb downward. At the tip of this force, lay off a 45° line with the vertical and a horizontal line through its tail. The intersection of these two lines establishes the force polygon as labeled in the figure. In this case force $\mathbf{F}_{CD}$ acts toward joint C (compression) and force $\mathbf{F}_{BC}$ acts away from the joint (tension).

In drawing the force polygon for joint D shown in Figure 4.29e, lay off force $\mathbf{F}_{CD}$, then from the tip of this vector lay off $\mathbf{F}_{DE}$. From the tip of $\mathbf{F}_{DE}$ lay off a line parallel to member AD and from the tail of $\mathbf{F}_{CD}$ lay off a vertical line. These latter two lines intersect to form the force polygon.

Figure 4.29f shows the force polygon for joint A, which established the force $\mathbf{F}_{AB}$. Figure 4.29g represents a check on the forces $\mathbf{F}_{AB}$, $\mathbf{F}_{BC}$, and $\mathbf{F}_{AD}$.

The Maxwell diagram is shown in Figure 4.29h. This diagram is constructed as we develop the force polygon at each joint. Indeed, we could construct Maxwell's diagram directly, without drawing each force polygon separately. If this ap-

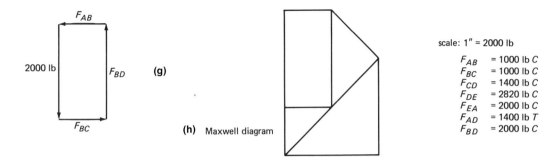

(h) Maxwell diagram

scale: 1" = 2000 lb

F_{AB} = 1000 lb C
F_{BC} = 1000 lb C
F_{CD} = 1400 lb C
F_{DE} = 2820 lb C
F_{EA} = 2000 lb C
F_{AD} = 1400 lb T
F_{BD} = 2000 lb C

proach is followed, it is advantageous to tabulate the forces in each member as we proceed from joint to joint. Write "C" after the force magnitude to indicate that the member is in compression and "T" to show that it is in tension. This is demonstrated by the tabulated forces in Figure 4.29.

Problems

4.4.1 Construct a force polygon to scale for the joints A, E, and D in Figure 4.14 (p. 106).

4.4.2 Construct a force polygon to scale for the forces acting at joints D and E in the truss in Figure 4.15 (p. 106).

4.4.3 Draw the force polygon for the joints A, B, and C of the truss shown in Figure 4.16 (p. 106).

4.4.4 Construct a force polygon to scale for all the joints in Figure 4.17 (p. 106).

4.4.5 Construct a force polygon for all the joints of the truss shown in Figure 4.18 (p. 106).

4.4.6 Construct Maxwell's diagram for the truss in Figure 4.18 (p. 106).

4.4.7 Construct Maxwell's diagram for the truss in Figure 4.19 (p. 107).

4.4.8 Obtain the force in member BC of the truss shown in Figure 4.20 (p. 107).

4.4.9 Construct Maxwell's diagram for the truss in Figure 4.23 (p. 107).

4.5 Method of Sections

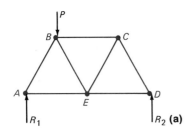

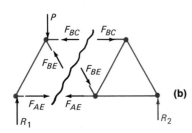

Figure 4.30

The method of joints and the graphical method provide the internal forces of each member of a plane truss, after the reaction forces are evaluated, by employing the conditions of equilibrium at each joint, i.e., $\Sigma F_x = 0$, $\Sigma F_y = 0$. This is possible because the forces acting at the joint are concurrent. However, it is possible to construct a free-body diagram of a portion of the truss and employ the third condition of equilibrium as well, namely, $\Sigma M = 0$. The free-body diagram of a part of a truss will generally contain nonconcurrent forces. This approach is called the method of sections; and with it, we can find the internal forces of selected members of a truss more rapidly than with an analysis which proceeds from one joint to the next.

Consider the truss shown in Figure 4.30a, which shows reactive forces $\mathbf{R}_1$ and $\mathbf{R}_2$ and an applied load $\mathbf{P}$. Let us find the forces in members BC, BE, and AE. First we cut the truss across these members and label the assumed directions of the internal forces as shown in Figure 4.30b. Now, since the truss to the left and to the right of the cut is in equilibrium, we can write for either section of the truss,

$$\Sigma F_x = 0 \qquad \Sigma F_y = 0 \qquad \Sigma M = 0$$

where the moments are taken about any convenient reference point, i.e., the reference point may be a point on the truss or off the truss. These three equations allow us to solve for the three unknown forces. Care must be exercised to insure that the part of the truss under consideration has no more than three cut members with unknown internal forces since only three unknown forces can be found from three conditions of equilibrium.

Example 4.5.1

Use the method of sections to find the forces in members KJ, DE, and EI for the truss shown in Figure 4.31a.

In Figure 4.31b, the left portion of the truss is shown with force F_{KJ} as the desired internal force. For convenience, sum moments about point C since internal forces F_{CD} and F_{CJ} pass through this point. Thus,

$$\Sigma M_C = 0 \qquad 25F_{KJ} + 1000(20) - 2000(60) - 0$$

$$F_{KJ} = 4000 \text{ lb } T \qquad \text{Answer}$$

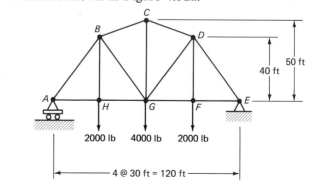

(a)

Figure 4.31c shows the right portion of the truss cut across members *DE*, *EI*, and *IH*. From this free-body diagram we have the following:

$$\Sigma F_y = 0$$

$$-\frac{25}{32.1}F_{EI} + 2000 - 1000 = 0$$

$$F_{EI} = 1280 \text{ lb } T \qquad \text{Answer}$$

$$\Sigma M_H = 0$$

$$-25F_{DE} + \frac{25}{32.1}F_{EI}(20) + \frac{20}{32.1}F_{EI}(25) + 2000(40) = 0$$

$$-25F_{DE} + 40,000 + 80,000 = 0$$

$$F_{DE} = 4800 \text{ lb } C \qquad \text{Answer}$$

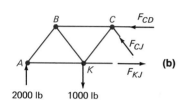

(b)

(c)

Figure 4.31

Example 4.5.2

Use the method of sections to find the force in member *BG* for the truss shown in Figure 4.32a.

(a)

Figure 4.32

The left portion of the truss, which is cut across members BC, BG, and HG, is shown in Figure 4.32b. The most convenient approach to finding F_{BG} is to extend the line BC to where it intersects with the extended line AH at point I, and then sum moments about point I:

$$\Sigma M_I = 0$$

$$4000(90) - 2000(120) - \tfrac{3}{5}F_{BG}(40) - \tfrac{4}{5}F_{BG}(120) = 0$$

$$F_{BG} = 1000 \text{ lb } T \qquad\qquad \text{Answer}$$

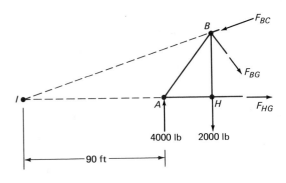

Figure 4.32   **(b)**

Problems

4.5.1 Find the forces in members BC and FE in Figure 4.33 by the method of sections.

4.5.2 Use the method of sections to find the forces in members BF and BC in Figure 4.24 (p. 108).

4.5.3 Use the method of sections to find the forces in member EG in Figure 4.27 (p. 108).

4.5.4 Find the forces in members BG and FG in Figure 4.28 (p. 108) by the method of sections.

4.5.5 Find the forces in members BC, CL, and LK in Figure 4.34 by the method of sections.

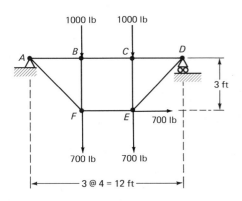

Figure 4.33

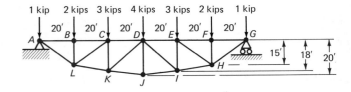

Figure 4.34

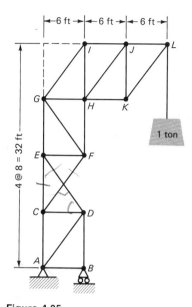

Figure 4.35

4.5.6 Find the forces in members *DI* and *JI* in Figure 4.34 by the method of sections.

4.5.7 Use the method of sections to find the forces in members *GI*, *IJ*, and *HK* in Figure 4.35.

4.5.8 Use the method of sections to find the forces in members *CE*, *ED*, and *CF* in Figure 4.35.

4.5.9 Find the forces in members *HJ* and *IL* in Figure 4.36 by the method of sections. (See suggested cut section.)

4.5.10 Find the force in member *JM* in Figure 4.36.

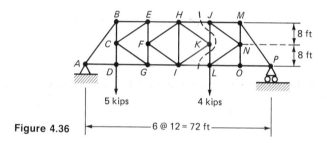

Figure 4.36

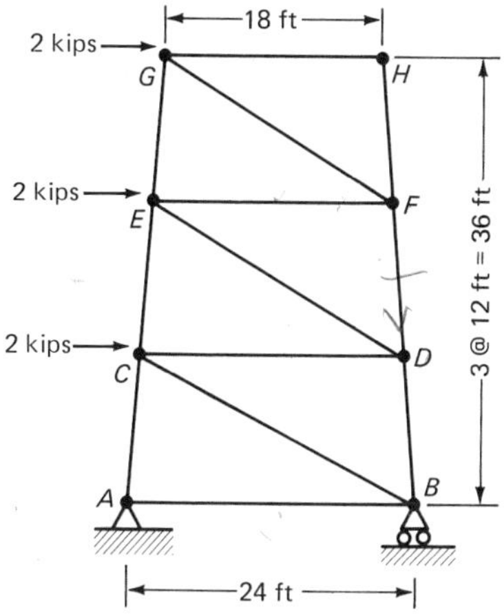

4.5.11 Find the force in member *FD* in Figure 4.37.

4.5.12 Find the force in member *BD* in Figure 4.38.

Figure 4.37

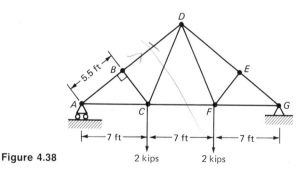

Figure 4.38

4.5.13 Find the force in member *HG* in Figure 4.39.

4.5.14 Find all the zero-force members in Figure 4.39.

4.5.15 Add a 3-kip vertical load at *L* in Figure 4.39 and find the force in member *EL*.

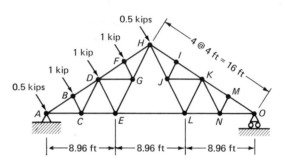

Figure 4.39

4.6 Equilibrium of Space Trusses

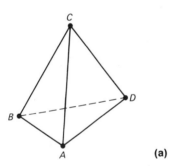

(a)

A three-dimensional truss is called a space truss. An elementary space truss consists of six straight members joined together to form a tetrahedron as shown in Figure 4.40a. Notice that we can add three new members, not in the same plane, to create another joint as shown in Figure 4.40b. This simple space truss starts with six members and four joints, and is expanded to nine members and five joints. In general, the number of joints *J* and members *M* of a simple space truss can be shown to be related by a simple formula.

$$M = 3J - 6 \qquad (4.2)$$

Since space trusses are in equilibrium and there are only six equilibrium equations, the truss system can involve no more than six force reactions in order to be statically determinate. Consequently, the supports of the truss must consist of rollers, ball and socket, or balls to insure no more than six unknown reactive forces.

Likewise, we assume that the members of a space truss are connected by ball and socket joints so that we are ignoring bending effects. This means that we are not applying couples to the members so that each member of the truss is a two-force member either in tension or compression.

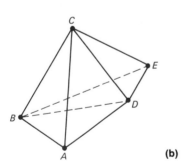

(b)

Figure 4.40

Once the free-body diagram of each joint is obtained, we can write the equations of equilibrium at each joint. Since we can write three equations at each joint, namely, $\Sigma F_x = 0$, $\Sigma F_y = 0$, $\Sigma F_z = 0$, we have $3J$ equations. And, since $3J = M + 6$, we can solve for the force in all the members M as well as for the six reaction forces. Often, however, it is easier to solve for the reactions by considering the equilibrium of the entire space truss just as we did for the plane truss.

The method of joints and the method of sections can be applied to the space truss. (A judicious selection of the order of analysis helps to avoid excessive algebraic equations.) In today's computerized age there exist numerous computer programs capable of solving the structural problems of large buildings, transmission towers, missiles, etc. The graphical method is, however, difficult to extend.

Example 4.5.3

Find the reactive forces at A, B, and D and internal forces for the space truss shown in Figure 4.41a. The reactions due to the supports are shown in Figure 4.41b.

Referring to Figure 4.41b, the equilibrium of the entire truss is first treated.

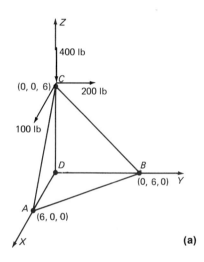

(a)

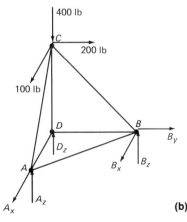

(b)

Figure 4.41

$$\Sigma M_x = 0 \qquad 6B_z - 200(6) = 0$$

$$B_z = 200 \text{ lb} \qquad \mathbf{B}_z = 200\mathbf{k} \quad \text{lb}$$

$$\Sigma M_y = 0 \qquad -6A_z + 100(6) = 0$$

$$A_z = 100 \text{ lb} \qquad \mathbf{A}_z = 100\mathbf{k} \quad \text{lb}$$

$$\Sigma M_z = 0 \qquad 6B_x = 0$$

$$B_x = 0$$

$$\Sigma F_x = 0 \qquad A_x + B_x + 100 = 0$$

$$A_x = -100 \text{ lb} \qquad \mathbf{A}_x = -100\mathbf{i} \quad \text{lb}$$

$$\Sigma F_y = 0 \qquad B_y + 200 = 0$$

$$B_y = -200 \text{ lb} \qquad \mathbf{B}_y = -200\mathbf{j} \quad \text{lb}$$

$$\Sigma F_z = 0 \qquad A_z + B_z + D_z - 400 = 0 \qquad D_z = -100 - 200 + 400$$

$$D_z = 100 \text{ lb} \qquad \mathbf{D}_z = 100\mathbf{k} \quad \text{lb}$$

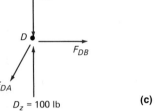

(c)

The equilibrium of the joints is now treated. For convenience, consider starting with joint D as shown in Figure 4.41c.

Joint D: $\qquad \Sigma F_x = 0 \qquad F_{DA} = 0$

$\qquad\qquad\qquad\qquad \Sigma F_y = 0 \qquad F_{DB} = 0$

$\qquad\qquad \Sigma F_z = 0 \qquad -F_{DC} + 100 = 0 \qquad F_{DC} = 100 \text{ lb } C$

Joint A: $\Sigma F_z = 0 \qquad 100 - 0.707 F_{AC} = 0 \qquad F_{AC} = 141.4 \text{ lb } C$

$\qquad \Sigma F_x = 0 \qquad -100 + 0.707 F_{AC} + 0.707 F_{AB} = 0 \qquad F_{AB} = 0$

Joint B: $\Sigma F_z = 0 \qquad 200 - 0.707 F_{BC} = 0 \qquad F_{BC} = 283 \text{ lb } C$

As a check, we can use

$$\Sigma F_y = 0 \qquad -200 + 0.707 F_{BC} = 0$$

$$F_{BC} = 283 \text{ lb} \qquad\qquad \text{(Checks)}$$

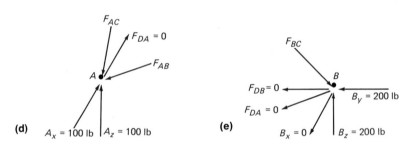

(d)

(e)

Joint C: The following calculations are a check on the resul already obtained.

$$\Sigma F_x = 0 \qquad 100 - 0.707 F_{AC} = 100 - 0.707(141.4) = 0$$

$$100 - 100 = 0 \qquad \text{(Checks)}$$

$$\Sigma F_y = 0 \qquad 200 - 0.707 F_{BC} = 200 - 0.707(283) = 0$$

$$200 - 200 = 0 \qquad \text{(Checks)}$$

$$\Sigma F_z = 0 \qquad -400 + 0.707 F_{AC} + F_{DC} + 0.707 F_{BC} = 0$$

$$-400 + 100 + 100 + 200 = 0 \qquad \text{(Checks)}$$

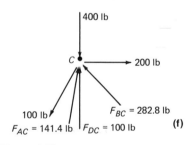

(f)

Figure 4.41

Problems

4.6.1 Find all the reaction forces in the space truss shown in Figure 4.42.

4.6.2 Find the reactions and the forces in members *AB* and *AC* for the truss shown in Figure 4.43.

4.6.3 Find the forces in members *AC*, *AD*, and *AB* of the truss of Figure 4.42.

4.6.4 Find the reactions and the force in member *AE* for the truss shown in Figure 4.44.

4.6.5 Obtain the force in member *CB* of the structure shown in Figure 4.42.

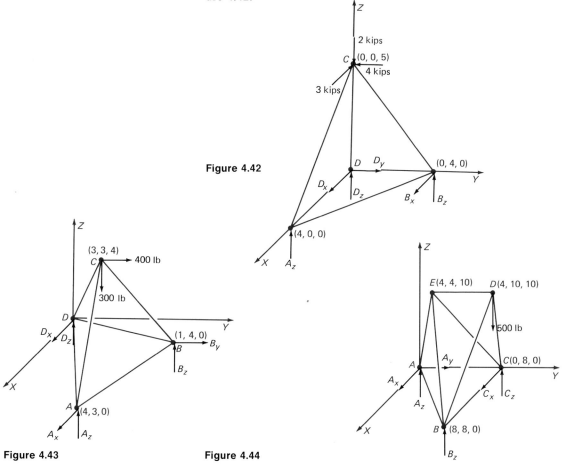

Figure 4.42

Figure 4.43

Figure 4.44

4.7 Frames and Machines

So far, we have analyzed only structures composed of two-force members where the forces are directed along the members upon which they act. When three or more forces are applied to a member, the member is called a *multiforce* member and the structure is referred to as a frame or machine. By way of example, the structure in Figure 4.1 is shown again in Figure 4.45. Here we have a frame consisting of a two-force member *EC*, and two multiforce members *EB* and *AD*. In analyzing multiforce members, the conditions of equilibrium are satisfied by the three equations of statics, namely, $\Sigma F_x = 0$, $\Sigma F_y = 0$, $\Sigma M = 0$, where we sum moments about some convenient reference point.

Figure 4.45

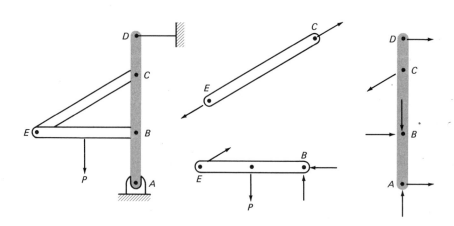

Frames A frame is usually a stationary structure consisting of one or more multiforce members. Frames can be further classified into two categories: (1) Rigid frame, wherein the shape of the frame does not change; and (2) nonrigid frame, wherein the removal or alteration of the supports of a frame causes the frame to change its shape. Figure 4.46 shows a four-link mechanism which is an example of a nonrigid frame. Notice that the ground itself forms the fourth link, and that if either support were removed, or replaced by a roller, this frame would alter its shape.

(a)

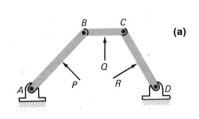

Figure 4.46

Rigid frames are analyzed by first drawing the free-body diagram of the entire structure so that the reactive forces may be determined. A free-body diagram of each member is then drawn and the equilibrium conditions are applied to each member in the most convenient order apparent to us in order to find the internal forces. We note that it is not customary to isolate the pin joints, but rather to assign the pin to one of the common members of the joint. This approach will be demonstrated in example 4.7.2.

Nonrigid frames are analyzed in a similar way. Not all the reaction forces can be obtained from the equilibrium of the entire nonrigid frame, however, as is apparent from Figure 4.46b. Here we have four unknown reactive forces and three equations of equilibrium. But, referring to Figure 4.46c, we see that the free-body diagrams of the members show eight unknown forces, the four reactive forces A_x, A_y, D_x, D_y, and four internal forces B_x, B_y, C_x, C_y. And for these, we have eight independent equilibrium equations, so that the structure is statically determinate.

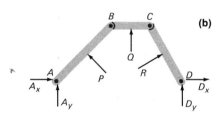

(b)

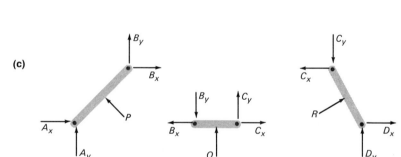

(c)

Machines A machine generally has moving parts and is usually not considered as a rigid structure. Machines are designed to transmit loads rather than to support them. For example, the pair of tongs shown in Figure 4.47 has a force P applied to each tong which transmits the gripping forces Q. Other forms of hand tools are further examples of familiar machines.

Machines and frames are analyzed in the same manner. Thus, analysis of a machine involves the unknown forces of multiforce members and the three equations of statics for each member.

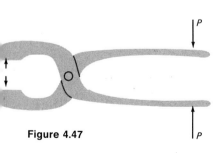

Figure 4.47

Figure 4.48

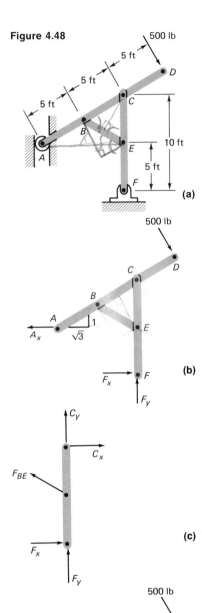

500 lb

5 ft

5 ft

D

5 ft

C

5 ft

B

E   10 ft

A

5 ft

F

(a)

500 lb

C   D

B

A

A_x $\sqrt{3}$ E

F_x F   (b)

F_y

C_y

C_x

F_{BE}

F_x

F_y (c)

500 lb

C_y

C_x

F_{BE}

A_x (d)

Example 4.7.1

Determine the components of all the forces acting on each member of the frame shown in Figure 4.48a.

The free-body diagram of the frame is shown in Figure 4.48b, while the members are shown in Figures 4.48c and 4.48d.

Equilibrium of the entire frame:

$$\Sigma M_F = 0 \qquad 5A_x - 500\frac{\sqrt{3}}{2}(4.34) - 500\frac{1}{2}(10 + 2.5) = 0$$

$$A_x = 1000 \text{ lb} \qquad \mathbf{A_x} = -1000\mathbf{i} \quad \text{lb}$$

$$\Sigma F_x = 0 \qquad -1000 + F_x + 500(\tfrac{1}{2}) = 0$$

$$F_x = 750 \text{ lb} \qquad \mathbf{F_x} = 750\mathbf{i} \quad \text{lb}$$

$$\Sigma F_y = 0 \qquad F_y - 500\frac{\sqrt{3}}{2} = 0$$

$$F_y = 434 \text{ lb} \qquad \mathbf{F_y} = 434\mathbf{j} \quad \text{lb}$$

Member CEF:

$$\Sigma M_C = 0 \qquad -\frac{\sqrt{3}}{2}F_{BE}(5) + F_x(10) = 0$$

$$F_{BE} = \frac{7500}{4.34} = 1730 \text{ lb}$$

$$\Sigma F_x = 0 \qquad C_x - \frac{\sqrt{3}}{2}F_{BE} + F_x = 0$$

$$C_x = 1500 - 750 = 750 \text{ lb}$$

$$\Sigma F_y = 0 \qquad C_y + \tfrac{1}{2}F_{BE} + F_y = 0$$

$$C_y = -865 - 434 = -1299 \text{ lb}$$

The equilibrium equations for member *ABCD* provide a check on our calculations. (Note the minus sign on C_y when drawing the free-body diagram, Figure 4.48d.)

$$\Sigma F_x = 0$$

$$-A_x + \frac{\sqrt{3}}{2}F_{BE} - C_x + \frac{1}{2}(500) = -1000 + 1500 - 750 + 250 = 0$$

$$-1750 + 1750 = 0 \qquad \text{(Checks)}$$

$$\Sigma F_y = 0$$

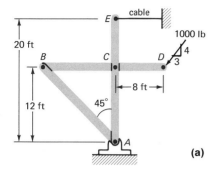

(a)

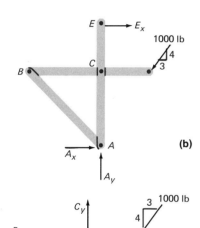

(b)

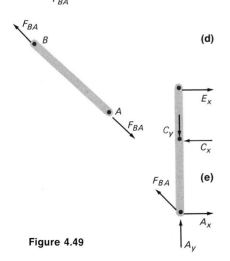

Figure 4.49

$$-\frac{1}{2}F_{BE} - C_y - \frac{\sqrt{3}}{2}(500) = -865 + 1299 - 434 = 0$$

$$-1299 + 1299 = 0 \qquad \text{(Checks)}$$

Example 4.7.2

Determine the components of all the forces acting on each member of the frame shown in Figure 4.49a.

The free-body diagram of the entire frame is shown in Figure 4.49b.

Equilibrium of the entire frame:

$$\Sigma M_A = 0 \qquad -20E_x - \tfrac{4}{5}(1000)(8) + \tfrac{3}{5}(1000)(12) = 0$$

$$20E_x = 800 \qquad E_x = 40 \text{ lb} \qquad \mathbf{E}_x = 40\mathbf{i} \quad \text{lb}$$

$$\Sigma F_x = 0 \qquad A_x + E_x - 600 = 0$$

$$A_x = 560 \text{ lb} \qquad \mathbf{A}_x = 560\mathbf{i} \quad \text{lb}$$

$$\Sigma F_y = 0 \qquad A_y - 800 = 0$$

$$A_y = 800 \text{ lb} \qquad \mathbf{A}_y = 800\mathbf{j} \quad \text{lb}$$

In drawing the free-body diagrams of the members of the truss, allow the pin at joint A to be in member ACE so that member AB is treated as a two-force member. These diagrams are shown in Figures 4.49c through 4.49e.

Member BCD: $\qquad \Sigma M_C = 0 \qquad 0.707F_{BA}(12) - 800(8) = 0$

$$F_{BA} = 754 \text{ lb}$$

$$\Sigma F_x = 0 \qquad 0.707F_{BA} + C_x - 600 = 0$$

$$C_x = 600 - 533 = 67 \text{ lb}$$

$$\Sigma F_y = 0 \qquad -0.707F_{BA} + C_y - 800 = 0$$

$$C_y = 533 + 800 = 1333 \text{ lb}$$

As a check on this calculation, the forces shown in Figure 4.49e should satisfy the equations of equilibrium.

$$\Sigma F_x = 0$$

$$-0.707F_{BA} + A_x - C_x + E_x = -533 + 560 - 67 + 40 = 0$$

$$-600 + 600 = 0 \qquad \text{(Checks)}$$

$$\Sigma F_y = 0 \qquad A_y + 0.707F_{BA} - C_y = 800 + 533 - 1333 = 0$$

$$1333 - 1333 = 0 \qquad \text{(Checks)}$$

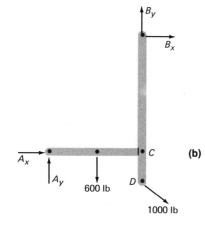

Figure 4.50

Example 4.7.3

Find the reaction forces for the nonrigid frame shown in Figure 4.50a.

The free-body diagram of the nonrigid frame shows four unknown reaction forces, as seen in Figure 4.50b. Since we have only three equilibrium equations, we cannot solve directly for the reaction forces. However, if we proceed to Figure 4.50c and 4.50d, we have six unknowns and six equilibrium equations.

Member AC: $\quad \Sigma M_A = 0 \qquad 10C_y - 600(5) = 0$

$$C_y = 300 \text{ lb}$$

$$\Sigma F_y = 0 \qquad A_y - 600 + C_y = 0$$

$$A_y = 300 \text{ lb} \qquad \mathbf{A}_y = 300\mathbf{j} \quad \text{lb}$$

Member BCD: $\qquad \Sigma M_B = 0 \qquad -12C_x + \frac{4}{5}(1000)(15) = 0$

$$C_x = 1000 \text{ lb}$$

$$\Sigma F_x = 0 \qquad B_x - C_x + \frac{4}{5}(1000) = 0$$

$$B_x = 1000 - 800 = 200 \text{ lb} \qquad \mathbf{B}_x = 200\mathbf{i} \quad \text{lb}$$

$$\Sigma F_y = 0 \qquad B_y - C_y - \frac{3}{5}(1000) = 0$$

$$B_y = 300 + 600 = 900 \text{ lb} \qquad \mathbf{B}_y = 900\mathbf{j} \quad \text{lb}$$

Member AC: $\qquad \Sigma F_x = 0 \qquad A_x + C_x = 0$

$$A_x = -1000 \text{ lb} \qquad \mathbf{A}_x = -1000\mathbf{i} \quad \text{lb}$$

As a check on the calculations, refer to Figure 4.50b.

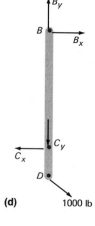

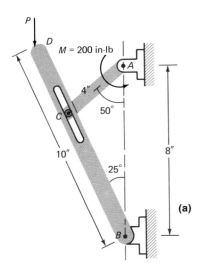

(a)

Figure 4.51

Equilibrium of entire frame:

$$\Sigma F_x = 0 \qquad A_x + 800 + B_x = -1000 + 800 + 200 = 0$$
(Checks)

$$\Sigma F_y = 0 \qquad A_y + B_y - 600 - 600 = 300 + 900 - 600 - 600 = 0$$
(Checks)

Example 4.7.4

Find the force P needed to keep the crank-shape mechanism in equilibrium for the applied moment M shown in Figure 4.51a.

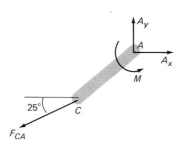

(b)

(c)   The free-body diagram for each member is shown in Figures 4.51b and 4.51c. Note that for this machine the force F_{CA} acts perpendicular to member BCD, since the pin at C slides along the grooved slot in the member BCD.

Member AC: $\Sigma M_A = 0$

$$-(F_{CA} \cos 25°)(4 \cos 50°) + (F_{CA} \sin 25°)(4 \sin 50°) + M = 0$$

$$-2.33 F_{CA} + 1.294 F_{CA} + 200 = 0$$

$$F_{CA} = 195 \text{ lb}$$

Member BCD: $\Sigma M_B = 0$

$$P(10 \sin 25°) - (F_{CA} \cos 25°)(7.26 \cos 25°) \\ - (F_{CA} \sin 25°)(7.26 \sin 25°) = 0$$

$$4.22 P = 1417 \qquad P = 335 \text{ lb} \qquad \text{Answer}$$

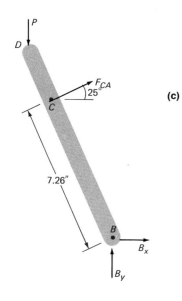

Problems

4.7.1 For the frame in Figure 4.52 find (a) the reactions at *A* and (b) the forces in members *DE* and *BE*.

Figure 4.52

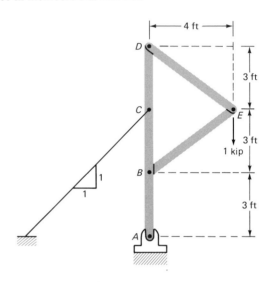

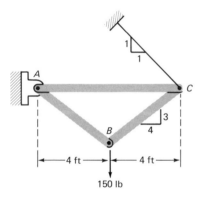

150 lb

Figure 4.53

4.7.2 Find the force acting on member *AB* in Figure 4.53.

4.7.3 Find the forces acting on member *AD* in Figure 4.54 if $\theta = 45°$.

4.7.4 Find the force in member *AC* in Figure 4.53.

4.7.5 For the structure in Figure 4.55, what is the maximum allowable load *w* if member *EG* has a compressive strength of 2500 lb?

4.7.6 If *w* = 4 kips in problem 4.7.5 and neglecting the restriction on member *EG*, find the forces acting on member *EG*.

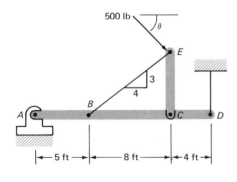

Figure 4.54

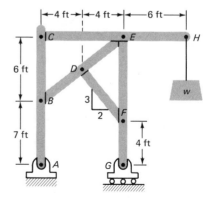

Figure 4.55

4.7.7 Find the forces acting on member BE in Figure 4.56 if $w = 1$ kip.

Figure 4.56

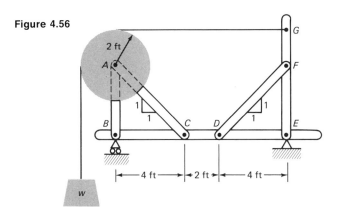

4.7.8 What are the forces acting on member AD in Figure 4.57?

4.7.9 What are the forces acting on member FC in Figure 4.58?

4.7.10 What are the forces acting on the member AE in the truss shown in Figure 4.58?

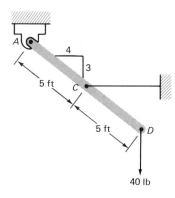

Figure 4.57

Figure 4.58

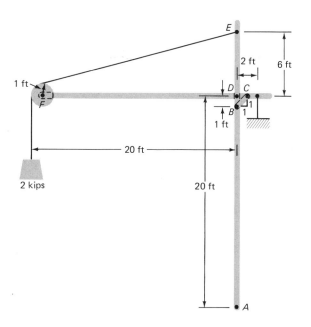

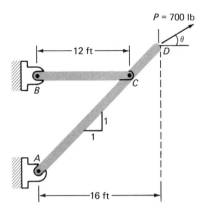

Figure 4.59

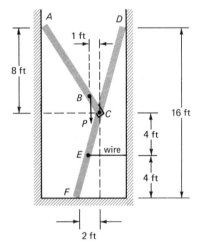

Figure 4.62

4.7.11 If $\theta = 30°$ in Figure 4.59, find the reactions at A and B.

4.7.12 Find the forces acting on member BE in Figure 4.60.

4.7.13 Find the reactions at A and B in Figure 4.61.

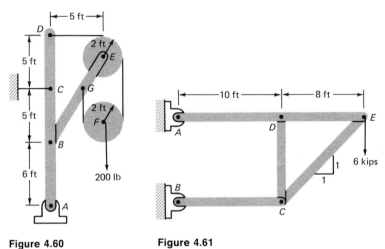

Figure 4.60   Figure 4.61

4.7.14 If the breaking load on the wire in Figure 4.62 is 80 lb, what is the maximum load P?

4.7.15 What forces are exerted on the bolt by the tongs in Figure 4.63?

4.7.16 The wire cutter in Figure 4.64 is to cut a wire which has a breaking strength of 75 lb. What is P if the wire is at A?

4.7.17 What is P if the wire, in the cutter shown in Figure 4.64, is at B?

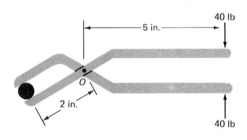

Figure 4.63

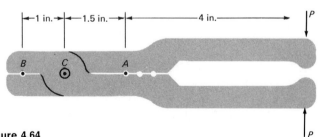

Figure 4.64

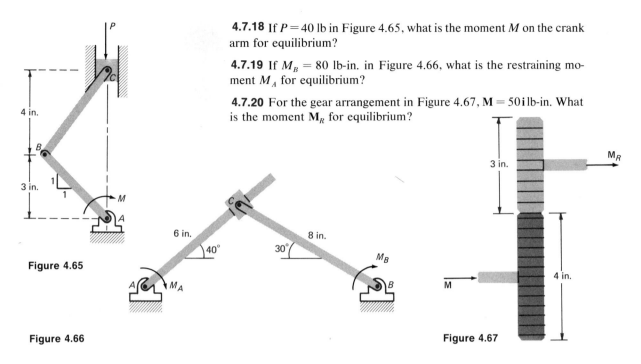

4.7.18 If $P = 40$ lb in Figure 4.65, what is the moment M on the crank arm for equilibrium?

4.7.19 If $M_B = 80$ lb-in. in Figure 4.66, what is the restraining moment M_A for equilibrium?

4.7.20 For the gear arrangement in Figure 4.67, $\mathbf{M} = 50\,\mathbf{i}$ lb-in. What is the moment $\mathbf{M}_R$ for equilibrium?

Figure 4.65

Figure 4.66

Figure 4.67

4.8 Summary

A   The important *ideas*:

1. Plane trusses and space trusses are formed by two-force members, that is, each member has a pair of forces in tension or compression. These forces are equal in magnitude, collinear, and act in opposite directions.

2. Frames and machines include multiforce members which are characterized by the action of three or more forces.

3. In analyzing frames, care must be taken to assign the pin to one of the common members at a joint.

B   The important *equations*:

Plane Truss

Method of joints: $\Sigma F_x = 0, \Sigma F_y = 0$

Method of sections: $\Sigma F_x = 0, \Sigma F_y = 0, \Sigma M = 0$

Space truss: $F_x = 0, \quad F_y = 0, \quad F_z = 0$

Frames and machines: $\Sigma F_x = 0, \Sigma F_y = 0, \Sigma M = 0$

Chapter 5
Distributed Forces

When a force is applied over a distributed area, it is called a distributed force. This fact, when included in our analysis, leads to the definition of the center of gravity and the centroid. We show how the centroids of lines, areas, and volumes may be obtained. Examples of distributed forces studied here include fluid pressure, buoyancy, and cables.

5.1 Introduction

We have represented a force as a vector which has magnitude, direction, and a point of application. In reality, most forces are applied over a distributed area rather than at a single point. The assumption of a point loading is valid in those cases where the area over which the force is applied is small in comparison with the size of the body. If, however, the area of loading is large relative to the body, the forces are called distributed forces and their distribution must be included in the analysis.

There is a distinction between push-pull forces and field forces such as the gravitational force. What is called the "weight" of a body is gravitational force. Since gravity applies a force to each particle of a body, its weight should be represented by many small forces distributed over the entire body. It will be seen, however, that these distributed forces reduce to a single force, that is, the weight going through the center of gravity.

In this chapter we introduce the center of gravity, centroids, and some theorems useful for the treatment of distributed forces. Applications of distributed forces introduced in this chapter include fluid pressures, buoyancy, and cables. The study of distributed forces is facilitated by the use of integral calculus which we shall briefly discuss.

5.2 Summation and Integration

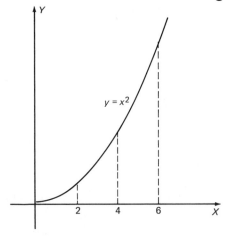

Figure 5.1

Suppose we wish to find an approximate value of the area under the curve $y = x^2$ between $x = 0$ to $x = 6$ as shown in Figure 5.1. To find this approximation, divide the X axis into three intervals, each of width $\Delta x = 2$. Evaluate y in each interval at its midpoint. Approximate the area of each interval by a rectangular strip, the area of each strip being the product of the width $\Delta x = 2$ and the midpoint value of y. Thus,

$$A \approx A_1 + A_2 + A_3$$
$$= 1(2) + 9(2) + 25(2) = 70$$

If we wish to improve this answer, we can reduce the interval, say to $\Delta x = 1$, so that we would have six rectangular strips. It is apparent that the answer can be further improved by reducing the interval Δx even further.

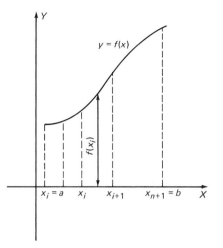

Figure 5.2

The problem can be generalized somewhat by considering the function $y = f(x)$ as shown in Figure 5.2. Let $(x_{i+1} - x_i) = \Delta x_i$ form the interval for one rectangular strip between $x = a$ and $x = b$, and let us find the area under the interval. For notation, let the value of the function in a given interval be $f(x_i)$. If we have n strips, the area is approximately given by

$$A \approx A_1 + A_2 + A_3 + \cdots + A_n$$

$$= f(x_1)(x_2 - x_1) + f(x_2)(x_3 - x_2) + \cdots + f(x_n)(x_{n+1} - x_n)$$

$$= \sum_{i=1}^{n} f(x_i)(x_{i+1} - x_i) = \sum_{i=1}^{n} f(x_i)\,\Delta x_i \qquad (5.1)$$

From calculus, we know that if the largest value of Δx_i approaches zero and the number of intervals approaches infinity, equation (5.1) can be written as follows:

$$A = \lim_{n \to \infty} \sum_{i=1}^{n} f(x_i)\,\Delta x_i = \int_a^b f(x)\,dx \qquad (5.2)$$

This expression, which will give us the correct value of the area, is called the definite integral of the function $f(x)$ evaluated between the limits of $x = a$ to $x = b$. The integral of a common function can, for example, be expressed as

$$\int_a^b x^n\,dx = \frac{x^{n+1}}{n+1}\Bigg]_a^b$$

$$= \frac{1}{n+1}[(b)^{n+1} - (a)^{n+1}] \qquad (5.3)$$

except when $n = -1$. Tables of integrals can be found in calculus textbooks and engineering handbooks.

Example 5.2.1

Find the area under the curve $y = x^2$ between the interval $x = 0$ to $x = 6$.

From equations (5.2) and (5.3) we find that

$$A = \int_0^6 x^2\,dx = \frac{x^3}{3}\Bigg]_0^6 = \frac{216}{3} = 72 \qquad \text{Answer}$$

This correct value for the area shows that our earlier crude approximation gave a reasonably good value.

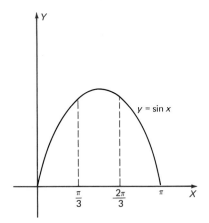

Figure 5.3

Example 5.2.2

Find the area under the curve $y = \sin x$ between $x = 0$ and $x = \pi$ radians (a) using the approximate approach for three equal strips and (b) using the definite integral.

(a) To satisfy $A = A_1 + A_2 + A_3$, let the function be evaluated at the midpoint of each interval, as shown in Figure 5.3. Thus, the areas of each strip are

$$A_1 = \left(\sin \frac{\pi}{6} \right) \frac{\pi}{3} = 0.5 \frac{\pi}{3}$$

$$A_2 = \left(\sin \frac{\pi}{2} \right) \frac{\pi}{3} = 1 \cdot \frac{\pi}{3}$$

$$A_3 = \left(\sin \frac{5\pi}{6} \right) \frac{\pi}{3} = 0.5 \frac{\pi}{3}$$

and

$$A = \frac{2\pi}{3} = 2.09 \qquad \text{Answer}$$

(b) From calculus, it is shown that

$$\int_a^b \sin x \, dx = -\cos x \Big]_a^b$$

therefore

$$A = \int_0^\pi \sin x \, dx = -\cos x \Big]_0^\pi = -(\cos \pi - \cos 0)$$

$$= -(-1 - 1) = 2 \qquad \text{Answer}$$

Problems

5.2.1 Find the approximate area under the curve $y = x^3$ between $x = 1$ to $x = 5$. Let $\Delta x = 2$ and evaluate the ordinate y at the midpoint of each strip.

5.2.2 Find the approximate area under the curve $y = e^{-0.2x}$ between $x = 2$ to $x = 5$. Let $\Delta x = 1$ and evaluate the ordinate y at the midpoint of each strip.

5.2.3 Evaluate the following definite integrals:

$$\int_1^5 x^3 \, dx$$

5.2.4 $\displaystyle\int_2^5 e^{-0.2x}\,dx$

5.2.5 $\displaystyle\int_{-2}^0 (10 + 2x)\,dx$

5.2.6 $\displaystyle\int_3^6 dx/x$

5.2.7 $\displaystyle\int_{-1}^1 (x + 2)^2\,dx$

5.2.8 $\displaystyle\int_0^{\pi/2} \cos\theta\,d\theta$

5.3 Center of Gravity

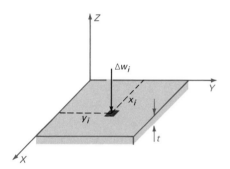

Figure 5.4

Consider a thin flat plate of uniform thickness t as shown in Figure 5.4. Let the plate be divided up into n small elements so that the weight of the ith element is Δw_i located at the coordinate point x_i, y_i as shown in the figure. The total weight of the plate is

$$w = \sum_{i=1}^n \Delta w_i$$

The moment about the X axis produced by all the elements of weight is

$$M_x = y_1\,\Delta w_1 + y_2\,\Delta w_2 + \cdots + y_n\,\Delta w_n$$

$$= \sum_{i=1}^n y_i\,\Delta w_i$$

If we let the size of the largest element approach zero and the number of elements approach infinity, we have the moment in integral form, i.e.,

$$M_x = \int_V y\,dw \tag{5.4a}$$

where the V means that the integration is taken over the entire volume of the plate. This is an example of a multiple integral as studied in calculus. Note that equation (5.4a) can be expressed in differential form as

$$dM_x = y\,dw$$

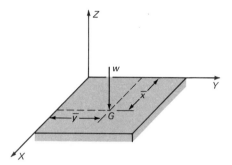

Figure 5.5

In a similar manner we can represent the moment about the *Y* axis due to the weight of the plate as

$$M_y = \int_V x \, dw \qquad (5.4b)$$

Let us select some point *G* with coordinates $\bar{x}$ and $\bar{y}$ and represent the total weight *w* of the plate at *G* by a force applied perpendicular to the plate, as seen in Figure 5.5. Now, the total weight of the plate in integral form is

$$w = \int_V dw \qquad (5.5)$$

We select point *G* so that the magnitudes of the moments caused by *w* about the *X* and *Y* axes,

$$M_x = w\bar{y} \qquad M_y = w\bar{x} \qquad (5.6)$$

are identical to the moments given by equations (5.4). Thus, equating the right sides of equations (5.4) and (5.6) and rearranging, we get

$$\bar{x} = \frac{1}{w} \int_V x \, dw \qquad (5.7a)$$

$$\bar{y} = \frac{1}{w} \int_V y \, dw \qquad (5.7b)$$

The point *G* is called the *center of gravity* of the body and its coordinates are obtained from equations (5.7a) and (5.7b).

We have assumed that the plate thickness *t* was small. If, however, we wish to consider the third dimension, it follows that

$$\bar{z} = \frac{1}{w} \int_V z \, dw \qquad (5.7c)$$

While equations (5.7) were derived for a flat plate, they may be applied to bodies with any geometrical properties.

If we let γ be the weight per unit volume of the body, then $dw = \gamma \, dV$ and equations (5.7) become

$$\bar{x} = \frac{\int_V x\gamma \, dV}{\int_V \gamma \, dV} \qquad \bar{y} = \frac{\int_V y\gamma \, dV}{\int_V \gamma \, dV} \qquad \bar{z} = \frac{\int_V z\gamma \, dV}{\int_V \gamma \, dV} \qquad (5.8)$$

5.4 Centroids

Equations (5.8) are simplified if the body is homogeneous so that γ is constant throughout. Thus, γ cancels in the numerator and denominator, giving

$$\bar{x} = \frac{1}{V}\int_V x\, dV \qquad \bar{y} = \frac{1}{V}\int_V y\, dV \qquad \bar{z} = \frac{1}{V}\int_V z\, dV \quad (5.9)$$

The coordinates $\bar{x}, \bar{y}, \bar{z}$, which are dependent only on the geometry of the body, locate the *centroid* of the body. Note that the centroid of a body equals the center of gravity if the body is homogeneous. Sometimes the integrals in equation (5.9) are called the *first moments* about the X, Y, Z axes.

Lines Let us assume that we have a homogeneous slender rod or wire of length L in the XY plane as shown in Figure 5.6. Let A be the uniform cross-sectional area of the wire, so that the differential volume is given by

$$dV = A\, dL \qquad\qquad (5.10)$$

Consequently, the total volume is

$$V = AL \qquad\qquad (5.11)$$

Now substitute equations (5.10) and (5.11) into (5.9) to get

$$\bar{x} = \frac{1}{L}\int x\, dL \quad \text{and} \quad \bar{y} = \frac{1}{L}\int y\, dL \qquad (5.12)$$

Depending upon the shape of the wire, $\bar{x}$ and $\bar{y}$ may or may not be on the wire itself. Since the wire is homogeneous, the center of gravity coincides with the centroid. If the origin of the XY axes is selected or moved to coincide with the centroid as shown in Figure 5.7, the axes are called *centroidal axes*. Note that in this case, if we compute the centroids using the centroidal axes as in Figure 5.7, we obtain a value of zero for both $\bar{x}$ and $\bar{y}$. Table 5.1 lists the centroids for common geometric shapes of lines in a plane.

Areas We will now consider a homogeneous thin plate of uniform thickness t. The differential element of volume is

$$dV = t\, dA \qquad\qquad (5.13)$$

The total volume is

$$V = tA \qquad\qquad (5.14)$$

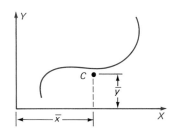

Figure 5.6

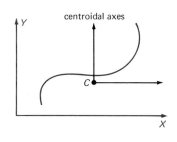

Figure 5.7

Table 5.1
Centroids for Lines in a Plane

	Centroid	Length

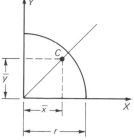

Quarter-circular arc

$\bar{x} = \dfrac{2r}{\pi}$ $\bar{y} = \dfrac{2r}{\pi}$ $\dfrac{\pi r}{2}$

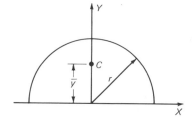

Semicircular arc

$\bar{x} = 0$ $\bar{y} = \dfrac{2r}{\pi}$ πr

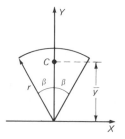

Arc of circle

$\bar{x} = 0$ $\bar{y} = \dfrac{r \sin \beta}{\beta}$ $2\beta r$

where A is the area of the plate shown in Figure 5.8. We can now substitute equations (5.13) and (5.14) into equation (5.9) to get

$$\bar{x} = \frac{1}{A} \int x \, dA \qquad \text{and} \qquad \bar{y} = \frac{1}{A} \int y \, dA \qquad (5.15)$$

Here, $\bar{x}$ and $\bar{y}$ are the coordinates of the centroid of the area as shown in Figure 5.8.

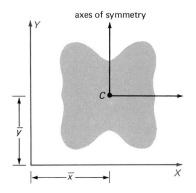

axes of symmetry

Figure 5.8

The integrals in equation (5.15) are called *first moments of area* about the *X* and *Y* axes. We note that in this example we have identified the axes of symmetry whose origin is at the centroid *C*. That is, the area of the plane is equally distributed on both sides of the axes. If two axes of symmetry are perpendicular to each other, they locate the centroid of an area. This observation enables us to locate centroids of regular shapes such as rectangles, circles, ellipses, etc., in a straightforward manner.

Since we are considering homogeneous cases, the weight on one side of an axis of symmetry equals that on the other side. This is why the centroid and the center of gravity coincide. Clearly, if we do not have homogeneity, the center of gravity will be different from the centroid. The centroids for a variety of areas are shown in Table 5.2.

Volumes The location of the centroid of a volume is given by equation (5.9).

$$\bar{x} = \frac{1}{V} \int_V x \, dV \qquad \bar{y} = \frac{1}{V} \int_V y \, dV \qquad \bar{z} = \frac{1}{V} \int_V z \, dV$$

$$(5.9)$$

Table 5.3 lists the centroids for some common volumes.

Example 5.4.1

Find the centroid of the line in Figure 5.9 from point *A* to point *B*.

The differential element *dL* shown in Figure 5.9 is

$$dL = \sqrt{dx^2 + dy^2} = dx\sqrt{1 + (dy/dx)^2}$$

Since $y = x - 2$,

$$\frac{dy}{dx} = 1$$

and therefore

$$dL = \sqrt{2} \, dx \qquad L = \sqrt{2} \int_0^6 dx = 6\sqrt{2}$$

From equations (5.12) we get

$$\bar{x} = \frac{1}{L} \int x \, dL = \frac{1}{L} \int_0^6 x(\sqrt{2} \, dx)$$

$$= \frac{1}{6} \left[\frac{x^2}{2} \right]_0^6 = 3 \qquad \qquad \text{Answer}$$

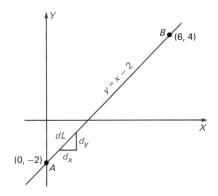

Figure 5.9

Table 5.2
Centroids for Areas

	Centroid	Area
Rectangle 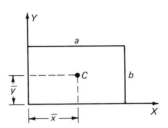	$\bar{x} = \dfrac{a}{2}$ $\bar{y} = \dfrac{b}{2}$	ab
Triangle 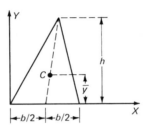	$\bar{y} = \dfrac{h}{3}$	$\dfrac{bh}{2}$
Circular sector 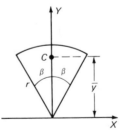	$\bar{x} = 0$ $\bar{y} = \dfrac{2r \sin \beta}{3\beta}$	βr^2
Semicircle 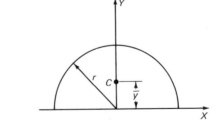	$\bar{x} = 0$ $\bar{y} = \dfrac{4r}{3\pi}$	$\dfrac{\pi r^2}{2}$

Table 5.2
Centroids for Areas

		Centroid	**Area**
Quarter-circular arc	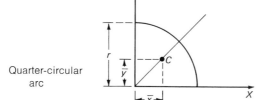	$\bar{x} = \dfrac{4r}{3\pi}$ $\bar{y} = \dfrac{4r}{3\pi}$	$\dfrac{\pi r^2}{4}$

Table 5.3
Centroids for Volumes

		Centroid	**Volume**
Cone or Pyramid	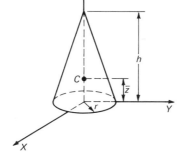	$\bar{z} = \dfrac{h}{4}$	$\dfrac{1}{3}\pi r^2 h$
Hemisphere	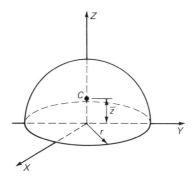	$\bar{z} = \dfrac{3r}{8}$	$\dfrac{2}{3}\pi r^3$

$$\bar{y} = \frac{1}{L} \int y \, dL = \frac{1}{L} \int_0^6 (x - 2)(\sqrt{2} \, dx)$$

$$= \frac{1}{6} \int_0^6 (x - 2) \, dx = \frac{1}{6} \left[\frac{x^2}{2} - 2x \right]_0^6 = 1 \quad \text{Answer}$$

We note that the centroid for a straight line is coincident with the midpoint of the X and Y projections. This is a useful property to remember.

Example 5.4.2

Locate the centroid for the triangle of base b and height h as shown in Figure 5.10.

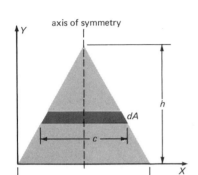

axis of symmetry

Figure 5.10

We notice that the triangle is symmetrical about an axis parallel to the Y axis as shown in Figure 5.10. This means that the centroid lies along this axis and $\bar{x} = b/2$. To find $\bar{y}$, select the element of area

$$dA = c \, dy$$

where

$$\frac{c/2}{b/2} = \frac{h - y}{h}$$

by similar triangles, so that

$$c = \frac{b}{h} (h - y)$$

Then, from equation (5.15), we find

$$\bar{y} = \frac{1}{A} \int y \, dA = \frac{2}{bh} \int yc \, dy$$

$$= \frac{2}{bh} \int_0^h \frac{b}{h} (h - y) y \, dy$$

$$= \frac{2}{h^2} \int_0^h (hy - y^2) \, dy$$

$$= \frac{2}{h^2} \left[\frac{hy^2}{2} - \frac{y^3}{3} \right]_0^h = \frac{h}{3}$$

Answer

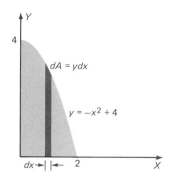

Figure 5.11

Example 5.4.3

Find the centroid of an area bounded by the curve $y = -x^2 + 4$, the Y axis, and the X axis as shown in Figure 5.11.

Let the element of area be

$$dA = y\,dx = (4 - x^2)\,dx$$

$$A = \int_0^2 (4 - x^2)\,dx = \left[4x - \frac{x^3}{3} \right]_0^2 = 5.33$$

Thus

$$\bar{x} = \frac{1}{A} \int x\,dA = \frac{1}{5.33} \int_0^2 (4x^2 - x^3)\,dx = 1.25$$

Answer

$$\bar{y} = \frac{1}{A} \int y\,dA = \frac{1}{5.33} \int y^2\,dx$$

$$= \frac{1}{5.33} \int_0^2 (4 - x^2)^2\,dx = 3.21$$

Answer

Example 5.4.4

Find the centroid for the inverted circular cone shown in Figure 5.12.

Since the Z axis is an axis of symmetry,

$$\bar{x} = \bar{y} = 0 \qquad \text{Answer}$$

To find $\bar{z}$, consider the element of volume as a circular disk of radius y and thickness dz. Thus,

$$dV = \pi y^2\,dz$$

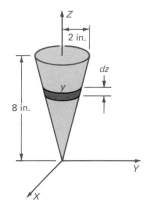

Figure 5.12

From the geometry we can get y in terms of z. That is,

$$\frac{y}{z} = \frac{2}{8} \qquad y = \frac{1}{4} z$$

therefore

$$V = \int \pi y^2\,dz = \frac{\pi}{16} \int_0^8 z^2\,dz$$

$$= \frac{\pi}{16} \frac{8^3}{3} = 33.5 \text{ in.}^3$$

Now

$$\bar{z} = \frac{1}{V} \int z \, dV = \frac{1}{33.5} \int z(\pi y^2 \, dz)$$

$$= \frac{\pi}{33.5} \int_0^8 \frac{z^3}{16} \, dz = 6.0 \text{ in.} \qquad \text{Answer}$$

Note that this checks with the data in Table 5.3, where $\bar{z} = h/4 = 2$ in. from the base.

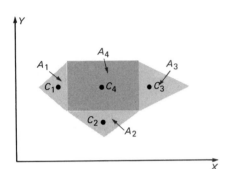

Figure 5.13

Composite Bodies

Often a complicated body can be represented as a combination of several common geometric shapes. When this is done, it is possible to obtain the centroid of the total body by making use of the known centroids of the simpler shapes. Consider a thin plate which is divided into four areas, as shown in Figure 5.13. The moment about the Y axis caused by the entire plate is

$$M_y = \gamma t A \bar{x} \qquad (5.16)$$

where

$$A = A_1 + A_2 + A_3 + A_4$$

and γ is the weight per unit volume and t is the plate thickness. This moment must equal the sum of the moments caused by the individual areas, namely

$$M_y = \bar{x}_1 A_1 \gamma t + \bar{x}_2 A_2 \gamma t + \bar{x}_3 A_3 \gamma t + \bar{x}_4 A_4 \gamma t \qquad (5.17)$$

Equating the right side of equations (5.16) and (5.17), we have

$$\bar{x} = \frac{\bar{x}_1 A_1 + \bar{x}_2 A_2 + \bar{x}_3 A_3 + \bar{x}_4 A_4}{A} \qquad \text{or} \qquad \bar{x} = \frac{\Sigma \bar{x}_i A_i}{A}$$

$$(5.18a)$$

Similarly, we can show that

$$\bar{y} = \frac{\Sigma \bar{y}_i A_i}{A} \qquad (5.18b)$$

In a similar manner, we can locate the centroid of a series of complicated lines by dividing it into a series of known line elements. It can be shown, following the above procedure for areas, that the centroid is given by

$$\bar{x} = \frac{\Sigma x_i L_i}{L} \qquad \bar{y} = \frac{\Sigma y_i L_i}{L} \tag{5.19}$$

where $L = \Sigma L_i$ = total length of the given line.

In the case of volumes, we can also represent volume elements for the total volume. The resulting equations for the centroid are:

$$\bar{x} = \frac{\Sigma \bar{x}_i V_i}{V} \qquad \bar{y} = \frac{\Sigma \bar{y}_i V_i}{V} \qquad \bar{z} = \frac{\Sigma \bar{z}_i V_i}{V} \tag{5.20}$$

where $\bar{x}_i, \bar{y}_i, \bar{z}_i$ locate the centroid of the element of volume V_i.

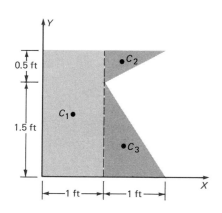

Figure 5.14

Example 5.4.5

Locate the centroid for the area shown in Figure 5.14.

The area is divided into three areas as shown, one rectangle and two triangles. The total area is

$$A = A_1 + A_2 + A_3$$
$$= 1(2) + \tfrac{1}{2}(0.5)(1) + \tfrac{1}{2}(1.5)(1) = 3 \text{ ft}^2$$

Using equations (5.18), we find

$$A\bar{x} = A_1\bar{x}_1 + A_2\bar{x}_2 + A_3\bar{x}_3$$
$$= 2(0.5) + 0.25(1 + 0.33) + 0.75(1 + 0.33) = 2.33$$
$$\bar{x} = 0.778 \text{ ft} \qquad\qquad \text{Answer}$$

and

$$A\bar{y} = A_1\bar{y}_1 + A_2\bar{y}_2 + A_3\bar{y}_3$$
$$= 2(1) + 0.25[1.5 + \tfrac{2}{3}(0.5)] + 0.75[\tfrac{1}{3}(1.5)] = 2.83$$
$$\bar{y} = 0.943 \text{ ft} \qquad\qquad \text{Answer}$$

Example 5.4.6

Locate the centroid for the area shown in Figure 5.15.

In this example, we will find it convenient to divide the area into three parts; a semicircle of area A_1, a 4 in. × 8 in. rectangle A_2, and a *negative* area A_3 representing the hole of radius 1 in. Thus, we include the hole in A_2 and subtract the contribution of A_3. This procedure can save calculations in many practical problems. (Could we have used this approach in example

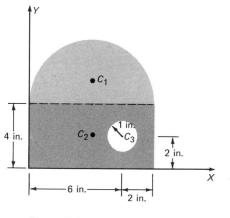

Figure 5.15

5.4.5?) Thus, the net area is:

$$A = A_1 + A_2 - A_3$$

$$= \frac{\pi(4)^2}{2} + 4(8) - \pi(1)^2$$

$$= 25.12 + 32 - 3.14 = 54.0 \text{ in.}^2$$

$$A\bar{x} = A_1\bar{x}_1 + A_2\bar{x}_2 - A_3\bar{x}_3$$

$$= 25.12(4) + 32(4) - 3.14(6) = 209$$

$$\bar{x} = 3.87 \text{ in.} \qquad\qquad \text{Answer}$$

$$A\bar{y} = A_1\bar{y}_1 + A_2\bar{y}_2 - A_3\bar{y}_3$$

$$= 25.12\left(4 + \frac{4}{3}\frac{4}{\pi}\right) + 32(2) - 3.14(2) = 201$$

$$\bar{y} = 3.72 \text{ in.} \qquad\qquad \text{Answer}$$

Example 5.4.7

Find $\bar{x}$ for the body shown in Figure 5.16.

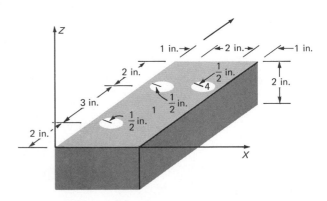

Figure 5.16

Let the body be represented by the 7 in. × 2 in. × 4 in. block and three negative volumes, each being a circular cylinder of radius $\frac{1}{2}$ in. and height 2 in. Consequently,

$$V = V_1 - V_2 - V_3 - V_4$$

$$= 7(4)(2) - \pi\left(\tfrac{1}{2}\right)^2(2) - \pi\left(\tfrac{1}{2}\right)^2(2) - \pi\left(\tfrac{1}{2}\right)^2(2)$$

$$= 56 - 1.57 - 1.57 - 1.57 = 51.3 \text{ in.}^3$$

$$V\bar{x} = V_1\bar{x}_1 - V_2\bar{x}_2 - V_3\bar{x}_3 - V_4\bar{x}_4$$

$$= 56(2) - 1.57(1) - 1.57(1) - 1.57(3) = 104.1$$

$$\bar{x} = 2.03 \text{ in.} \qquad\qquad \text{Answer}$$

Problems

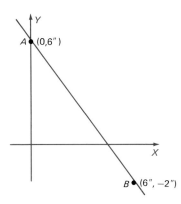

Figure 5.17

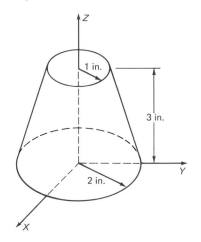

Figure 5.18

5.4.1 Verify the centroid location of the quarter-circular arc shown in Table 5.1 (p. 138).

5.4.2 Verify the centroid location of the semicircular arc shown in Table 5.1 (p. 138).

5.4.3 Verify the centroid location of the arc of the circle shown in Table 5.1 (p. 138).

5.4.4 Find the centroid of the line in Figure 5.17 from point A to point B.

5.4.5 Find the centroid of the line $y = |x|$ between $x = -2$ in. and $x = 2$ in.

5.4.6 Repeat problem 5.4.5 between $x = -2$ in. and $x = 4$ in.

5.4.7 Verify the centroid location of the area enclosed by a circular sector shown in Table 5.2 (p. 140).

5.4.8 Verify the centroid location of the area enclosed by a semi-circle shown in Table 5.2 (p. 140).

5.4.9 Verify the centroid location of the area enclosed by the quarter-circle arc shown in Table 5.2 (p. 141).

5.4.10 Find the centroid for the area bounded by $x = 4$ in., $y = x$, and $y = 0$.

5.4.11 Find the centroid for the area bounded by $y = 6$ in. and $y = |x|$.

5.4.12 Find the centroid for the area bounded by $y = 0.5x$ and $y = x(x - 4)$.

5.4.13 Verify the centroid location for the cone or pyramid shown in Table 5.3 (p. 141).

5.4.14 Verify the centroid location for the hemisphere shown in Table 5.3 (p. 141).

5.4.15 Find the centroid of the frustum of a cone shown in Figure 5.18. Use the composite-body approach.

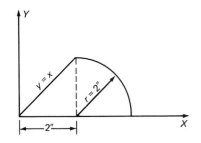

Figure 5.19

5.4.16 Using the composite-body approach, find the centroid for the lines shown in Figure 5.19.

5.4.17 Using the composite-body approach, find the centroid of the line segments forming the three-quarter circle shown in Figure 5.20.

5.4.18 Using the composite-body approach, find the centroid for the four lines shown in Figure 5.21.

5.4.19 Using the composite-body approach, find the centroid for the lines shown in Figure 5.22.

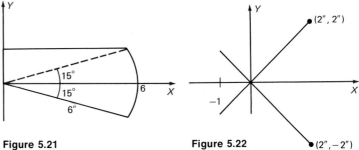

Figure 5.21   **Figure 5.22**

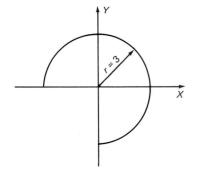

Figure 5.20

5.4.20 Find the centroid of the enclosed area in Figure 5.19.

5.4.21 Find the centroid of the enclosed area of Figure 5.20.

5.4.22 Find the centroid of the enclosed area of Figure 5.21.

Find the centroid of the enclosed area in:

5.4.23 Figure 5.23.

5.4.24 Figure 5.24.

5.4.25 Figure 5.25.

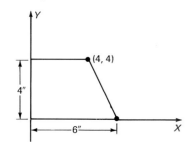

Figure 5.23

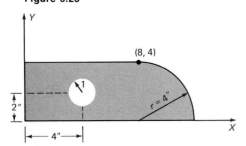

Figure 5.24

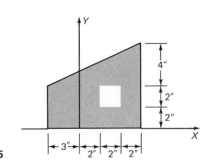

Figure 5.25

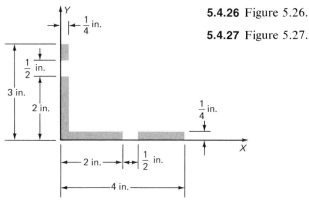

Figure 5.26

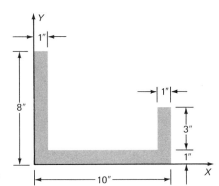

Figure 5.27

5.4.26 Figure 5.26.

5.4.27 Figure 5.27.

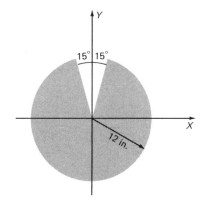

Figure 5.28

5.4.28 Figure 5.28.

5.4.29 Figure 5.29.

5.4.30 Find the centroid of the body composed of a cone and hemisphere as shown in Figure 5.30.

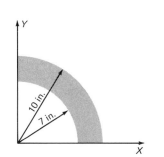

Figure 5.29

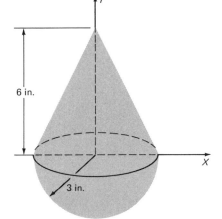

Figure 5.30

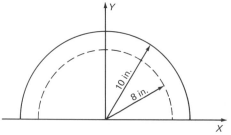

Figure 5.31

5.4.31 The hemispheric shell in Figure 5.31 has an inner radius of 8 in. and an outer radius of 10 in. Find the centroid of the body.

5.4.32 Find the centroid of the block containing two circular holes in Figure 5.32.

5.4.33 Find the centroid of the two plates welded together in Figure 5.33.

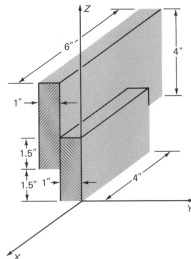

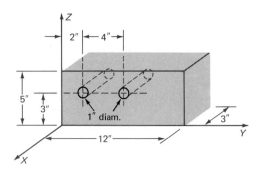

Figure 5.32

Figure 5.33

5.5 Two Useful Theorems

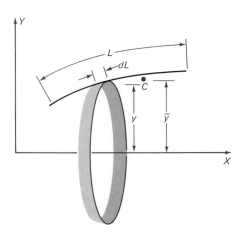

Figure 5.34

A Greek geometer named Pappus, and later, a Swiss mathematician named Guldinus formulated theorems that yield simple methods for obtaining surface areas and volumes generated by revolving a line or surface about a nonintersecting axis. As we shall see, these theorems take advantage of our knowledge of centroids for lines and areas.

Theorem 1

The surface area obtained by revolving a curve of length L about a fixed, nonintersecting axis equals the curve length L times the distance traveled by the centroid of the generating line.

This theorem is proved in the following way. Consider the line of length dL in Figure 5.34 which revolves about the X axis.

The surface area dA of the ring obtained by revolving dL is

$$dA = 2\pi y \, dL$$

If the entire line of length L is revolved about the X axis, the total surface area is

$$A = 2\pi \int_0^L y \, dL \tag{5.21}$$

Since

$$\bar{y} = \frac{1}{L} \int y \, dL \tag{5.12}$$

we can rewrite equation (5.21) as

$$A = 2\pi \bar{y} L \tag{5.22}$$

where $2\pi\bar{y}$ is the distance traveled by the centroid in generating the surface area. Consequently, the theorem is verified. Of course, if $\theta\bar{y}$ is the distance traveled by the centroid, then $A = \theta\bar{y}L$, where θ is in radians.

The consequences of this theorem may be used to compute the area for a variety of surfaces. Examples are shown in Figure 5.35. Here we see that a cylinder, torus, sphere, disk, or cone may be generated by revolving the appropriate line about the X axis. The generated surface areas are found using the theorem.

Figure 5.35

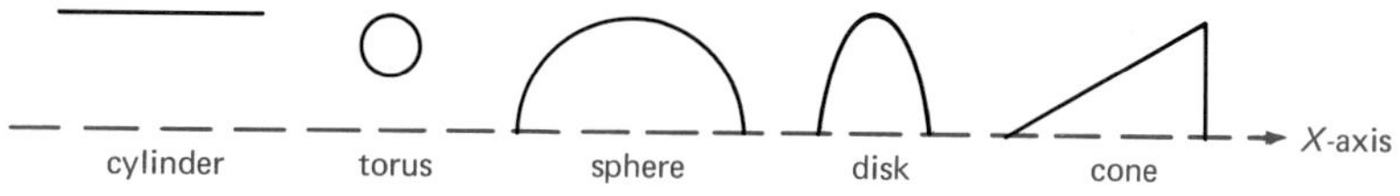

cylinder   torus   sphere   disk   cone X-axis

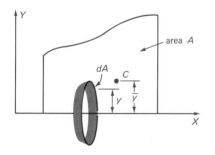

Figure 5.36

Theorem 2

The volume obtained by revolving a surface area A about a fixed nonintersecting axis equals the surface area A times the distance traveled by the centroid of the generating surface area.

Consider the area A in Figure 5.36 which is to be revolved about the X axis. The element of volume obtained by revolving the area dA is

$$dV = 2\pi y \, dA$$

so that the total volume obtained by revolving A is

$$V = 2\pi \int y \, dA$$

But from equation (5.15) we have

$$\bar{y} = \frac{1}{A} \int y \, dA \qquad (5.15)$$

so that

$$V = 2\pi \bar{y} A \qquad (5.23)$$

Since the term $2\pi\bar{y}$ is the distance traveled by the centroid relative to the fixed axis, the theorem is verified. Once again, if $\theta\bar{y}$ is traveled by the centroid, then $V = \theta\bar{y}A$. Figure 5.37 shows how the volume of a cylinder, sphere, or cone can be generated.

cylinder   sphere   cone

Figure 5.37

Example 5.5.1

Find the surface area obtained by revolving the triangle in Figure 5.38 (a) about the X axis and (b) about the Y axis.

(a) We recall from example 5.4.1 that the centroid of a straight line is the midpoint. Therefore,

$$\bar{y}L = (3)(6) + 6(3) + 3(6.7)$$
$$= 18 + 18 + 20.1 = 56.1$$

The area is

$$A = 2\pi\bar{y}L \qquad (5.22)$$
$$= 2(3.14)(56.1)$$
$$= 353 \text{ in.}^2 \qquad \text{Answer}$$

(b) For rotation about the Y axis, we have

$$\bar{x}L = 1.5(3) + 1.5(6.7) = 14.55$$

and

$$A = 2\pi\bar{x}L = 2(3.14)(14.55)$$
$$= 91.6 \text{ in.}^2 \qquad \text{Answer}$$

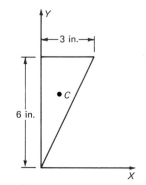

Figure 5.38

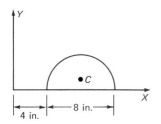

Figure 5.39

Example 5.5.2

Find the volume generated by revolving the area shown in Figure 5.39 (a) about the X axis, and (b) about the Y axis.

The area of the semicircle is

$$A = \frac{\pi r^2}{2} = \frac{\pi(4)^2}{2} = 25.1 \text{ in.}^2$$

(a) The generated volume about the X axis is

$$V = 2\pi \bar{y} A \qquad (5.23)$$

where

$$\bar{y} = \frac{4r}{3\pi} = \frac{4(4)}{3\pi} = 1.70 \text{ in.}$$

therefore

$$V = 2\pi(25.1)(1.70) = 268 \text{ in.}^3 \qquad \text{Answer}$$

(b) The generated volume about the Y axis is

$$V = 2\pi \bar{x} A$$

where

$$\bar{x} = 4 + 4 = 8 \text{ in.}$$

and therefore

$$V = 2\pi(25.1)(8) = 1260 \text{ in.}^3 \qquad \text{Answer}$$

Example 5.5.3

The area shown in Figure 5.40 is measured to be 6.25 in.^{2} The area, revolved about the X axis, generates a body which is later submerged in a circular cylinder tank of water. The tank's radius measures 5 in. and the water rises 1 in. when the body is submerged. What is $\bar{y}$ in Figure 5.40?

The volume of the body equals the volume of water displaced. Therefore,

$$V = \pi r^2 \, \Delta h = \pi(25)(1) = 25\pi \text{ in.}^3$$

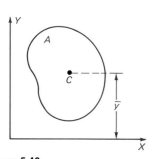

Figure 5.40

and, since

$$V = 2\pi \bar{y} A$$

we find that

$$\bar{y} = \frac{V}{2\pi A} = \frac{25\pi}{2\pi(6.25)} = 2 \text{ in.} \qquad \text{Answer}$$

Problems

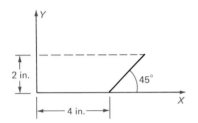

Figure 5.41

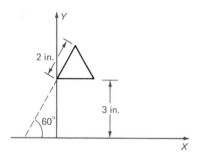

Figure 5.42

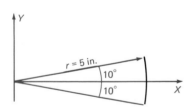

Figure 5.43

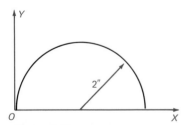

Figure 5.44

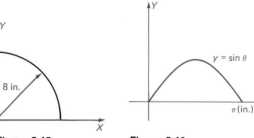

Figure 5.45   **Figure 5.46**

5.5.1 Find the surface area by revolving the line segment in Figure 5.41 about the Y axis.

5.5.2 Find the surface area if the three line segments which form the isosceles triangle in Figure 5.42 is revolved around the X axis.

5.5.3 Find the surface area if the arc segment in Figure 5.43 is revolved around the Y axis.

5.5.4 Find the surface area if the semicircle in Figure 5.44 is revolved around, (a) the X axis, and (b) the Y axis.

5.5.5 The circular arc in Figure 5.45 is revolved around the X axis to find the surface area of a hemisphere. Find this area and check your result with the surface area of a sphere by doubling your answer.

5.5.6 Find the volume generated by revolving the enclosed area in Figure 5.42 about the X axis.

5.5.7 Find the volume generated by revolving the area enclosed by the θ axis and the sine curve in Figure 5.46 about the θ axis.

5.5.8 Find the volume generated by revolving the area enclosed by the X axis, Y axis, and the circular segment in Figure 5.45 around the X axis.

5.5.9 The square shown in Figure 5.47 is revolved around the Y axis. The volume generated is 30 in.^{3} Find the dimension a.

5.5.10 Find the volume generated by revolving the area formed by the curve in Figure 5.48 about the X axis.

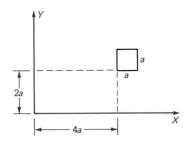

Figure 5.47

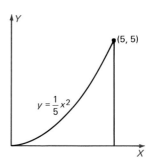

Figure 5.48

5.6 Surface Forces

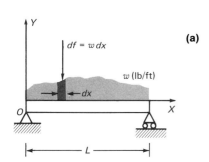

(a)

Beams

The concept of centroids is useful when dealing with distributed forces. For example, consider a beam subjected to the distributed load of w lb/ft as shown in Figure 5.49a. The total magnitude of this load is

$$F = \int_0^L w \, dx \qquad (5.24)$$

that is, it is the area under the w curve.

We now wish to place F on the beam so that it produces the same moment about any point on the beam as the actual distributed load. To locate this point, let us take moments about point O. The moment due to the element of force df is

$$dM_O = x \, df \qquad (5.25)$$

where $df = w \, dx$. The total moment is

$$M_O = \int_0^L x \, df = \int_0^L x \, w \, dx \qquad (5.26)$$

Let the moment about point O be

$$M_O = \bar{x} F \qquad (5.27)$$

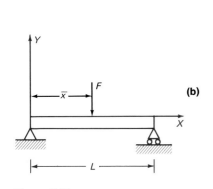

(b)

where $\bar{x}$ locates the position of F as shown in Figure 5.49b. Equating the right sides of equations (5.26) and (5.27) and using equation (5.24), we get

$$\bar{x} = \frac{\int_0^L x \, w \, dx}{\int_0^L w \, dx} \qquad (5.28)$$

Figure 5.49

From our earlier discussion of centroids, equation (5.28) locates one coordinate for the centroid of the area under the load diagram. In this case we are only interested in the $\bar{x}$ coordinate which we call the *center of force distribution*. Note that this point generally does not coincide with the $\bar{x}$ for the beam.

Example 5.6.1

The beam shown in Figure 5.50a has an applied load of 200 lb at its center and a triangular distributed load whose ordinate value at point A is 100 lb/ft. Find (a) the reactions at the supports, and (b) the resultant force for the applied loads.

(a) Figure 5.50b shows the free-body diagram of the forces on the beam. Force F is the resultant force for the distributed load w (now shown by the dashed line) and is located at $\bar{x} = \frac{1}{3}(12) = 4$ ft for the triangular load. Its magnitude is

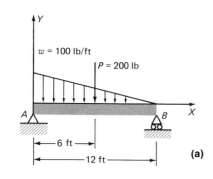

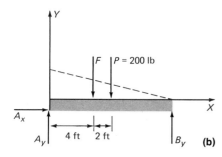

Figure 5.50

$$F = \int_0^L w \, dx = \int_0^{12} 100\left(\frac{12-x}{12}\right) dx$$

$$= \tfrac{1}{2}(100)(12) = 600 \text{ lb}$$

Note that for a triangular loading, F equals the area under the triangle whose base equals the length of loading and whose height equals the maximum magnitude of w. To find the beam reactions we use

$$\Sigma M_A = 0 \qquad 12B_y - 4(600) - 6(200) = 0$$

$$B_y = 300 \text{ lb} \qquad \text{Answer}$$

$$\Sigma F_y = 0 \qquad A_y - 600 - 200 + 300 = 0$$

$$A_y = 500 \text{ lb} \qquad \text{Answer}$$

and

$$\Sigma F_x = 0$$

$$A_x = 0 \qquad \text{Answer}$$

(b) The resultant of the applied loads is

$$R = 600 + 200 = 800 \text{ lb} \qquad \text{Answer}$$

The location of the applied load is

$$\bar{x} = \frac{600(4) + 200(6)}{800} = 4.5 \text{ ft} \qquad \text{Answer}$$

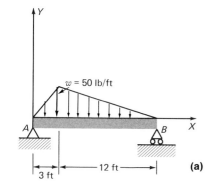

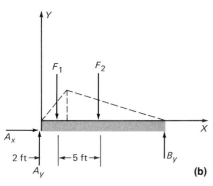

Figure 5.51

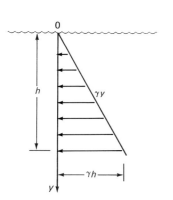

Figure 5.52

Example 5.6.2

For the beam shown in Figure 5.51a find (a) the reactions at the supports, and (b) the resultant force for the applied loads.

(a) Figure 5.51b shows two resultant forces, F_1 and F_2, where F_1 is due to the triangular load on the left of $x = 3$ ft and F_2 is due to the triangular load to the right of $x = 3$ ft. Their magnitudes are

$$F_1 = \tfrac{1}{2}(50)(3) = 75 \text{ lb} \qquad F_2 = \tfrac{1}{2}(50)(12) = 300 \text{ lb}$$

The beam reactions are computed as follows:

$$\Sigma M_A = 0 \qquad 15B_y - 2(75) - 7(300) = 0$$

$$B_y = 150 \text{ lb} \qquad\qquad \text{Answer}$$

$$\Sigma F_y = 0 \qquad A_y - 75 - 300 + 150 = 0$$

$$A_y = 225 \text{ lb} \qquad\qquad \text{Answer}$$

$$\Sigma F_x = 0$$

$$A_x = 0 \qquad\qquad \text{Answer}$$

(b) The resultant of the applied load is

$$R = 75 + 300 = 375 \text{ lb} \qquad\qquad \text{Answer}$$

The location of the load is

$$\bar{x} = \frac{75(2) + 300(7)}{375} = 6 \text{ ft} \qquad\qquad \text{Answer}$$

Fluid Pressure

When a body is submerged in a fluid, it is subjected to a surface force or pressure and is usually measured in lb/ft² or lb/in.² This pressure, called the *hydrostatic pressure,* is due to the weight of the fluid above the point in question. The hydrostatic pressure varies linearly with the depth as shown in Figure 5.52. Consequently, the pressure at a depth y is

$$p = p_0 + \gamma y \qquad\qquad (5.29)$$

where

p_0 = atmospheric pressure at the surface of the fluid

γ = specific weight of the fluid in lb/ft³

Usually, we can neglect p_0, so that

$$p = \gamma y \qquad\qquad (5.30)$$

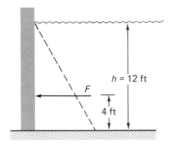

Figure 5.53

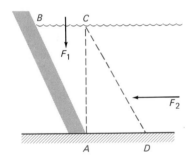

Figure 5.54

This equation can be applied as follows. Consider a dam retaining a body of water as shown in Figure 5.53. Since the pressure distribution varies in accord with equation (5.30), we can think of the hydrostatic pressure loading as a distributed load acting on a beam turned 90°. Consequently, the resultant force is 4 ft above ground level and its magnitude is

$$F = \tfrac{1}{2}(\gamma h)(h)(L) \tag{5.31}$$

where

$$h = \text{depth of the water}$$

$$L = \text{width of the wall}$$

Thus, letting $L = 1$ ft, we have

$$F = \frac{1}{2}\left(62.4\,\frac{\text{lb}}{\text{ft}^3}\right)(12 \text{ ft})^2(1 \text{ ft}) = 4500 \text{ lb}$$

Should the wall be inclined as shown in Figure 5.54, the most convenient approach to finding the resultant force due to the liquid is to partition the loads as shown in the figure. Here F_1 is the weight of the water contained in the triangle ABC, while F_2 is the force due to the hydrostatic pressure shown by the triangle ACD. Having these two forces, we can find their resultant by the techniques developed thus far.

Example 5.6.3

Find the reactions at A and B in Figure 5.55a assuming a simple support at A. Consider only a 1-ft section of the wall which weighs 4000 lb/ft.

Figure 5.55b shows the free-body diagram of the forces acting on the wall, where

$$F = \tfrac{1}{2}(62.4)(15)^2(1) = 7020 \text{ lb}$$

The reactions are then

$$\Sigma M_A = 0 \qquad -B \cos 30°(18) + F(5) = 0$$

$$B = \frac{7020(5)}{18 \cos 30°} = 2250 \text{ lb} \qquad \text{Answer}$$

$$\Sigma F_x = 0 \qquad A_x - F + B \cos 30° = 0$$

$$A_x = 5070 \text{ lb} \qquad \text{Answer}$$

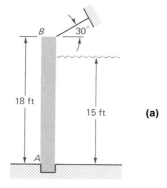

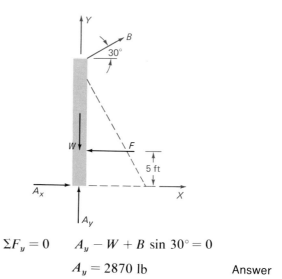

(a)

18 ft

15 ft

Figure 5.55

(b)

$$\Sigma F_y = 0 \qquad A_y - W + B \sin 30° = 0$$

$$A_y = 2870 \text{ lb} \qquad \text{Answer}$$

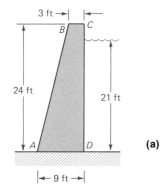

(a)

Example 5.6.4

Find the reactions of the concrete dam shown in Figure 5.56a assuming that the concrete weighs 150 lb/ft³ and the liquid is water at 62.4 lb/ft³. Treat only a 1-ft section of the dam.

Figure 5.56b shows a free-body diagram of the forces acting on the dam. Note that we are including a moment M as a reaction. For convenience, the weight of the dam is divided into two values, W_1 and W_2. The magnitudes of the applied forces are

$$W_1 = \tfrac{1}{2}(150)(6)(24)(1) = 10,800 \text{ lb}$$

$$W_2 = 150(3)(24)(1) = 10,800 \text{ lb}$$

$$F = \tfrac{1}{2}(62.4)(21)^2(1) = 13,750 \text{ lb}$$

The reactions are therefore

$$\Sigma F_x = 0 \qquad A_x - F = 0$$

$$A_x = 13,750 \text{ lb} \qquad \text{Answer}$$

$$\Sigma F_y = 0 \qquad A_y - W_1 - W_2 = 0$$

$$A_y = 21,600 \text{ lb} \qquad \text{Answer}$$

$$\Sigma M_A = 0 \qquad M - W_1(4) - W_2(7.5) + F(7) = 0$$

$$M = 27,800 \text{ lb-ft} \qquad \text{Answer}$$

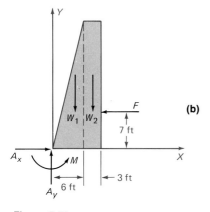

(b)

Figure 5.56

If we wish, we could replace A_y and M by an equivalent force of 21,600 lb placed at a distance

$$x = \frac{M}{A_y} = \frac{27,800}{21,600} = 1.29 \text{ ft}$$

Buoyancy

A body submerged in a liquid undergoes a buoyant effect due to the increase of hydrostatic pressure with depth. For example, consider the submerged body shown in Figure 5.57. For convenience, let the element of force on a differential element of cross-sectional area dA at a depth y_1 be

$$d\mathbf{f}_1 = \gamma y_1 \, dA \, \mathbf{j}$$

and at a depth y_2 be

$$d\mathbf{f}_2 = -\gamma y_2 \, dA \, \mathbf{j}$$

The net differential force $d\mathbf{F}$ is

$$d\mathbf{F} = d\mathbf{f}_1 + d\mathbf{f}_2 = -\gamma(y_2 - y_1) \, dA \, \mathbf{j}$$

The term $(y_2 - y_1) \, dA$ may be viewed as a differential volume of a small cylinder dV. Thus,

$$d\mathbf{F} = -\gamma \, dV \, \mathbf{j}$$

so that the total buoyant force is

$$\mathbf{F} = -\gamma \int dV \, \mathbf{j} = -\gamma V \mathbf{j} \qquad (5.32)$$

Notice that the net resultant force on the submerged body in the x direction due to the hydrostatic pressure is zero. This is because each element of force in the x direction acting on the body due to hydrostatic pressure has an equal and opposite element of force, the summation of which is zero.

The resultant buoyant force given by equation (5.32) passes through the centroid of the body as in the case of the other examples of distributed forces.

Example 5.6.5

Water is contained by the gate AB which is pinned at point A, and restrained by the wire at B and the counterweight D as

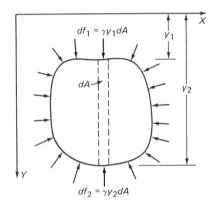

$df_1 = \gamma y_1 dA$

dA

$df_2 = \gamma y_2 dA$

Figure 5.57

shown in Figure 5.58a. The gate weighs 200 lb, and the counterweight is a sphere which weighs 300 lb. Neglecting the

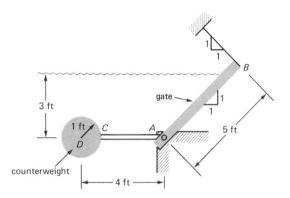

(a)

weight and volume of member AC, find the tensile force in the wire at B if the gate is 2 ft wide.

Figure 5.58b shows the free-body diagram of the forces. Forces F_1 and F_2 are due to the hydrostatic pressure and F_3 is the buoyant force acting on the sphere. Since we are neglecting the volume of member AC, there is no buoyant force for this member. The magnitudes of these forces are:

$$F_1 = 62.4 \frac{(3)(3)(2)}{2} = 562 \text{ lb}$$

$$F_2 = \tfrac{1}{2}(62.4)(3)^2(2) = 562 \text{ lb}$$

$$F_3 = 62.4 \left(\tfrac{4}{3}\pi \ 1^3\right) = 261 \text{ lb}$$

$$W_1 = 200 \text{ lb} \qquad W_2 = 300 \text{ lb}$$

The force B in the wire is found thus:

$$\Sigma M_A = 0$$

$$5B - W_1(2.5)(.707) - F_1(1) + (W_2 - F_3)4 - F_2(1) = 0$$

$$B = \frac{1321}{5} = 262 \text{ lb} \qquad\qquad \text{Answer}$$

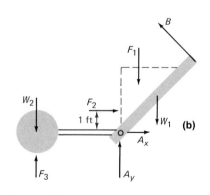

Figure 5.58

(b)

Problems

Find (a) the reactions at the supports and (b) the resultant force for the applied loads:

5.6.1 For the loaded beam in Figure 5.59.

5.6.2 For the loaded beam in Figure 5.60.

5.6.3 For the loaded beam in Figure 5.61.

5.6.4 For the loaded beam in Figure 5.62.

5.6.5 For the loaded beam in Figure 5.63.

5.6.6 For the loaded beam in Figure 5.64.

5.6.7 For the loaded beam in Figure 5.65.

5.6.8 For the loaded beam in Figure 5.66.

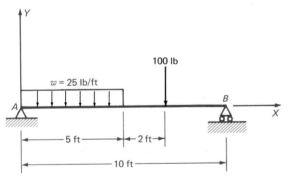

Figure 5.59

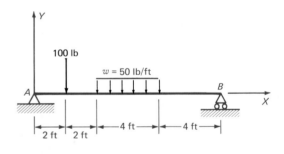

Figure 5.60

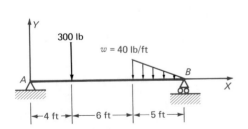

Figure 5.61

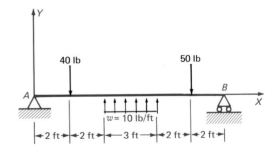

Figure 5.62

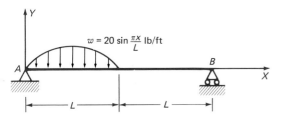

Figure 5.63

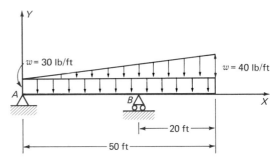

Figure 5.64

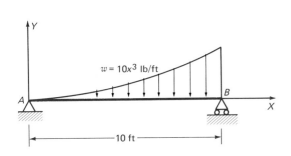

Figure 5.65

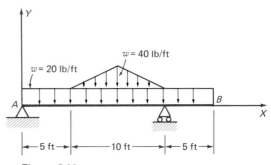

Figure 5.66

5.6.9 Draw the pressure distribution of the soil acting on the face AB of the retaining wall in Figure 5.67. If the specific weight of the soil is 120 lb/ft³, find the resultant force acting on a 1-ft section of the face AB of the retaining wall.

5.6.10 The retaining wall in Figure 5.68 has water on one side, $\gamma = 62.4$ lb/ft³, and soil on the other side, $\gamma = 115$ lb/ft³. For a 1-ft section of wall, draw the distributed forces on the wall AB, and find the resultant force acting on the wall.

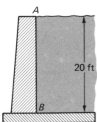

Figure 5.67

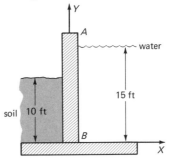

Figure 5.68

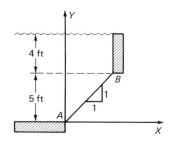

Figure 5.69

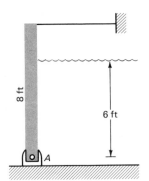

Figure 5.70

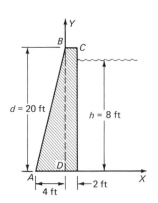

Figure 5.72

5.6.11 The gate AB in Figure 5.69 is 3 ft wide. Find the resultant force from the water acting on the gate.

5.6.12 Find the tension in the cable used to support a 1-ft section of a gate as shown in Figure 5.70. The water level is $h = 6$ ft.

5.6.13 If the breaking strength of the cable shown in Figure 5.71 is 500 lb, what is the allowable water level h?

5.6.14 Find the reactions of the concrete dam shown in Figure 5.72 if $\gamma = 150$ lb/ft³ for the concrete. Use a 1-ft section of the dam and idealize the problem by assuming all the reactions occurring at D.

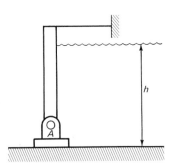

Figure 5.71

5.6.15 The earth dam in Figure 5.73 weighs 125 lb/ft³. Due to seepage of water under the base AD, an uplifting pressure results which, for approximation purposes, varies linearly across the base starting with zero pressure at A to a maximum hydrostatic pressure at D. Find the reaction at A of the dam for a 1-ft section of the dam.

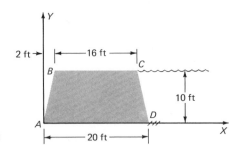

Figure 5.73

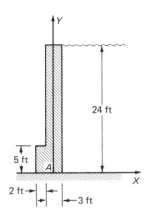

Figure 5.74

Figure 5.75

5.6.16 Find the reactions of the concrete dam about the point A shown in Figure 5.74 if $\gamma = 150$ lb/ft³ for the concrete. Use a 1-ft section of the dam.

5.6.17 Two boys make a raft out of wood which has an average thickness of 2 in. and weighs 30 lb/ft³. If the total weight of the boys is 250 lb, what is the minimum area of raft that will support the boys?

5.6.18 The float-valve arrangement in Figure 5.75 consists of a plastic 3-in. radius sphere which weighs 3 lb/ft³. The rod AB weighs 2 lb and is uniform. The rod is pivoted at O. At the instant shown, find the force transmitted to the spring at A.

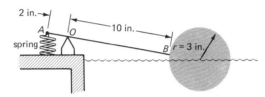

5.6.19 A package of scientific instruments weighing 75 lb is to be sent aloft by a spherical balloon containing helium. What is the minimum diameter of the balloon that will permit the package to be airborne?

5.6.20 Find the force in the spring if the sphere is totally submerged in problem 5.6.18.

5.6.21 The 8-ft-long block in Figure 5.76 is secured to the floor of a tank by four strings, each having a breaking strength of 15 lb. How high must the water rise for the block to break away assuming $\gamma = 20$ lb/ft³ for the block and that its cross section is a 6-in. square?

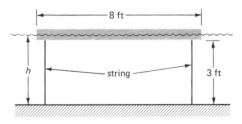

Figure 5.76

5.6.22 Solve problem 5.6.21 assuming that the block has a circular cross section with an 8-ft diameter and is 6 in. high.

5.7 Cables

In engineering, cables have many uses, of which suspension bridges, telephone lines, and electrical power lines are commonly observed examples. The successful use of cables is dependent on a knowledge of what happens to a cable when a load is applied. That is, for a given use, it is necessary to know the length of the cable and its tension, the reactions at its supports, its span, and its sag.

Concentrated Load

For purposes of analysis, cables are assumed to have no resistance to bending and to carry tensile forces only. By way of introduction to a study of cables, let us first treat the case of concentrated loads on a cable as shown in Figure 5.77a. We will assume that the distances x_1, x_2, x are known while y_1 and y_2 are unknowns. Figure 5.77b shows the free-body diagram of the cable, wherein there are four unknowns, A_x, A_y, B_x, and B_y. Note that we are presently neglecting the weight of the cable. Since we have only three equations of statics, the problem appears indeterminate. However, if we know the coordinates of some point on the cable, say point C in Figure 5.77b, the problem becomes solvable.

Consider the free-body diagram shown in Figure 5.77c. The figure shows the cable cut at the point C and a tension T acting on the cable. If we sum moments about point C, $\Sigma M_C = 0$, we obtain an additional relationship between the reaction components A_x and A_y. Now all the reactions can be found. The forces in each cable can also be established using appropriate free-body diagrams and remembering that the cable acts as a two-force member.

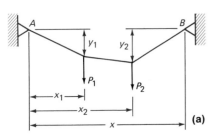

(a)

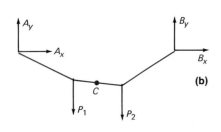

(b)

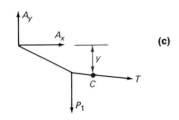

(c)

Figure 5.77

Distributed Load

Let us now consider a cable carrying a uniformly distributed load w (lb/ft) as shown in Figure 5.78a. Also shown in this figure is an element of load $dw = w\,dx$ acting on the differential element of cable dx.

The total vertical load is

$$w = \int dw = \int w\,dx = w \int dx = wL$$

since w is constant and L is the length of the cable. The moment caused by w at some distance $\bar{x}$ from the origin must equal the sum of the moments caused by dw, that is,

$$\bar{x}w = \int x \, dw \qquad \text{or} \qquad \bar{x} = \frac{\int x \, dw}{w}$$

Thus, if a cable is subjected to a uniformly distributed load, the resultant load w passes through the centroid of the load, as in the case of beams carrying distributed loads.

In order to determine the shape of the cable for this case, let us consider the free-body diagram of the cable in Figure 5.78b. Here we show the cable having an angle θ with the horizontal and $\theta + d\theta$ with the horizontal a distance dx away. The

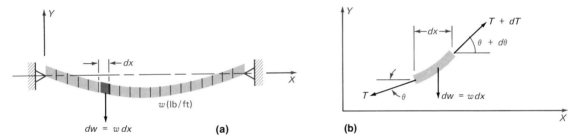

(a)   **(b)**

Figure 5.78

tension also changes from T to $T + dT$ over this increment. We apply the equations of equilibrium to the element as follows:

$$\Sigma F_x = 0$$

$$(T + dT)\cos(\theta + d\theta) - T\cos\theta = 0$$

$$(T + dT)(\cos\theta\cos d\theta - \sin\theta\sin d\theta) - T\cos\theta = 0$$

$$\Sigma F_y = 0$$

$$(T + dT)\sin(\theta + d\theta) - T\sin\theta - w\,dx = 0$$

$$(T + dT)(\sin\theta\cos d\theta + \cos\theta\sin d\theta) - T\sin\theta - w\,dx = 0$$

For a small change in θ, $\sin d\theta \approx d\theta$ and $\cos d\theta \approx 1$, so that

$$(T + dT)(\cos\theta - d\theta\sin\theta) - T\cos\theta = 0$$

$$(T + dT)(\sin\theta + d\theta\cos\theta) - T\sin\theta = w\,dx$$

If we neglect the product of differentials, these equations become

$$-T \, d\theta \sin \theta + dT \cos \theta = 0$$

$$T \, d\theta \cos \theta + dT \sin \theta = w \, dx$$

or

$$d(T \cos \theta) = 0 \tag{5.33}$$

$$d(T \sin \theta) = w \, dx \tag{5.34}$$

Since the derivative of a constant is zero, we can write equation (5.33) as

$$T \cos \theta = \text{constant} = T_0 \tag{5.35}$$

Now multiply both sides of equation (5.35) by $\sin \theta$ and rearrange to get

$$T \sin \theta = T_0 \tan \theta \tag{5.36}$$

Substitute this into equation (5.34) to obtain

$$d(T_0 \tan \theta) = w \, dx \tag{5.37}$$

But the slope $dy/dx = \tan \theta$, so that this becomes

$$d \left(T_0 \frac{dy}{dx} \right) = w \, dx \qquad \text{or} \qquad \frac{d}{dx} \frac{dy}{dx} = \frac{w}{T_0}$$

therefore,

$$\frac{d^2y}{dx^2} = \frac{w}{T_0} \tag{5.38}$$

Equation (5.38) is a *differential equation* that governs the flexible cable loaded continuously by a uniformly distributed load w (lb/ft). The solution of the differential equation must also satisfy the *boundary conditions* at each end of the cable. In general, however, the equations governing the cable can become rather complex. In what follows we will be content in analyzing two types of cables that have wide application and are not too difficult to study.

Parabolic Cable

When the distributed load w is constant and the weight of the cable is neglected, the equilibrium shape of the cable is a parabola. Such a situation exists approximately in suspension bridges where w is the road load and the weight of the cable is small relative to the road load.

Consider a suspension cable, as shown in Figure 5.79a,

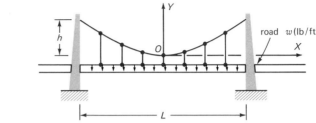

(a)

Figure 5.79

which carries a uniform load w from the road. Now equation (5.38) is applicable with w and T_0 as constants. Let us integrate this equation twice to get

$$\frac{dy}{dx} = \frac{wx}{T_0} + C_1 \tag{5.39}$$

and

$$y = \frac{wx^2}{2T_0} + C_1 x + C_2 \tag{5.40}$$

where C_1 and C_2 are constants of integration. From Figure 5.79a we see that the boundary conditions are that at $x = 0$,

$$\frac{dy}{dx} = 0 \tag{5.41}$$

$$y = 0 \tag{5.42}$$

Substituting equation (5.41) into equation (5.39) and equation (5.42) into equation (5.40), we get $C_1 = 0$ and $C_2 = 0$, respectively. Thus,

$$y = \frac{wx^2}{2T_0} \tag{5.43}$$

We can now evaluate T_0 since we notice that at $x = L/2$, $y = h$. Thus,

$$T_0 = \frac{wL^2}{8h}$$

so that

$$y = \frac{4h}{L^2} x^2 \tag{5.44}$$

which is the equation of a parabola.

The tension in the cable at any point can be found by considering the free-body diagram in Figure 5.79b. Note that T_0

(b)

(c)

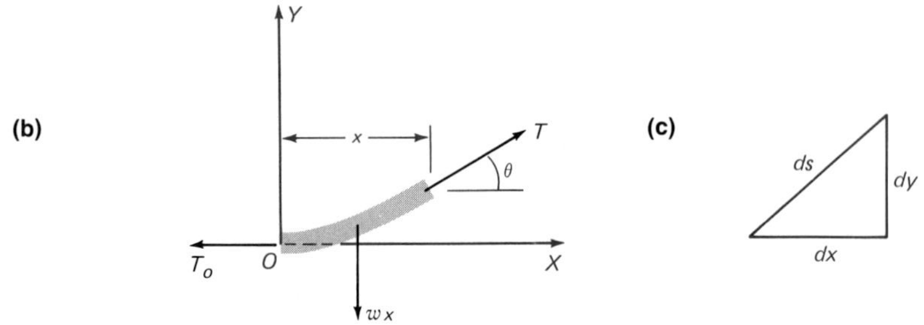

Figure 5.79

acts in the horizontal direction at the origin where the slope of the cable is zero. The equilibrium equations are:

$$T \cos \theta = T_0 \qquad T \sin \theta = wx \qquad (5.45)$$

Squaring both sides of each equation and adding, we get

$$T^2 = T_0^2 + w^2x^2 \qquad \text{or} \qquad T = \sqrt{T_0^2 + w^2x^2} \qquad (5.46)$$

where

$$T_{\text{max}} = \sqrt{T_0^2 + \frac{w^2L^2}{4}}$$

Eliminating T in equation (5.45) gives

$$\tan \theta = \frac{wx}{T_0} \qquad (5.47)$$

To determine the length of the cable, consider a differential length of cable ds in Figure 5.79c. Thus,

$$ds = \sqrt{(dx)^2 + (dy)^2} = dx\sqrt{1 + \left(\frac{dy}{dx}\right)^2} \qquad (5.48)$$

Now the derivative of equation (5.43) is

$$\frac{dy}{dx} = \frac{wx}{T_0}$$

so that equation (5.48) can be written

$$ds = dx\sqrt{1 + \left(\frac{wx}{T_0}\right)^2} \qquad (5.49)$$

The integral of this equation is

$$s = \int_0^{L/2} \sqrt{1 + \left(\frac{wx}{T_o}\right)^2}\, dx \qquad (5.50)$$

which represents half the total length of the cable. This integration can be simplified if we use the binomial series expansion as follows:

$$\sqrt{1 + \left(\frac{wx}{T_o}\right)^2} = 1 + \frac{1}{2}\frac{w^2x^2}{T_o^2} - \frac{1}{8}\frac{w^4x^4}{T_o^4} + \cdots \qquad (5.51)$$

Substitution of this into equation (5.50) gives

$$s = \int_0^{L/2}\left(1 + \frac{1}{2}\frac{w^2x^2}{T_o^2} - \frac{1}{8}\frac{w^4x^4}{T_o^4} + \cdots\right) dx$$

$$= L\left(\frac{1}{2} + \frac{w^2L^2}{48T_o^2} - \frac{w^4L^4}{1280T_o^4} + \cdots\right)$$

The total length of the cable is

$$S = 2s = L\left(1 + \frac{w^2L^2}{24T_o^2} - \frac{w^4L^4}{640T_o^4} + \cdots\right)$$

Since $w/T_o = 8h/L^2$, we substitute this to get

$$S = L\left[1 + \frac{8}{3}\left(\frac{h}{L}\right)^2 - \frac{32}{5}\left(\frac{h}{L}\right)^4 + \cdots\right]$$

If $h/L < \frac{1}{4}$, this series converges. In most practical cases, h is much less than $L/4$ and a good approximation for the total length of the cable is

$$S \approx L\left[1 + \frac{8}{3}\left(\frac{h}{L}\right)^2\right]$$

Example 5.7.1

A cable is to span 200 ft across a canyon as shown in Figure 5.80. Point B is known to be 30 ft higher than point A. If the breaking strength of the cable is 100,000 lb, find the maximum uniform load w (lb/ft) that the cable can carry.

Since the distributed load is uniform, equations (5.43) and (5.46) are applicable for this case. The first step in our solution is to locate the origin of the coordinate system. Label point A

as $(x_A, 8)$ and point B as $(x_A + 200, 38)$. Using equation (5.43), we have

$$8 = \frac{wx_A^2}{2T_0} \qquad (5.52)$$

and

$$38 = \frac{w(x_A + 200)^2}{2T_0} \qquad (5.53)$$

Substitute equation (5.52) for $w/2T_0$ into equation (5.53) to obtain

$$38 = \frac{8}{x_A^2}(x_A + 200)^2$$

$$x_A = 53.3 \pm 116.3$$

We choose $x_A = -63.0$ so that $x_B = 137.0$ ft. If we choose $x_A = 169.6$, then $x_B = 369.6$ ft which is impossible.

Now, at $x_B = 137$ ft, the maximum tension occurs in the cable. Rewriting equation (5.46) at this coordinate, we have

$$T_{\max} = \sqrt{T_0^2 + w^2 x_B^2} \qquad (5.54)$$

Figure 5.80

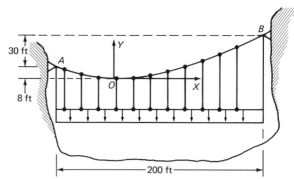

But, from equation (5.53), $T_0 = wx_B^2/76$, so that equation (5.54) becomes

$$T_{\max}^2 = w^2\left(\frac{x_B^2}{76}\right)^2 + w^2 x_B^2$$

$$= w^2 x_B^2\left[\left(\frac{x_B}{76}\right)^2 + 1\right] = 4.24 w^2 x_B^2$$

and, therefore,

$$w = \frac{T_{\max}}{2.06 x_B} = \frac{100,000}{2.06(137)} = 354 \text{ lb/ft}$$

Answer

Catenary Cable

A catenary cable is one which is loaded by its own weight as shown in Figure 5.81. By considering an element of length ds,

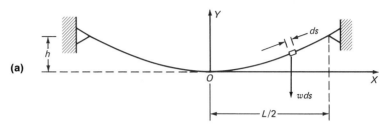

(a)

Figure 5.81

we can derive expressions similar to equations (5.33) and (5.34) except that ds now replaces dx. Thus,

$$d(T \cos \theta) = 0$$

$$d(T \sin \theta) = w \, ds$$

so that the governing differential equation for the catenary cable is

$$\frac{d^2y}{dx^2} = \frac{w}{T_0} \frac{ds}{dx} \qquad (5.55)$$

Recall that

$$ds = dx\sqrt{1 + \left(\frac{dy}{dx}\right)^2} \qquad (5.48)$$

so that equation (5.55) can be written

$$\frac{d^2y}{dx^2} = \frac{w}{T_0}\sqrt{1 + \left(\frac{dy}{dx}\right)^2}$$

To solve this differential equation, let $u = dy/dx$. Then

$$\frac{du}{dx} = \frac{w}{T_0}\sqrt{1 + u^2} \qquad (5.56)$$

Since w is a constant, this equation can be integrated directly (see a table of integrals) to give

$$\ln\left(u + \sqrt{1 + u^2}\right) = \frac{w}{T_0}x + C_1 \qquad (5.57)$$

where C_1 is the constant of integration. The origin of the coordinate system is selected in Figure 5.81 such that at $x = 0$,

$$\frac{dy}{dx} = u = 0$$

Using this boundary condition in equation (5.57), we find that $C_1 = 0$, and therefore

$$\ln\left(u + \sqrt{1 + u^2}\right) = \frac{wx}{T_0} \qquad \text{or} \qquad \sqrt{1 + u^2} = e^{wx/T_0} - u$$

Squaring both sides and simplifying, we obtain

$$u = \frac{e^{wx/T_0} - e^{-wx/T_0}}{2} = \sinh\frac{wx}{T_0}$$

Now,

$$u = \frac{dy}{dx} = \sinh\frac{wx}{T_0} \tag{5.58}$$

and we can integrate this equation to get

$$y = \frac{T_0}{w}\cosh\frac{wx}{T_0} + C_2 \tag{5.59}$$

The second boundary condition is that at $x = 0$, $y = 0$. Using this condition in equation (5.59), we have

$$C_2 = -\frac{T_0}{w}$$

so that

$$y = \frac{T_0}{w}\left(\cosh\frac{wx}{T_0} - 1\right) \tag{5.60}$$

Equation (5.60) is the curve of the catenary cable. Thus, the sag h is given by

$$h = \frac{T_0}{w}\left(\cosh\frac{wL}{2T_0} - 1\right)$$

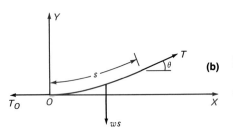

Figure 5.81

provided the cable supports are at the same elevation.

To determine length, we can consider a section of the caternary cable as shown in Figure 5.81b. For equilibrium,

$$T\cos\theta = T_0 \qquad \text{and} \qquad T\sin\theta = ws$$

or, by combining these equations,

$$\tan\theta = \frac{dy}{dx} = \frac{ws}{T_0} \tag{5.61}$$

Referring to equation (5.58), we can rewrite this equation as

$$\frac{ws}{T_0} = \sinh\frac{wx}{T_0}$$

and therefore

$$s = \frac{T_0}{w} \sinh \frac{wx}{T_0} \qquad (5.62)$$

which provides the basic equation for the length of the catenary cable.

The tension T is obtained as before:

$$T = \sqrt{T_0^2 + w^2 s^2} = \sqrt{T_0^2 + T_0^2 \sinh^2 \frac{wx}{T_0}}$$

$$= T_0 \sqrt{1 + \sinh^2 \frac{wx}{T_0}}$$

$$= T_0 \cosh \frac{wx}{T_0} \qquad (5.63)$$

As a final comment on the catenary cable, we observe that equation (5.60) is the basic expression for the curve. Notice that if we wish to find T_0, we need the appropriate x and y coordinate as well as the load w. With this information, however, we will require a trial-and-error process to find T_0. This is illustrated by the next example.

Example 5.7.2

A cable weighing 2 lb/ft is strung between two points at the same elevation across a horizontal span of 400 ft. If the sag is 100 ft, find the maximum tension in the cable.

Referring to equation (5.60), we have for $x = 200$, $y = 100$,

$$100 = \frac{T_0}{2} \left[\cosh \frac{2(200)}{T_0} - 1 \right] \text{ or } \cosh \frac{400}{T_0} - \frac{200}{T_0} = 1$$

A trial and error approach to finding T_0 is tabulated below.

Table 5.4

T_0	$\cosh \dfrac{400}{T_0}$	$\dfrac{200}{T_0}$	$\cosh \dfrac{400}{T_0} - \dfrac{200}{T_0}$	
200	3.76	1	2.76	
300	2.03	0.667	1.35	
400	1.543	0.500	1.043	
410	1.515	0.488	1.025	
420	1.489	0.476	1.011	
430	1.4648	0.465	0.9997	(close enough)

From the tabulated data, we find that $T_o = 430$ lb. The maximum tension in the cable occurs when $x = 200$ ft. Thus, using equation (5.63), we obtain

$$T_{max} = T_o \cosh \frac{2(200)}{T_o}$$

$$= 430 \cosh 0.930$$

$$= 630 \text{ lb} \qquad \text{Answer}$$

Problems

5.7.1 Find the tensional force in the cable section AB in Figure 5.82.

5.7.2 Find the reactions at A and D for the cable in Figure 5.83.

5.7.3 If the maximum deflection of the cable in Figure 5.84 is $\frac{1}{2}$ ft, find the reactions at A and E.

Figure 5.82

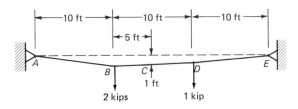

Figure 5.83

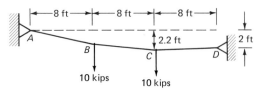

Figure 5.84

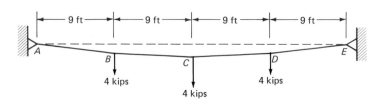

5.7.4 A force of 8 kips is known to be the vertical reaction at D for the cable shown in Figure 5.85. Find the reaction at A and deflection at C.

5.7.5 The cable in Figure 5.86 carries a uniform load $w = 200$ lb/ft. Find the magnitude of the reactions at the supports A and B.

5.7.6 A cable whose breaking strength is 150 kips is to carry a uniform load $w = 100$ lb/ft across a span. If both the supports are at the same level, what is the maximum span if the sag must be limited to 10 ft?

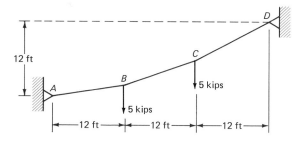

Figure 5.85

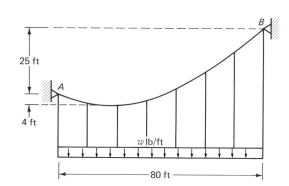

Figure 5.86

5.7.7 The breaking strength of the cable in Figure 5.87 is 120 kips. Find the maximum uniform load w that the cable can support.

5.7.8 A cable weighing 50 lb/ft spans a river 200 ft wide. The cable supports are at the same elevation and the breaking strength of the cable is 10,000 lb. Find the sag of the cable.

5.7.9 An electric transmission line, weighing 90 lb per 1000 ft, spans 400 ft between towers at the same elevation. If the cable sags 15 ft, find the maximum tension in the cable.

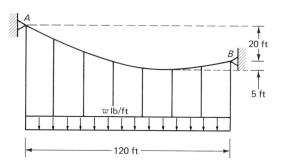

Figure 5.87

5.8 Summary

A   The important *ideas:*

1. The centroid is coincident with the center of gravity if the body is homogeneous.

2. The centroid of a composite body is found by treating the body as a combination of simpler geometric shapes.

3. The theorems of Pappus and Guldinus provide convenient formulas to find areas and volumes of bodies of revolution.

4. Distributed loads on beams, fluid pressure, and buoyancy are examples of distributed forces which can be replaced by a resultant force applied at the center of force distribution.

5. Complete analysis of cables subjected to distributed forces includes the solution of a differential equation with boundary conditions.

B   The important *equations:*

Centroids

$$\text{Lines:}\quad \bar{x} = \frac{1}{L}\int x\, dL,\ \bar{y} = \frac{1}{L}\int y\, dL \tag{5.12}$$

$$\text{Areas:}\quad \bar{x} = \frac{1}{A}\int x\, dA,\ \bar{y} = \frac{1}{A}\int y\, dA \tag{5.15}$$

$$\text{Volumes:}\quad \bar{x} = \frac{1}{V}\int x\, dV,\ \bar{y} = \frac{1}{V}\int y\, dV,\ \bar{z} = \frac{1}{V}\int z\, dV \tag{5.9}$$

Area of a surface of revolution: $A = 2\pi \bar{y} L$ $\tag{5.22}$

Volume of a body of revolution: $V = 2\pi \bar{y} A$ $\tag{5.23}$

Fluid pressure: $p = \gamma y$ $\tag{5.30}$

Parabolic cable: $y = \dfrac{wx^2}{2T_0}$ $\tag{5.43}$

$$T = \sqrt{T_0^2 + w^2 x^2} \tag{5.46}$$

Catenary cable: $y = \dfrac{T_0}{w}\left(\cosh \dfrac{wx}{T_0} - 1\right)$ $\tag{5.60}$

$$T = T_0 \cosh \frac{wx}{T_0} \tag{5.63}$$

Chapter 6
Moments of Area and Inertia

Whereas first moments are useful in determining centroids, second moments are useful in stress analysis and in dynamics. The second moment of area and the second moment of mass are derived here. The meaning and relationships between centroidal axes, principal axes, product moments, and the maximum as well as minimum second moments are established.

6.1 Introduction

In Chapter 5, which was concerned with distributed forces, the integral of the product of distance and an element of length, area, or volume was used to introduce the concept of a centroid. Two other integrals which also appear very often in problems of mechanics will be considered in this chapter: The *second moment of area* is an integral of distance squared times an element of area. The *second moment of mass* is an integral of distance squared times an element of mass.

6.2 The Moment of Area

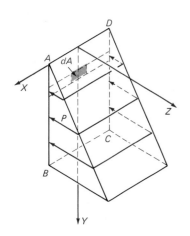

Figure 6.1

Consider a flat surface *ABCD* submerged in a fluid as shown in Figure 6.1. We wish to evaluate the moment about the *X* axis due to the force on the area *ABCD*. The magnitude of the moment, due to the differential force $dF = p\,dA$ on area dA, is

$$dM_x = yp\,dA$$

where p is the fluid pressure on the element of area dA. The magnitude of the moment due to the pressure on the entire area *ABCD* is expressed as

$$M_x = \int_{\text{area}} dM_x$$

so that

$$M_x = \int_{\text{area}} yp\,dA$$

The hydrostatic pressure is a linear function of distance, i.e.,

$$p = p_0 + \gamma y$$

where γ is the weight per unit volume of the fluid and p_0 is the atmospheric pressure at the surface of the fluid, which is usually assumed negligible. Substituting γy for p, we obtain for the moment,

$$M_x = \int \gamma y^2\,dA$$

If γ is assumed to be constant, then

$$M_x = \gamma \int y^2\,dA \tag{6.1}$$

The integral $\int y^2 \, dA$ is the second moment of area about the X axis. In this text, we shall call this integral simply the *moment of area*. Since the second moment is about the X axis, the symbol I_x is used. If the axis were the Y axis, the moment of area is written as I_y. The second moments, therefore, are defined as

$$I_x = \int y^2 \, dA \qquad I_y = \int x^2 \, dA \qquad (6.2)$$

Rectangular Areas

If the areas under consideration are rectangular, equation (6.2) can be simplified. Consider the area shown in Figure 6.2, where

$$dA = L \, dy$$

Substituting this into the first of equations (6.2), we have

$$I_x = \int y^2 \, dA = \int_0^h Ly^2 \, dy$$

which, upon integration, yields

$$I_x = \frac{Lh^3}{3}$$

But we know that the area is given by $A = Lh$, so that

$$I_x = \frac{Ah^2}{3}$$

We can similarly show that

$$I_y = \frac{AL^2}{3}$$

Let us now assume that for a given body we concentrate all of the area A in a strip as shown in Figure 6.3. The moment of area of this strip about the X axis is

$$I_x = k_x^2 A \qquad (6.3)$$

Here, k_x is called the *radius of gyration* and is a measure of the distribution of area from the X axis. For the rectangle shown in Figure 6.2, we have

$$I_x = \frac{Ah^2}{3} = k_x^2 A$$

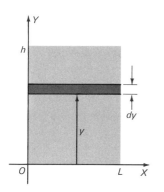

Figure 6.2

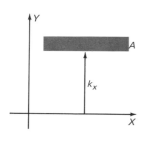

Figure 6.3

so that

$$k_x = \frac{h}{\sqrt{3}}$$

Similarly, the radius of gyration about the Y axis for the rectangle in Figure 6.2 is given by

$$k_y = \frac{L}{\sqrt{3}} \tag{6.4}$$

Polar Moment of Area

The moment of area about the axis passing through O and perpendicular to the XY plane in Figure 6.4 is the polar moment of area. This moment is very important in rotational problems. It is designated as J and is defined mathematically as

$$J = \int r^2 \, dA \tag{6.5}$$

Since

$$r^2 = x^2 + y^2$$

we have

$$J = \int (x^2 + y^2) \, dA$$
$$= \int x^2 \, dA + \int y^2 \, dA$$
$$= I_y + I_x \tag{6.6}$$

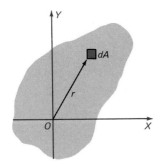

Figure 6.4

i.e., the polar moment of area is the sum of the two moments of area I_x and I_y. The radius of gyration about the polar axis (actually the Z axis) is

$$k = \sqrt{\frac{J}{A}} \tag{6.7}$$

We can establish a relationship between k, k_x, and k_y by substituting

$$J = k^2 A \qquad I_x = k_x^2 A \qquad I_y = k_y^2 A$$

into equation (6.6) to obtain

$$k^2 A = k_x^2 A + k_y^2 A$$

or

$$k = \sqrt{k_x^2 + k_y^2} \tag{6.8}$$

Table 6.1 lists the moments of area for some common geometric shapes. The moments of area are important in the stress analysis of structures, which are studied in courses concerned with strength of materials, machine design, and theory of elasticity.

Table 6.1

Moments of Area

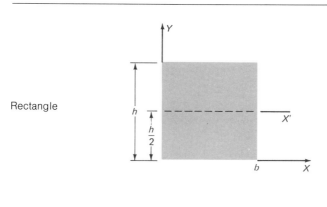

Rectangle

$$I_{x'} = \frac{1}{12} bh^3$$

$$I_x = \frac{1}{3} bh^3$$

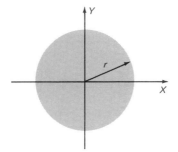

Solid Circle

$$J = \frac{1}{2} \pi r^4$$

$$I_x = I_y = \frac{1}{4} \pi r^4$$

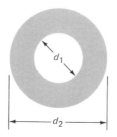

Tube

$$J = \frac{\pi}{64} (d_2{}^4 - d_1{}^4)$$

Table 6.1
Moments of Area

Triangle

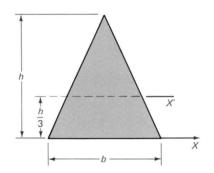

$$I_{x'} = \frac{1}{36} bh^3$$

$$I_x = \frac{1}{12} bh^3$$

Semicircle

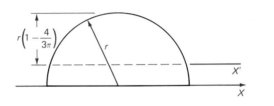

$$I_{x'} = r^4\left(\frac{\pi}{8} - \frac{8}{9\pi}\right)$$

$$I_x = \frac{\pi r^4}{8}$$

Quarter Circle

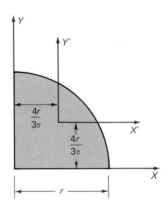

$$I_x = I_y = \frac{\pi r^4}{16}$$

$$J = \frac{\pi r^4}{8}$$

$$I_{x'} = I_{y'} = r^4\left(\frac{\pi}{16} - \frac{4}{9\pi}\right)$$

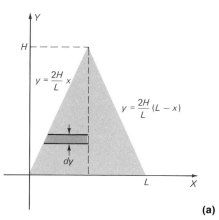

Figure 6.5

(a)

Example 6.2.1

For the triangle shown in Figure 6.5a determine (a) the moments of area about the X and Y axes and the respective radii of gyration and (b) the polar moment of area about O and the polar radius of gyration.

(a) For obtaining the moment of area about the X axis it is convenient to treat half of the triangle by a differential element of area dA as shown in Figure 6.5. The differential area dA is

$$dA = \left(\frac{L}{2} - x\right) dy$$

Since $y = 2Hx/L$, we have $dy = 2H\,dx/L$. Thus

$$I_x = \int y^2\, dA$$

$$= 2 \int_0^{L/2} \frac{4H^2}{L^2} x^2 \left(\frac{L}{2} - x\right) \frac{2H}{L}\, dx$$

where we are computing I_x for half the triangle and then multiplying by 2. The above integral becomes

$$I_x = \frac{16H^3}{L^3} \left[\frac{Lx^3}{6} - \frac{x^4}{4}\right]_0^{L/2}$$

$$= \frac{16H^3}{L^3} \frac{L^4}{192}$$

$$= \frac{H^3 L}{12} \qquad \text{Answer}$$

The radius of gyration is

$$k_x = \sqrt{\frac{I_x}{A}}$$

Since the area of the triangle is $A = LH/2$

$$k_x = \sqrt{\frac{H^3 L}{12} \frac{2}{LH}}$$

$$= \frac{H}{\sqrt{6}} \qquad \text{Answer}$$

The moment of area about the Y axis is

$$I_y = \int x^2\, dA \qquad dA = y\, dx$$

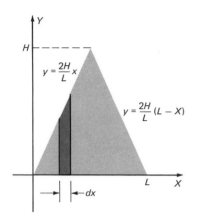

Figure 6.5

(b)

This element of area is shown in Figure 6.5b. Note that y is given by two equations depending upon the particular side of the triangle.

$$I_y = \int_0^{L/2} \frac{2H}{L} x^3 \, dx + \int_{L/2}^L \frac{2H}{L} (L - x) x^2 \, dx$$

$$= \frac{HL^3}{8} + \frac{11}{96} HL^3$$

$$= \frac{23}{96} HL^3 \qquad \text{Answer}$$

The radius of gyration is

$$k_y = \sqrt{\frac{23}{96} HL^3 \frac{2}{HL}}$$

$$= L \sqrt{\frac{23}{48}} \qquad \text{Answer}$$

(b) The polar moment of area is

$$J = I_x + I_y$$

$$= \frac{H^3 L}{12} + \frac{23 HL^3}{96}$$

$$= \frac{HL}{12} \left(H^2 + \frac{23}{8} L^2 \right) \qquad \text{Answer}$$

and

$$k = \sqrt{\frac{23}{48} L^2 + \frac{H^2}{6}} \qquad \text{Answer}$$

Example 6.2.2

Determine the moment of area I_x and polar moment of area J for the circle shown in Figure 6.6.

In this problem it is convenient to use polar coordinates. The differential area is

$$dA = 2\pi r \, dr$$

so the polar moment of area becomes

$$J = \int r^2 \, dA$$

$$= \int_0^R 2\pi r^3 \, dr$$

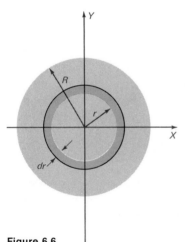

Figure 6.6

$$= \frac{\pi R^4}{2} \qquad \text{Answer}$$

From symmetry, $I_x = I_y$, so that

$$J = I_x + I_y = 2I_x$$

and

$$I_x = \frac{J}{2}$$

$$= \frac{\pi R^4}{4} \qquad \text{Answer}$$

Example 6.2.3

Calculate I_y for the shaded area of Figure 6.7 for $a = 2$ in. and $b = 10$ in.

From the figure, we establish the differential area parallel to the Y axis as $dA = y\,dx$, and since $x = ky^3$, we have

$$dx = 3ky^2\,dy$$

so that

$$dA = 3ky^3\,dy$$

The moment of area becomes

$$I_y = \int x^2\,dA$$

$$= \int_0^b (k^2 y^6)\,3ky^3\,dy$$

$$= \int_0^b 3k^3 y^9\,dy$$

$$= \frac{3k^3 b^{10}}{10}$$

Since $x = a$ when $y = b$, $k = a/b^3$, so that

$$I_y = \frac{3b^{10}}{10}\frac{a^3}{b^9} = \frac{3ba^3}{10}$$

Substituting $a = 2$ in. and $b = 10$ in. results in

$$I_y = 24 \text{ in.}^4 \qquad \text{Answer}$$

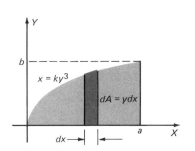

Figure 6.7

Problems

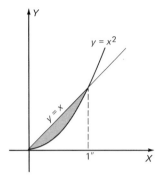

Figure 6.8

Obtain the moment of area:

6.2.1 About the X axis for the shaded area of Figure 6.8.

6.2.2 About the X axis for the shaded area of Figure 6.9.

6.2.3 About the X axis for the shaded area of Figure 6.10.

6.2.4 About the X axis for the shaded area of Figure 6.11.

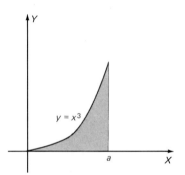

Figure 6.9

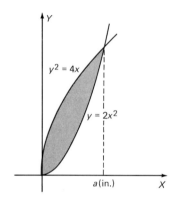

Figure 6.10

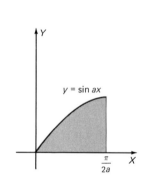

Figure 6.11

6.2.5 About the Y axis for the shaded area of Figure 6.12.

6.2.6 About the Y axis for the shaded area of Figure 6.13.

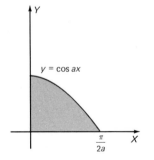

Figure 6.12

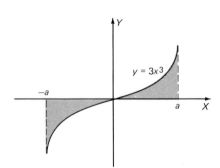

Figure 6.13

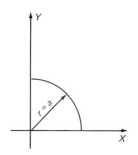

Figure 6.14

6.2.7 About the Y axis for the shaded area of Figure 6.8.

6.2.8 About the Y axis for the shaded area of Figure 6.9.

6.2.9 About the Y axis for the shaded area of Figure 6.10.

6.2.10 About the Y axis for the shaded area of Figure 6.11.

6.2.11 Find (a) the polar moment of area for the quarter circle in Figure 6.14. (b) What is the radius of gyration about the X axis?

6.2.12 Find (a) the polar moment of area about the Z axis for the half circle in Figure 6.15, and (b) the corresponding radius of gyration.

6.2.13 Find the polar moment of area for the shaded area shown in Figure 6.16.

6.2.14 Find the moment of area about the X axis for the ellipse shown in Figure 6.17.

6.2.15 Find the polar radius of gyration for the hollow tube shown in Figure 6.16.

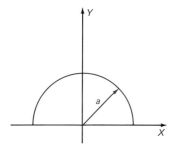

Figure 6.15

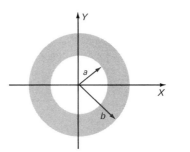

Figure 6.16

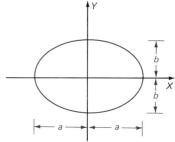

Figure 6.17

6.3 Parallel-Axis Theorem

We mentioned earlier that the moment of area depends upon the axis chosen. Here we shall derive a simple formula that enables us to obtain the moment of area about any parallel axis once we obtain the moment of area about the centroidal axis. Consider the area shown in Figure 6.18 where the moment of area about the Y axis is

$$I_y = \int x^2 \, dA$$

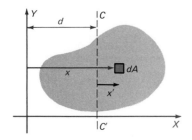

Figure 6.18

We now select an axis CC' parallel to the Y axis at a distance d. We can therefore write $x = x' + d$, so that

$$I_y = \int (x' + d)^2 \, dA = \int x'^2 \, dA + d^2 \int dA + 2d \int x' \, dA$$

If we select the CC' to pass through the centroid of the area, then

$$\int x' \, dA = 0$$

and the previous expression reduces to

$$I_y = \int x'^2 \, dA + d^2 \int dA$$

But the first integral is the moment of area about CC' and the second integral is simply the total area. If $\bar{I}_y{}'$ is the moment of area about the centroidal axis, that is,

$$\bar{I}_{y'} = \int x'^2 \, dA$$

then substituting we have

$$I_y = \bar{I}_{y'} + d^2 A \qquad\qquad (6.9)$$

This is known as the *parallel-axis theorem*. It states that the moment of area about an axis parallel to the centroidal axis is equal to the sum of the moment of area about the centroidal axis and $d^2 A$, where d is the distance between the centroidal axis and the axis parallel to the centroidal axis.

If we introduce the radius of gyration into equation (6.9), we get

$$k_y^2 A = \bar{k}_{y'}^2 A + d^2 A \qquad \text{then} \qquad k_y^2 = \bar{k}_{y'}^2 + d^2$$

We may, in a similar manner, show that for the polar moment of area

$$J = \bar{J} + A d^2 \qquad \text{and} \qquad k^2 = \bar{k}^2 + d^2$$

where d is the distance between the centroid and the origin of the parallel axes.

Composite Areas

The results of the parallel-axis theorem may be used to advantage for obtaining the moment of area of composite areas. Consider the two areas A_1 and A_2 shown in Figure 6.19. Let us assume the moments of area of A_1 and A_2 about the

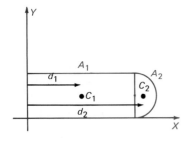

Figure 6.19

centroidal axis parallel to the Y axis are $I_{1y'}$ and $I_{2y'}$, respectively. Then the moments of area of areas A_1 and A_2 about the Y axis are

$$\overline{I}_{1y'} + A_1 d_1^2 \qquad \text{and} \qquad \overline{I}_{2y'} + A_2 d_2^2$$

so that the total moment of area about the Y axis is

$$I_y = (\overline{I}_{1y'} + \overline{I}_{2y'}) + (A_1 d_1^2 + A_2 d_2^2) \tag{6.10}$$

For the case of many areas, these results lead to the expression

$$I_y = \Sigma \overline{I}_{y'} + \Sigma A d_x^2 \tag{6.11a}$$

Similarly,

$$I_x = \Sigma \overline{I}_{x'} + \Sigma A d_y^2 \tag{6.11b}$$

The radius of gyration of a composite area cannot be obtained by adding the radii of gyration of individual areas. Instead, it is necessary to compute the moment of area by equation (6.11) and substitute the result into equation (6.3).

Example 6.3.1

Determine the moment of area about the X' axis of the triangle shown in Figure 6.20.

In this example, the X' axis passes through the centroid of the triangle so that we are in effect finding $\overline{I}_{x'}$. Thus, we can make use of the parallel-axis theorem. From example 6.2.1 we have

$$I_x = \frac{H^3 L}{12}$$

The area of the triangle is

$$A = \frac{HL}{2}$$

Thus, by the parallel-axis theorem,

$$\overline{I}_{x'} = I_x - A d^2$$

$$= \frac{H^3 L}{12} - \frac{HL}{2} \frac{H^2}{9}$$

$$= \frac{H^3 L}{36} \qquad\qquad \text{Answer}$$

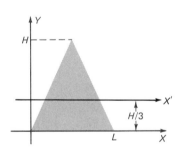

Figure 6.20

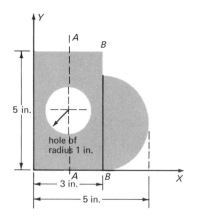

Figure 6.21

Example 6.3.2

What is the moment of area of the composite area of Figure 6.21 about the Y axis?

The moment of area of the rectangle is

$$I_y\Big]_{\text{rectangle}} = \frac{AL^2}{3}$$

$$= \frac{(5)(3)(3)^2}{3} = 45 \text{ in.}^4$$

The moment of area of the 1-in. radius circle about the A axis is

$$\bar{I}_A = \frac{\pi(1)^4}{4} = \frac{\pi}{4} \text{ in.}^4$$

Now we shift this to the Y axis, i.e.,

$$I_y\Big]_{\text{circle}} = \frac{\pi}{4} + \pi(1)^2\left(\frac{3}{2}\right)^2$$

$$= 7.85 \text{ in.}^4$$

The moment of area of the semicircle about the centroidal axis is obtained by using the formula from Table 6.1,

$$\bar{I}\Big]_{\text{semicircle}} = (2)^4\left(\frac{\pi}{8} - \frac{8}{9\pi}\right)$$

$$= 2\pi - \frac{128}{9\pi}$$

$$= 1.756 \text{ in.}^4$$

For shifting to the Y axis, we note that $A = 2\pi$ and the x distance between the Y axis and the semicircle centroid is

$$d = 3 + \frac{4r}{3\pi}$$

$$= 3 + \frac{4(2)}{3(3.14)}$$

$$= 3.85 \text{ in.}$$

The moment of area about Y axis becomes

$$I_y\Big]_{\text{semicircle}} = 1.756 + (3.85)^2(2\pi)$$

$$= 95.0 \text{ in.}^4$$

The moment of area of the composite area is obtained by adding the moment of areas for the rectangle and the semicircle and subtracting that due to the circle. Thus,

$$I_y = \left[I_y \right]_{\text{rectangle}} - \left[I_y \right]_{\text{circle}} + \left[I_y \right]_{\text{semicircle}}$$

$$= 45 - 7.85 + 95$$

$$= 132.2 \text{ in.}^4 \qquad\qquad \text{Answer}$$

Problems

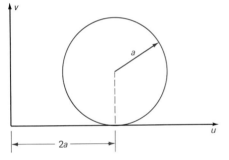

Figure 6.22

6.3.1 Using the parallel-axis theorem and the data from Table 6.1, find the moment of area about the u, v axes for the area shown in Figure 6.22.

6.3.2 Using the parallel-axis theorem and the data from Table 6.1, find the moment of area about the u,v axes for the area shown in Figure 6.23.

6.3.3 Using the parallel-axis theorem and the data from Table 6.1, find the moment of area about the u axis for the area shown in Figure 6.24.

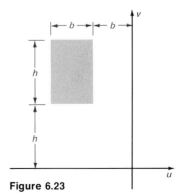

Figure 6.23

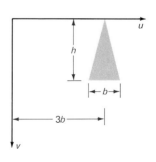

Figure 6.24

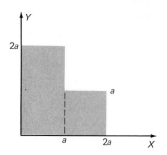

Figure 6.25

Using the composite area method, find the moment of area about the X axis for the following:

6.3.4 The shaded area shown in Figure 6.25.

6.3.5 The shaded area shown in Figure 6.26.

6.3.6 The shaded area shown in Figure 6.27.

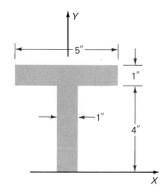

Figure 6.26

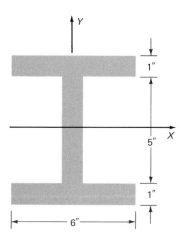

Figure 6.27

6.3.7 The shaded area shown in Figure 6.28.

6.3.8 The shaded area shown in Figure 6.29.

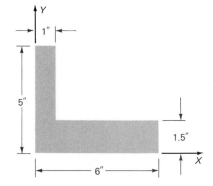

Figure 6.28

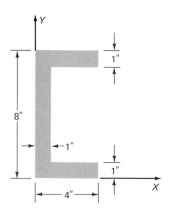

Figure 6.29

6.3.9 The shaded area shown in Figure 6.30.

6.3.10 The shaded area shown in Figure 6.31.

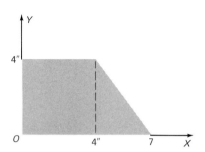

Figure 6.30

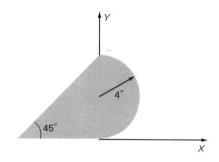

Figure 6.31

6.3.11 The shaded area shown in Figure 6.32.

6.3.12 The shaded area shown in Figure 6.33.

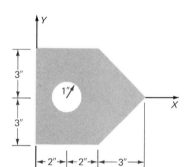

Figure 6.32

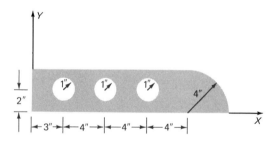

Figure 6.33

6.3.13 Obtain the polar moment of area about the center of the area shown in Figure 6.34.

6.3.14 Obtain the polar moment of area about the origin for the area shown in Figure 6.25.

6.3.15 Calculate the moment of area about the Y axis for the area shown in Figure 6.26.

6.3.16 Calculate the moment of area about the Y axis for the area shown in Figure 6.27.

6.3.17 Calculate the moment of area about the Y axis for the area shown in Figure 6.28.

6.3.18 Find the moment of area about the Y axis for the area shown in Figure 6.29.

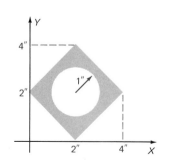

Figure 6.34

6.3.19 Find the moment of area about the Y axis for the area shown in Figure 6.30.

6.3.20 Find the moment of area about the Y axis for the area shown in Figure 6.31.

6.3.21 Find the moment of area about the Y axis for the area shown in Figure 6.32.

6.4 Product Moment of Area

Let us return to the example in section 6.2 where we computed the moment of the force about the X axis. Referring to Figure 6.1, let us compute the moment about the Y axis. Thus,

$$M_y = \int_{\text{area}} xp \, dA$$

and if $p = \gamma y$, we have

$$M_y = \gamma \int_{\text{area}} xy \, dA$$

The term $\int xy \, dA$ is called the *product moment of area* and is written as I_{xy}, i.e.,

$$I_{xy} = \int_{\text{area}} xy \, dA \qquad (6.12)$$

In this text we shall call this integral simply the *product of area*.

By way of example, let us evaluate the product of area for the elliptical cross section shown in Figure 6.35. We have placed the Y axis so that the ellipse is symmetrical about this axis. The product of area becomes

$$I_{xy} = \int_{A_1} xy \, dA + \int_{A_2} (-x)y \, dA + \int_{A_3} (-x)(-y) \, dA + \int_{A_4} x(-y) \, dA$$

Since $A_1 = A_2$, $A_3 = A_4$, and these areas are symmetrical about the Y axis, the expression for I_{xy} goes to zero. In general, the product of area is zero if the X or the Y axis is a symmetrical axis of the body.

Let the product of area about the centroidal axes X' and Y' axes be $\overline{I}_{x'y'}$ for the area in Figure 6.36. Then

$$I_{xy} = \int (x' + d_x)(y' + d_y) \, dA$$

$$= (\int x'y' \, dA) + (d_x \int y' \, dA) + (d_y \int x' \, dA) + (d_x d_y \int dA)$$

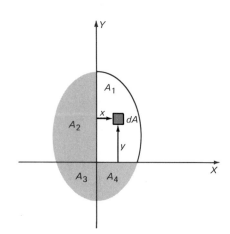

Figure 6.35

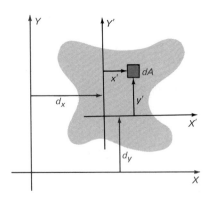

Figure 6.36

Since the X' and Y' axes are centroidal, the middle two terms go to zero and

$$I_{xy} = \bar{I}_{x'y'} + d_x d_y A \qquad (6.13)$$

This is the parallel-axis theorem for the product of area.

Example 6.4.1

For the triangle shown in Figure 6.37, determine the product of area about (a) the X and Y axes and (b) the X' and Y' axes.

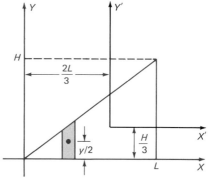

Figure 6.37

(a) Select a differential area as $dA = y\,dx$ so that the coordinate of the centroid of the element is $(x, y/2)$. When we substitute these coordinates for x and y in equation (6.12), we obtain

$$I_{xy} = \int \frac{xy^2}{2}\,dx$$

Substituting $y = (H/L)x$ and the limits for x gives us

$$I_{xy} = \int_0^L \frac{H^2}{2L^2} x^3\,dx$$

$$= \frac{H^2 L^2}{8} \qquad \text{Answer}$$

(b) The product of area about the X' and Y' axes is

$$\bar{I}_{x'y'} = I_{xy} - d_x d_y A$$

$$= \frac{H^2 L^2}{8} - \frac{2L}{3}\frac{H}{3}\frac{HL}{2}$$

$$= \frac{1}{72} H^2 L^2 \qquad \text{Answer}$$

Problems

6.4.1 Find the product of area about the XY axes for the area shown in Figure 6.38.

6.4.2 Find the product of area about the XY axes for the area shown in Figure 6.39.

6.4.3 Obtain the product of area about the $X'Y'$ axes for the area shown in Figure 6.38. Use the parallel-axis theorem.

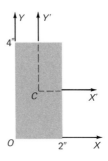

Figure 6.38

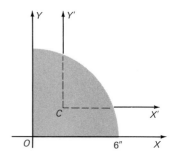

Figure 6.39

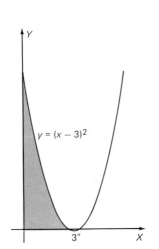

Figure 6.40

$y = (x - 3)^2$

6.4.4 Find the product of area about the XY axes of the area shown in Figure 6.40.

6.4.5 Find the product of area about the XY axes and the centroidal axes parallel to the XY axes of the area shown in Figure 6.41.

6.4.6 Obtain the product of area about the XY axes for the shape shown in Figure 6.42.

6.4.7 Obtain the product of area about the XY axes for the shape shown in Figure 6.43.

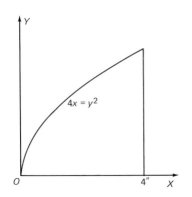

$4x = y^2$

Figure 6.41

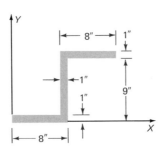

Figure 6.42

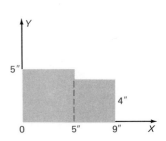

Figure 6.43

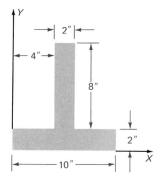

Figure 6.44

6.4.8 Obtain the product of area about the XY axes for the shape shown in Figure 6.44.

6.4.9 Obtain the product of area about the XY axes for the shape shown in Figure 6.45.

6.4.10 Obtain the product of area about the XY axes for the shape shown in Figure 6.46.

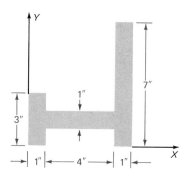

Figure 6.45

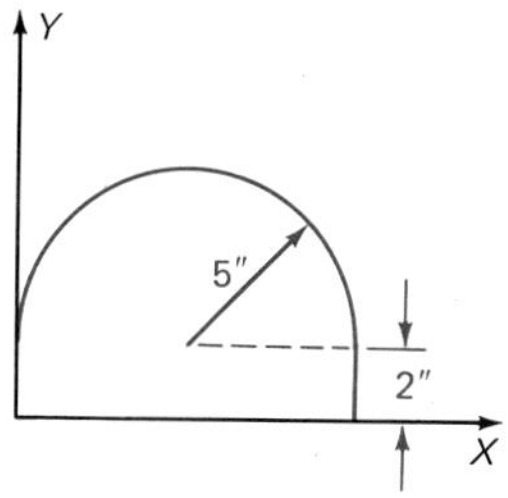

Figure 6.46

6.5 Principal Axes

The problem of finding the axis about which the moment of area is a maximum or a minimum is of importance in the study of structural mechanics. These axes can be determined with the aid of the product of area which was introduced in the previous section.

Consider the area shown in Figure 6.47 where the two sets of centroidal axes are related by following transformation equations:

$$x' = y \sin \theta + x \cos \theta$$
$$y' = y \cos \theta - x \sin \theta$$
$$(6.14)$$

The moments of area about the X' and Y' axis are

$$\bar{I}_{x'} = \int y'^2 \, dA \qquad \bar{I}_{y'} = \int x'^2 \, dA$$

Substituting equations (6.14), we obtain

$$\bar{I}_{x'} = \int (y \cos \theta - x \sin \theta)^2 \, dA$$
$$\bar{I}_{y'} = \int (y \sin \theta + x \cos \theta)^2 \, dA$$

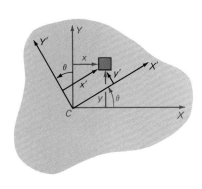

Figure 6.47

Expanding and using the trigonometric identities

$$2 \sin^2 \theta = 1 - \cos 2\theta$$

$$2 \cos^2 \theta = 1 + \cos 2\theta$$

$$\sin 2\theta = 2 \sin \theta \cos \theta$$

we obtain

$$\bar{I}_{x'} = \frac{\bar{I}_x + \bar{I}_y}{2} + \frac{\bar{I}_x - \bar{I}_y}{2} \cos 2\theta - \bar{I}_{xy} \sin 2\theta \qquad (6.15a)$$

$$\bar{I}_{y'} = \frac{\bar{I}_x + \bar{I}_y}{2} - \frac{\bar{I}_x - \bar{I}_y}{2} \cos 2\theta + \bar{I}_{xy} \sin 2\theta \qquad (6.15b)$$

where we have substituted $\bar{I}_x, \bar{I}_y, \bar{I}_{xy}$ for $\int y^2 \, dA$, $\int x^2 \, dA$, and $\int xy \, dA$, respectively.

Next we evaluate the product of area,

$$\bar{I}_{x'y'} = \int x'y' \, dA$$

Again substituting from equations (6.14), we have

$$\bar{I}_{x'y'} = \int (y \sin \theta + x \cos \theta)(y \cos \theta - x \sin \theta) \, dA$$

which simplifies to

$$\bar{I}_{x'y'} = \frac{\bar{I}_x - \bar{I}_y}{2} \sin 2\theta + \bar{I}_{xy} \cos 2\theta \qquad (6.16)$$

Since we wish to determine the maximum or minimum of the moment of area, we set

$$\frac{d\bar{I}_{x'}}{d\theta} = 0 \qquad \text{or} \qquad \frac{d\bar{I}_{y'}}{d\theta} = 0$$

Referring to equation (6.15a), we have

$$\frac{d\bar{I}_{x'}}{d\theta} = -(\bar{I}_x - \bar{I}_y) \sin 2\theta - 2\bar{I}_{xy} \cos 2\theta = 0$$

Solving this, we obtain

$$\tan 2\theta = -\frac{2\bar{I}_{xy}}{\bar{I}_x - \bar{I}_y} = q \qquad (6.17)$$

Since $\tan 2\theta = \tan (2\theta - \pi)$, we shall expect two solutions, one for maximum and one for minimum moment of area. Thus,

$$2\theta_m = \tan^{-1} q \qquad \text{and} \qquad 2\theta_m - \pi = \tan^{-1} q$$

so that

$$\theta_m = \frac{1}{2}\tan^{-1} q \qquad \text{and} \qquad \theta_m = \frac{\pi}{2} + \frac{1}{2}\tan^{-1} q \qquad (6.18)$$

where q is defined in equation (6.17). These two solutions for θ locate the X' and Y' axes relative to the X and Y axes. The X' and Y' axes are called the principal axes and for the case under consideration are also centroidal axes. Note that positive θ is measured counterclockwise as shown in Figure 6.47.

If we now substitute the value of θ from equation (6.18) into equations (6.15), we obtain

$$\bar{I}_{\max} = \frac{\bar{I}_x + \bar{I}_y}{2} + \sqrt{\left(\frac{\bar{I}_x - \bar{I}_y}{2}\right)^2 + \bar{I}_{xy}^2} \qquad (6.19a)$$

$$\bar{I}_{\min} = \frac{\bar{I}_x + \bar{I}_y}{2} - \sqrt{\left(\frac{\bar{I}_x - \bar{I}_y}{2}\right)^2 + \bar{I}_{xy}^2} \qquad (6.19b)$$

The axes about which $\bar{I}_{\max}$ and $\bar{I}_{\min}$ occur are called the principal axes. About these axes the product of area is zero, as verified by substituting equation (6.18) into (6.16).

Mohr's Circle

The relations between the maximum and minimum values of the moment of area can be shown graphically by plotting the moment of area versus the product of area. We begin by defining

$$\frac{\bar{I}_x + \bar{I}_y}{2} = I_s \qquad \frac{\bar{I}_x - \bar{I}_y}{2} = I_d$$

then, referring to equations (6.15) and (6.16), we have

$$\bar{I}_{x'} = I_s + I_d \cos 2\theta - \bar{I}_{xy} \sin 2\theta$$
$$\bar{I}_{y'} = I_s - I_d \cos 2\theta + \bar{I}_{xy} \sin 2\theta \qquad (6.20)$$
$$\bar{I}_{x'y'} = I_d \sin 2\theta + \bar{I}_{xy} \cos 2\theta$$

The above three equations are the parametric equations of a circle. This is seen by casting these equations in a slightly different form.

Let us eliminate the angle θ from the first and third equation of equations (6.20) so that

$$(\bar{I}_{x'} - I_s)^2 + \bar{I}_{x'y'}^2 = (I_d \cos 2\theta - \bar{I}_{xy} \sin 2\theta)^2$$
$$+ (I_d \sin 2\theta + \bar{I}_{xy} \cos 2\theta)^2$$
$$= I_d^2 + \bar{I}_{xy}^2$$

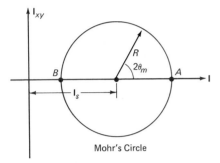

Mohr's Circle

Figure 6.48

If we set

$$R^2 = I_d^2 + \bar{I}_{xy}^2 \qquad (6.21)$$

then

$$(\bar{I}_{x'} - I_s)^2 + \bar{I}_{x'y'}^2 = R^2 \qquad (6.22)$$

which is the equation of a circle of radius R, having its center at $\bar{I}_{x'} = I_s$ and $\bar{I}_{x'y'} = 0$ as shown in Figure 6.48. The point A is a point of maximum moment of area and point B of minimum moment of area. These values are

$$I_A = I_s + R \qquad I_B = I_s - R$$

Substituting for I_s and R gives us

$$I_A = \frac{\bar{I}_x + \bar{I}_y}{2} + \sqrt{\left(\frac{\bar{I}_x - \bar{I}_y}{2}\right)^2 + \bar{I}_{xy}^2} \qquad (6.23a)$$

$$I_B = \frac{\bar{I}_x + \bar{I}_y}{2} - \sqrt{\left(\frac{\bar{I}_x - \bar{I}_y}{2}\right)^2 + \bar{I}_{xy}^2} \qquad (6.23b)$$

Equations (6.23) are identical to the equations derived analytically as given by equations (6.19).

The circle shown in Figure 6.48 is called *Mohr's circle* and was first introduced by the German engineer Otto Mohr (1835–1918). This circle may be used to graphically determine (i) the principal axes and principal moments of area, and (ii) the moment of area and product of area with respect to any centroidal axes, provided the moment of area and product of area are known about a set of axes having the same origin.

Consider the area A shown in Figure 6.49 and let us assume that we know $\bar{I}_x$, $\bar{I}_y$, and $\bar{I}_{xy}$. This is represented by plotting a point $P_1(\bar{I}_x, \bar{I}_{xy})$ and a point $P_2(\bar{I}_y, -\bar{I}_{xy})$ on a coordinate system where the X axis is called the $\bar{I}$ axis and the Y axis is the $\bar{I}_{xy}$ axis as shown in Figure 6.50. We join P_1 and P_2 and define the point O which is the intersection of P_1P_2 with the $\bar{I}$ axis. We draw a circle with center at O and diameter P_1P_2. We notice that the radius of this circle is R and the abscissa value of O is I_s. This circle is the Mohr circle. The points A

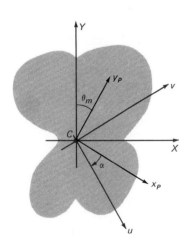

Figure 6.49

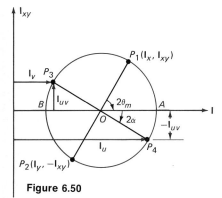

Figure 6.50

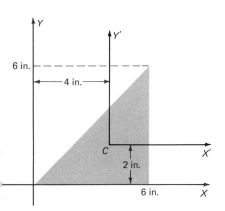

Figure 6.51

and B are points of maximum and minimum moments of area. The angle between the $\bar{I}$ axis and line P_1P_2 is $2\theta_m$, where

$$\tan 2\theta_m = -\frac{2\bar{I}_{xy}}{\bar{I}_x - \bar{I}_y}$$

The principal axes may be obtained by rotating the X and Y axis through $2\theta_m$ as shown in Figure 6.50. This is equivalent to a rotation of θ_m of the original axes as shown in Figure 6.49.

The moments of area about any other axis may be readily obtained now. Let us select the u and v axes which make an angle α with the principal axes in Figure 6.49. A line is drawn through the center of the Mohr circle in Figure 6.50 intersecting the circle at P_3 and P_4. The abscissa of P_3 and P_4 is $\bar{I}_v$ and $\bar{I}_u$, whereas the ordinate is $\bar{I}_{uv}$ and $-\bar{I}_{uv}$. Notice that if $\alpha = 45°$, the moments of area about the two rectangular axes are equal and the product of area is a maximum.

Example 6.5.1

For the triangle shown in Figure 6.51, determine the (a) centroidal moments of area, (b) the principal axes, and (c) the maximum and minimum moments of area about the centroidal axes.

(a) The moments of area and product of area for the triangle are

$$I_x = \frac{LH^3}{12} \qquad I_y = \frac{HL^3}{4} \qquad I_{xy} = \frac{H^2L^2}{8}$$

Since $H = L = 6$ in.,

$$I_x = 108 \text{ in.}^4 \qquad I_y = 324 \text{ in.}^4 \qquad I_{xy} = 162 \text{ in.}^4$$

Shifting to the centroidal axes and noting that $A = 18$ in.², we find that

$$\bar{I}_x = 108 - (2)^2(18) = 36 \text{ in.}^4$$
$$\bar{I}_y = 324 - (4)^2(18) = 36 \text{ in.}^4 \qquad \text{Answer}$$
$$\bar{I}_{xy} = 162 - (4)(2)(18) = 18 \text{ in.}^4$$

(b) We can determine the principal axes by using equation (6.17).

$$\tan 2\theta_m = -\frac{18}{0} = \infty \qquad 2\theta_m = 90°$$

therefore

$$\theta_m = 45° \text{ and } 135° \qquad \text{Answer}$$

(c) The maximum and minimum moments of area become

$$\bar{I}_{max, min} = \frac{\bar{I}_x + \bar{I}_y}{2} \pm \sqrt{\left(\frac{\bar{I}_x - \bar{I}_y}{2}\right)^2 + \bar{I}_{xy}^2} = 36 \pm \sqrt{(18)^2}$$

$$\bar{I}_{max} = 54 \text{ in.}^4 \qquad \bar{I}_{min} = 18 \text{ in.}^4 \qquad \text{Answer}$$

Example 6.5.2

Using the product of area and moments of area of the triangle shown in Figure 6.51, draw the Mohr circle. From the circle check the answers obtained in example 6.5.1. Determine the product of area and moments of area about the *u* and *v* axes shown in Figure 6.52a.

(a) The moments of area and product of area are

$$\bar{I}_x = 36 \text{ in.}^4 \qquad \bar{I}_y = 36 \text{ in.}^4 \qquad \bar{I}_{xy} = 18 \text{ in.}^4$$

We plot two points $P_1(36,18)$ and $P_2(36,-18)$ as shown in Figure 6.52b. A circle is drawn with P_1P_2 as diameter. The points of intersection with the $\bar{I}$ axis determine the minimum and maximum moments of area, thus

$$\bar{I}_{max} = 54 \text{ in.}^4 \qquad \bar{I}_{min} = 18 \text{ in.}^4 \qquad \text{Answer}$$

which checks with the answer obtained by the analytical approach.

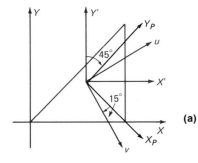

(a)

(b)

Figure 6.52

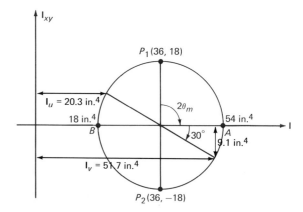

(b) For the moments of area about the u and v axes, we rotate through $2(15°)$ or $30°$ on the Mohr circle. And, referring to Figure 6.52b, find that

$$\overline{I}_u = 20.3 \text{ in.}^4 \qquad \overline{I}_v = 51.7 \text{ in.}^4 \qquad \overline{I}_{uv} = 9.1 \text{ in.}^4$$

Answer

Problems

6.5.1 Verify the derivation of equations (6.15a) and (6.15b).

6.5.2 Verify the derivation of equation (6.16).

6.5.3 Verify the derivation of equations (6.19a) and (6.19b).

6.5.4 For the area shown in Figure 6.53, find the moment and product of area about the centroidal axes parallel to (a) the XY axes and (b) the principal axes.

6.5.5 For the area shown in Figure 6.54, find the moment and product of area about the centroidal axes parallel to (a) the XY axes and (b) the principal axes.

6.5.6 For the area shown in Figure 6.55, find the moment and product of area about the centroidal axes parallel to (a) the XY axes and (b) the principal axes.

6.5.7 Determine the maximum and minimum moments of area for the shape of Figure 6.54.

6.5.8 Determine the maximum and minimum moments of area for the shape of Figure 6.55.

6.5.9 Verify the results obtained in problem 6.5.5 by using the Mohr circle.

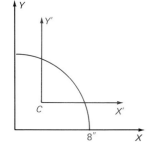

Figure 6.53

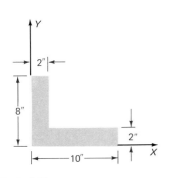

Figure 6.54

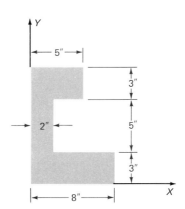

Figure 6.55

6.5.10 Verify the results obtained in problem 6.5.6 by using the Mohr circle.

6.5.11 Find $\bar{I}_u$, $\bar{I}_v$, and $\bar{I}_{uv}$ for the structural beam, Figure 6.56, whose properties are: $\bar{I}_x = 5454.2$ in.^{4}, $\bar{I}_y = 1986.0$ in.^{4} and $\bar{I}_{xy} = 0$.

6.5.12 Find $\bar{I}_u$, $\bar{I}_v$, and $\bar{I}_{uv}$ for the American Standard Channel, Figure 6.57, whose properties are: $\bar{I}_x = 128.1$ in.^{4}, $\bar{I}_y = 3.9$ in.^{4}, and $\bar{I}_{xy} = -15$ in.^{4}

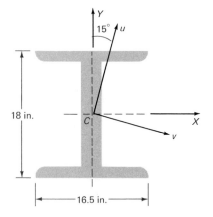

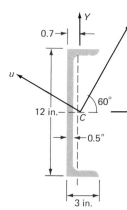

Figure 6.56

Figure 6.57

6.6 The Moment of Inertia

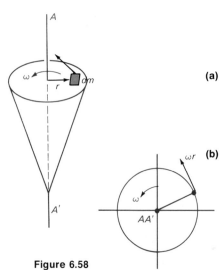

Figure 6.58

Consider a body rotating about the axis AA' as shown in Figure 6.58a. If the differential element of mass dm is rotating at the rate of ω radians per second about AA', then its velocity is of magnitude ωr and acts in a direction tangent to the radius vector as shown in Figure 6.58b. The angular momentum of this mass about the AA' axis is $r^2 \omega \, dm$. The angular momentum of the entire body becomes

$$\int_{\text{mass}} r^2 \omega \, dm$$

Since the angular velocity is the same for all the elements of mass dm, the angular momentum may be written as

$$\omega \int r^2 \, dm$$

The term described by $\int r^2 \, dm$ is the second moment of the mass about AA'; it is called the *moment of inertia* and written as I, so that the angular momentum becomes $I\omega$. This expression is of fundamental importance in dynamics, since, from

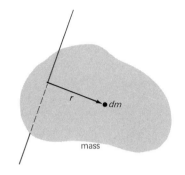

Figure 6.59

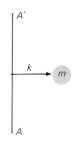

Figure 6.60

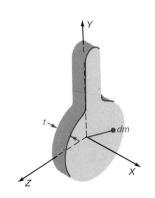

Figure 6.61

Newton's second law, the moment applied about AA' causes a change in the angular momentum $I\omega$. It is not our purpose to rigorously develop this thought process. What we wish to emphasize is the usefulness of the moment of inertia and its place in the study of mechanics. We therefore relegate additional consideration of the dynamical significance to the course in dynamics. Here we shall show how the moment of inertia may be computed.

The moment of inertia I of the body shown in Figure 6.59 is given by

$$I = \int_{\text{mass}} r^2 \, dm \tag{6.24}$$

where r is the perpendicular distance between the differential element of mass dm and the axis. We must naturally specify the axis. If the mass is assumed to be concentrated at a point as shown in Figure 6.60, then

$$I = k^2 m$$

so that the radius of gyration k becomes

$$k = \sqrt{\frac{I}{m}} \tag{6.25}$$

where m is the mass of the body. If the moment of inertia is $\bar{I}$ where the axis is a centroidal axis, then the moment of inertia about a parallel axis is

$$I = \bar{I} + md^2 \tag{6.26}$$

where d is the perpendicular distance between the two axes. If the units for mass are lb-sec^2/ft (or slug) and distance is in ft, then the units for I are lb-ft-sec^2 or slug-ft^2.

Thin Plates

The moments of inertia of thin plates are relatively simple to evaluate. Consider the plate shown in Figure 6.61. We wish to obtain the moment of inertia about the X, Y, and Z axes. A differential mass of the thin plate is given by

$$dm = \rho \, dV$$

where ρ is the density and is assumed to be constant. Since the plate thickness is t, the differential mass becomes

$$dm = \rho t \, dA$$

The moments of inertia about the X, Y, and Z axes become

$$I_y = \int z^2 \, dm = \rho t \int z^2 \, dA$$
$$I_z = \int y^2 \, dm = \rho t \int y^2 \, dA$$
$$I_x = \int (z^2 + y^2) \, dm = I_y + I_z$$

The products of inertia are defined as follows:

$$I_{yx} = I_{xy} = \int xy \, dm = \rho t \int xy \, dA$$
$$I_{zx} = I_{xz} = \int xz \, dm = \rho t \int xz \, dA$$
$$I_{zy} = I_{yz} = \int yz \, dm = \rho t \int yz \, dA$$

We note that $I_{yx} = I_{xy}$ and there are three different products of inertia. If the axes are axes of symmetry, the products of inertia are zero.

Three-Dimensional Bodies

Consider the differential mass dm shown in Figure 6.62. The moment of inertia about the Y axis is

$$I_y = \int r_y^2 \, dm$$

We notice that, in this case,

$$r_y^2 = x^2 + z^2$$

so that

$$I_y = \int (x^2 + z^2) \, dm$$

If we consider constant density ρ, then

$$dm = \rho \, dV$$

where dV is the volume of the differential mass dm. Substituting this, the moment of inertia about the Y axis becomes

$$I_y = \rho \int_{\text{volume}} (x^2 + z^2) \, dV$$

Similarly

$$I_x = \rho \int_{\text{volume}} (y^2 + z^2) \, dV$$

$$I_z = \rho \int_{\text{volume}} (x^2 + y^2) \, dV$$

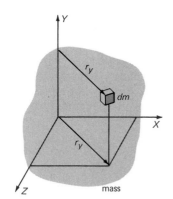

Figure 6.62

The products of inertia are given by the following expressions:

$$I_{xy} = I_{yx} = \rho \int_{\text{volume}} xy \, dV$$

$$I_{xz} = I_{zx} = \rho \int_{\text{volume}} xz \, dV$$

$$I_{yz} = I_{zy} = \rho \int_{\text{volume}} yz \, dV$$

The moments of inertia for some common geometric bodies are given in Table 6.2. For composite bodies, the moments of inertia can be found by finding the moment of inertia of each member about its centroidal axis, and then using the parallel-axis theorem for each member. This approach is demonstrated below in example 6.6.3.

Example 6.6.1

Determine the moment of inertia of the prismatic bar shown in Figure 6.63 about (a) the X axis, and (b) the centroidal X' axis.

Figure 6.63

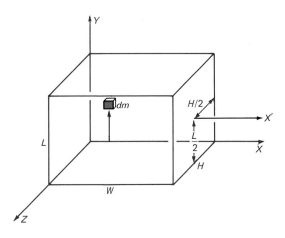

Table 6.2

*Mass Moments of Inertia of
Common Geometric Bodies*

Body	**Moments of Inertia**

Slender
Rod

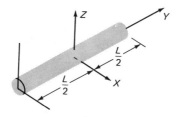

$$I_x = I_z = \tfrac{1}{12}mL^2$$

Thin
Rectangular
Plate

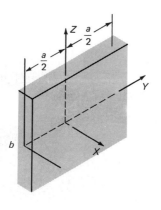

$$I_y = \tfrac{1}{12}mb^2$$
$$I_x = \tfrac{1}{12}m(a^2 + b^2)$$
$$I_z = \tfrac{1}{12}ma^2$$

Rectangular
Prism

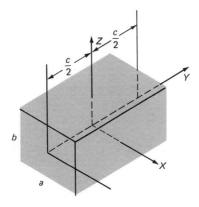

$$I_x = \tfrac{1}{12}m(b^2 + c^2)$$
$$I_y = \tfrac{1}{12}m(b^2 + a^2)$$
$$I_z = \tfrac{1}{12}m(a^2 + c^2)$$

	Body	**Moments of Inertia**

Sphere

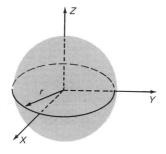

$$I_x = I_y = I_z = \tfrac{2}{5}mr^2$$

Thin
Circular
Plate

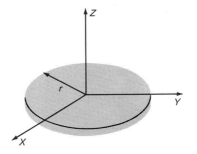

$$I_x = I_y = \tfrac{1}{4}mr^2$$
$$I_z = \tfrac{1}{2}mr^2$$

Circular
Cylinder

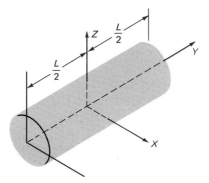

$$I_y = \tfrac{1}{2}mr^2$$
$$I_x = I_z = \tfrac{1}{12}m(3r^2 + L^2)$$

Body	**Moments of Inertia**

Semicylinder

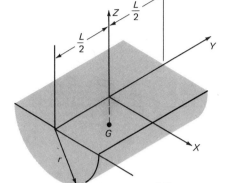

$$I_x = I_z = \tfrac{1}{4}mr^2 + \tfrac{1}{12}mL^2$$
$$I_y = \tfrac{1}{2}mr^2$$

Right
Circular
Cone

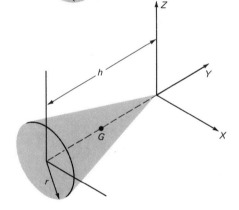

$$I_y = \tfrac{3}{10}mr^2$$
$$I_z = I_x = \tfrac{3}{20}mr^2 + \tfrac{3}{5}mh^2$$

(a) The differential mass becomes,

$$dm = \rho\, dx\, dy\, dz$$

The moment of inertia about the X axis is

$$I_x = \int (y^2 + z^2)\, dm$$

Substituting for dm, we find that

$$I_x = \rho \int y^2\, dx\, dy\, dz + \rho \int z^2\, dx\, dy\, dz$$

that is,

$$I_x = \rho \frac{WHL^3}{3} + \rho \frac{H^3LW}{3}$$

The mass of the prismatic bar is

$$m = LWH\rho$$

so that

$$I_x = \frac{m}{3}(L^2 + H^2) \qquad \text{Answer}$$

(b) The moment of inertia about the centroidal axis is

$$\bar{I}_{x'} = I_x - md^2$$

but

$$d^2 = \left(\frac{L}{2}\right)^2 + \left(\frac{H}{2}\right)^2 = \frac{1}{4}(L^2 + H^2)$$

so that

$$\bar{I}_{x'} = \frac{m}{3}(L^2 + H^2) - \frac{m}{4}(L^2 + H^2)$$

$$= \frac{m}{12}(L^2 + H^2) \qquad \text{Answer}$$

Example 6.6.2

Determine the moment of inertia about the X, Y, and Z axes of the thin disk shown in Figure 6.64.

The differential mass is

$$dm = \rho t\, 2\pi r\, dr$$

where t is the disk thickness. The moment of inertia is

$$I_x = \int (y^2 + z^2)\, dm$$

and since

$$r^2 = y^2 + z^2$$

we have

$$I_x = \int_0^R r^2 \rho t 2\pi r\, dr$$

$$= \rho t\, \frac{2\pi R^4}{4} = \rho t\, \frac{\pi R^4}{2}$$

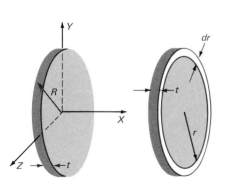

Figure 6.64

Since the mass is $m = \pi R^2 \rho t$,

$$I_x = \frac{mR^2}{2}$$ Answer

From symmetry we notice that $I_z = I_y$ and that, for a thin disk,

$$I_z = \int y^2 \, dm \qquad I_y = \int z^2 \, dm$$

so that

$$I_z + I_y = I_x$$

and

$$I_z = I_y = \frac{mR^2}{4}$$ Answer

Example 6.6.3

A circular cylinder has a right circular cone attached to it as shown in Figure 6.65. If the body weighs 490 lb/ft³, find the moment of inertia about the AA' axis.

This is an example of a composite body so that

$$I_{AA'} = (I_{AA'})_{\text{cylinder}} + (I_{AA'})_{\text{cone}}$$

For the cylinder,

$$\text{Volume} = \pi(4)^2(10) = 502 \text{ in.}^3 = 0.291 \text{ ft}^3$$

$$\text{Weight} = w = 490(0.291) = 142.5 \text{ lb}$$

$$\text{Mass} = m = \frac{w}{g} = \frac{142.5}{32.2} = 4.43 \; \frac{\text{lb-sec}^2}{\text{ft}}$$

Using Table 6.2 and shifting the axis,

$$(I_{AA'})_{\text{cylinder}} = \frac{m}{12} (3r^2 + 4L^2)$$

$$= \frac{4.43}{12} \left[3\left(\frac{4}{12}\right)^2 + 4\left(\frac{10}{12}\right)^2 \right]$$

$$= 1.149 \text{ lb-ft-sec}^2$$

For the circular cone,

$$\text{Volume} = \tfrac{1}{3} \pi r^2 h = \tfrac{1}{3} \pi(4)^2(8) = 134 \text{ in.}^3 = 0.0776 \text{ ft}^3$$

$$\text{Weight} = w = 490(0.0776) = 38.0 \text{ lb}$$

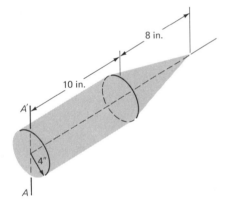

8 in.

10 in.

4"

A'

A

Figure 6.65

$$\text{Mass} = m = \frac{38.0}{32.2} = 1.18 \ \frac{\text{lb-sec}^2}{\text{ft}}$$

Referring to the data in Table 6.2 and shifting the axis, we obtain the moment of inertia about the base of the cone. Then by the parallel-axis theorem we get

$$\bar{I} = I_x - md^2$$

$$= \left(\frac{3}{20}mr^2 + \frac{1}{10}mh^2\right) - m\left(\frac{h}{3}\right)^2$$

$$= \frac{3}{20}mr^2 - \frac{1}{90}mh^2$$

$$= 0.0138 \ \text{lb-ft-sec}^2$$

Now

$$(I_{AA})_{\text{cone}} = \bar{I} + md^2$$

$$= 0.0138 + 1.18 \left(\frac{10 + 8/3}{12}\right)^2$$

$$= 1.329 \ \text{lb-ft-sec}^2$$

therefore

$$I_{AA} = 1.149 + 1.329 = 2.48 \ \text{lb-ft-sec}^2 \quad \text{Answer}$$

Problems

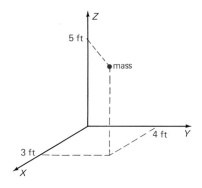

Figure 6.66

6.6.1 Verify the expressions for I_x and I_z, for the slender rod shown in Table 6.2.

6.6.2 Verify the equations for I_x and I_z, for the thin rectangular plate shown in Table 6.2.

6.6.3 Verify the equation for I_x for the sphere shown in Table 6.2.

6.6.4 Verify the equation for I_x for the circular cylinder shown in Table 6.2.

6.6.5 A 10-slug mass is located as shown in Figure 6.66. Obtain the moment of inertia about the X, Y, and Z axes.

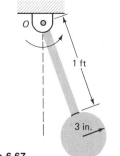

Figure 6.67

6.6.6 The brass pendulum shown in Figure 6.67 consists of a thin rod 1 ft in length and 1 in. in diameter with a sphere of radius 3 in. attached at the end. If the specific weight of brass is 534 lb/ft³, find the moment of inertia about the axis through O.

6.6.7 A 10-slug mass is located at (3,4,5). Obtain the moment of inertia of the mass about an axis coincident with the unit vector $\lambda = 0.577\mathbf{i} + 0.577\mathbf{j} + 0.577\mathbf{k}$. Let the distance be in feet.

6.6.8 Find the moment of inertia for the spinning body about the AA' axis as shown in Figure 6.68. The body is made of aluminum which has a specific weight of 165 lb/ft³ and is assumed to consist of two similar thin circular disks and a slender rod. Let $d = 1$ in. be the diameter of the rod and $t = 1$ in. be the thickness of each disk.

6.6.9 The half cylinder rocks back and forth as shown in Figure 6.69. If the body is homogeneous having a mass of 100 slugs, find the moment of inertia about the AA' axis.

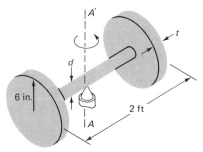

Figure 6.68

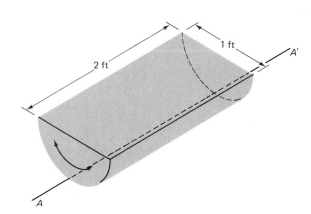

Figure 6.69

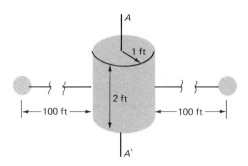

Figure 6.70

6.6.10 A spinning satellite shown in Figure 6.70 releases a pair of masses m to reduce the amount of spin about the AA' axis. The satellite, excluding the masses, weighs 50 lb and each mass is 0.01 slug. Neglecting the weight of the cord, find the moment of inertia of the body about the AA' axis.

6.6.11 Find the moment of inertia about the AA' axis of the hollow cylinder shown in Figure 6.71. The specific weight of the material is 490 lb/ft³.

6.6.12 Find the moment of inertia about the AA' axis of the hollow sphere shown in Figure 6.72. The specfic weight of the material is 500 lb/ft³.

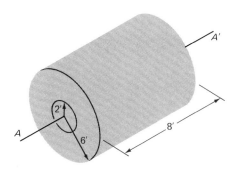

Figure 6.71

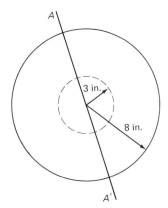

Figure 6.72

6.7 Summary

A   The important *ideas:*

1. The moment of area is useful in the study of stress analysis of structures such as beams.

2. The moment of inertia is fundamental in the study of rotational motion in dynamics.

3. The product of inertia is zero about the principal axes.

4. Mohr's circle is a graphical method for finding principal moments of inertia.

B   The important *equations:*

Moments of Area: $I_x = \int y^2 \, dA$

$$I_y = \int x^2 \, dA \tag{6.2}$$

$$I_x = k_x^2 A \tag{6.3}$$

Polar moment of area: $J = \int r^2 \, dA$ (6.5)

$$J = I_x + I_y \tag{6.6}$$

$$k = \sqrt{k_x^2 + k_y^2} \tag{6.8}$$

Parallel axis theorem: $I_y = \bar{I}_{y'} + d^2 A$ (6.9)

Product of area: $I_{xy} = \int xy \, dA$ (6.12)

Moment of inertia: $I = \int_{\text{mass}} r^2 \, dm$ (6.24)

Chapter 7
Analysis of Beams

Beams are commonly used structural members which offer strong resistance to externally applied loads. When external loads are applied to a beam, the beam develops internal bending moments as well as internal shear forces. To determine the proper size of beams for various engineering applications, it is necessary to know the relationships between the bending moments, the shear forces, and the applied loads. Here we develop these important relationships.

7.1 Introduction

Beams are perhaps the most important structural members used in engineering. It is, therefore, important that we understand fully the fundamentals of beam analysis.

We analyzed beams for their support reactions to concentrated and distributed loads in Chapter 5. Here, we will extend our analysis to include the relationship between these applied loads and the consequential effects of shear and bending of the beam. This information is necessary in order to design beams of proper size, a task normally taken up in a Strength of Materials course.

7.2 Types of Beams

When the reactions of a beam can be found from the equations of statics, that beam is classified as "statically determinate." If, however, there are more unknown reactions at the supports than there are equations of statics, a beam is classified as "statically indeterminate." Complete analysis of this latter group must include the load−deformation properties of the beams along with the equilibrium equations of statics. In this text, we will limit ourselves to statically determinate beams. Table 7.1 shows some common beam supports and their classification.

Figure 7.1 shows selected beam loads with which we will be concerned in our study of beams; namely, the concentrated load, an applied couple, and the distributed load. Beam reactions to distributed loads can be determined by placing the equivalent resultant load at the centroid of the distributed load and then applying the equations of equilibrium as discussed in Chapter 5.

When simple structures were analyzed earlier, a structural member was considered to be either in tension or compression. Such members we called two-force members. In the case of beams, the behavior of the internal forces is more complicated. For example, Figure 7.2a shows a simply supported beam carrying a concentrated load w. Figure 7.2b shows two free-body diagrams, if the beam is cut to the left of the applied load w. The diagram to the left of the cut section shows forces Q and T and a couple M which result internally when the beam supports the applied load. In the free-body diagram to the

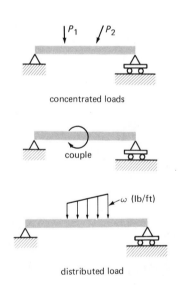

concentrated loads

couple

distributed load

Figure 7.1

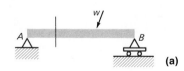

(a)

Figure 7.2

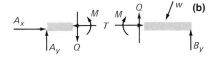

right of the cut section, we have the same forces Q and T and couple M applied in equal but opposite directions. This is in accord with Newton's third law. We shall consider the forces Q and T and the couple M as being constant over the cross section of the beam. In Strength of Materials we study the associated stresses in the beam as they vary across the beam cross section.

7.3 Beam Analysis

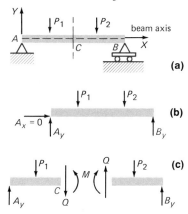

Figure 7.3

Concentrated Load

Consider a beam subjected to concentrated loads P_1 and P_2, as shown in Figure 7.3a. The free-body diagram of the entire beam is shown in Figure 7.3b. Using this diagram and the three equations of statics,

$$\Sigma F_x = 0 \qquad \Sigma F_y = 0 \qquad \Sigma M = 0$$

we can find the beam reactions $A_x, A_y,$ and B_y. Note that $A_x = 0$ for this case.

To investigate the internal forces, let us consider the free-body diagram in Figure 7.3c for a section of the beam cut at point C. We note that the resultant force Q, called the *shear force*, is perpendicular to the beam axis. Since there is no load applied in the x direction, there is no *axial force* acting on the beam. The moment M is called the *bending moment* developed by the beam. We can calculate the shear force Q and the bending moment M acting at the cross section under consideration by applying the equations of statics to either free-body diagram in Figure 7.3c. For example, considering the left section, $\Sigma F_y = 0$ will give us Q, while $\Sigma M = 0$ about any point on the left section will give us M. Note that the magnitudes of Q and M depend upon the cross section selected. In other words, if we selected a section between A and P_1, we would calculate a new set of values for Q and M associated with the new cross section.

In the above example, we assumed the directions of the shear force Q and bending moment M when we drew Figure 7.3c. Let us adopt these assumed directions as the positive directions for the shear and the bending moment. This assumption identifies shear forces as positive when the external forces tend to deform the beam as shown in Figure 7.4a, and the bending moment as positive if it deforms the beam as indicated in Figure 7.4b. In problem solving, we assume positive shear

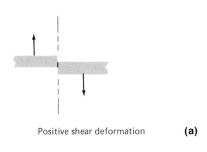

Positive shear deformation (a)

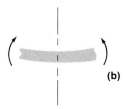

(b)

Figure 7.4 Positive bending deformation

Table 7.1

Type of Beam		Classification
Simply supported		Statically determinate
Overhanging		Statically determinate
Cantilever (fixed–free)		Statically determinate
Fixed at both ends (fixed–fixed)		Statically indeterminate
Fixed–simply supported		Statically indeterminate
Continuous beam		Statically indeterminate

Type of Beam		Classification
Beam with elastic support	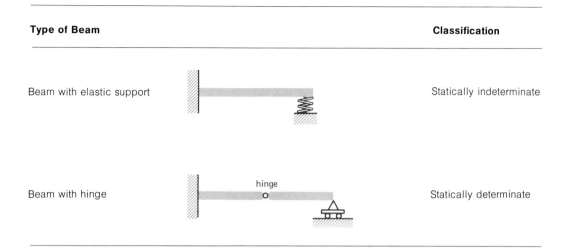	Statically indeterminate
Beam with hinge		Statically determinate

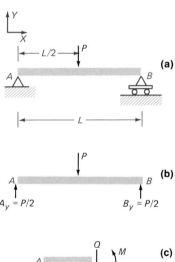

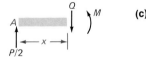

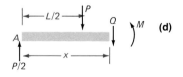

Figure 7.5

and bending moment as shown in Figure 7.3c. We know these assumptions are correct when computation for Q, or M, provides a positive value. If Q, or M, is computed as a negative quantity, we know that the shear force, or bending moment, acts in the reverse direction.

In our example in Figure 7.3 we noted that the shear force and bending moment are influenced by the point at which we cut the beam. In general, we wish to know how this force and moment vary throughout the length of the beam. It is, therefore, necessary that the shear and bending moment be computed everywhere and recorded in a convenient manner. To this end, we draw a shear diagram and a bending-moment diagram. By way of example, consider the beam carrying the load P in Figure 7.5a. The free-body diagram for the entire beam is shown in Figure 7.5b. From the equations of statics, we obtain $A_x = 0$, $A_y = B_y = P/2$.

To establish the shear and bending moment in the beam, consider the free-body diagrams in Figures 7.5c and d. In Figure 7.5c, a section at a distance x is taken to the left of the applied load P. From this diagram we can write the following: For $0 < x < L/2$,

$$\Sigma F_y = 0 \qquad \frac{P}{2} - Q = 0$$

$$Q = \frac{P}{2} \qquad\qquad (7.1)$$

$$\Sigma M_x = 0 \qquad M - \frac{Px}{2} = 0$$

$$M = \frac{Px}{2} \qquad (7.2)$$

Since Q and M are calculated as positive quantities, our assumed directions are correct.

Referring to the section to the right of the load P as shown in Figure 7.5d, we have the following: For $L/2 < x < L$,

$$\Sigma F_y = 0 \qquad \frac{P}{2} - P - Q = 0$$

$$Q = -\frac{P}{2} \qquad (7.3)$$

and

$$\Sigma M_x = 0 \qquad M - \frac{Px}{2} + P\left(x - \frac{L}{2}\right) = 0$$

$$M = P\left(\frac{L}{2} - \frac{x}{2}\right) \qquad (7.4)$$

In this section our assumed direction on Q was incorrect, while the direction on M is correct.

The results for the shear throughout the beam, given by equations (7.1) and (7.3), are plotted as a shear diagram in Figure 7.5e. Thus, the shear force begins at A with a value of $P/2$ until we reach the location of the applied load P, at which point the shear changes by an amount $(-P)$. Beyond $x = L/2$, the shear remains $(-P/2)$ throughout until we reach the reaction at B at which point the shear changes by an amount $(P/2)$.

Equations (7.2) and (7.4) are plotted in Figure 7.5f, which is called the bending-moment diagram. Note that the boundary conditions for a simply supported beam are satisfied, that is, $M = 0$ at $x = 0$ and $x = L$. In this case, the maximum bending moment occurs at $x = L/2$ and has a magnitude equal to $PL/4$.

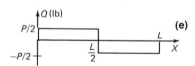

(e)

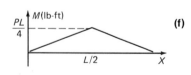

(f)

Figure 7.5

In order to adequately design beams, it is essential to know the location of their maximum shears and bending moments; this information is supplied by the shear and bending-moment diagrams.

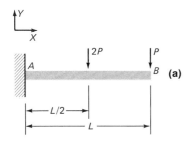

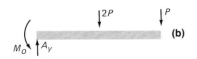

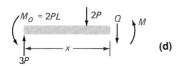

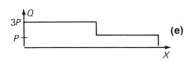

Figure 7.6

Example 7.3.1

Find the equations for the shear and bending moment and draw the shear and bending-moment diagrams for the cantilever beam in Figure 7.6a.

The free-body diagram of the total beam is shown in Figure 7.6b. Here we see reaction A_y and a moment M_0 due to the fixed-support condition. For equilibrium conditions, we have the following:

$$\Sigma F_y = 0 \qquad A_y = 3P$$

and

$$\Sigma M_A = 0 \qquad -M_0 + 2P\left(\frac{L}{2}\right) + P(L) = 0 \qquad M_0 = 2PL$$

The free-body diagram to the left of the load $2P$ is shown in Figure 7.6c. For this case, where $0 < x < L/2$, we find

$$\Sigma F_y = 0$$
$$Q = 3P \qquad\qquad \text{Answer}$$

and

$$\Sigma M_x = 0 \qquad M + 2PL - 3Px = 0$$
$$M = 3Px - 2PL \qquad\qquad \text{Answer}$$

The free-body diagram for a section cut between the applied loads is shown in Figure 7.6d. For this case, where $L/2 < x < L$, we find

$$\Sigma F_y = 0 \qquad 3P - 2P - Q = 0$$
$$Q = P \qquad\qquad \text{Answer}$$

and

$$\Sigma M_x = 0 \qquad M + 2PL - 3Px + 2P\left(x - \frac{L}{2}\right) = 0$$
$$M = P(x - L) \qquad\qquad \text{Answer}$$

The Q equations are plotted to give Figure 7.6e for the shear diagram. Again we note that wherever we have a concentrated load (including the reactions), we have a corresponding step change in the shear magnitude. In this case, it occurs at $x = 0$, $x = L/2$, and $x = L$. The bending-moment diagram (Figure 7.6f) is obtained from the M equations. Again we note that the

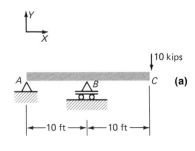

(a)

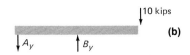

(b)

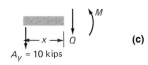

(c)

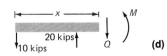

(d)

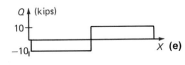

(e)

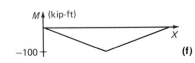

(f)

Figure 7.7

boundary conditions are met in the diagram, that is, $M_0 = -2PL$ at $x = 0$ and $M = 0$ at $x = L$. The negative sign on M_0 follows the sign convention for bending moments discussed earlier.

Example 7.3.2

Find the equations for the shear and bending moment and draw the shear and bending-moment diagrams for the overhanging beam in Figure 7.7a.

From the free-body diagram in Figure 7.7b we have the following:

$$\Sigma M_A = 0 \qquad 10B_y - 10(20) = 0 \qquad B_y = 20 \text{ kips}$$

and

$$\Sigma F_y = 0 \qquad -A_y + B_y - 10 = 0 \qquad A_y = 10 \text{ kips}$$

For the free-body diagram of a section between A and B in Figure 7.7c. where $0 < x < 10$, we have the following:

$$\Sigma F_y = 0 \qquad -Q - 10 = 0$$
$$Q = -10 \text{ kips} \qquad \qquad \text{Answer}$$

and

$$\Sigma M_x = 0 \qquad M + 10x = 0$$
$$M = -10x \text{ kip-ft} \qquad \qquad \text{Answer}$$

From Figure 7.7d. where $10 < x < 20$, we have

$$\Sigma F_y = 0 \qquad -Q - 10 + 20 = 0$$
$$Q = 10 \text{ kips} \qquad \qquad \text{Answer}$$

and

$$\Sigma M_x = 0 \qquad M + 10x - 20(x - 10) = 0$$
$$M = 10x - 200 \text{ kip-ft} \qquad \qquad \text{Answer}$$

The Q equations are plotted in Figure 7.7e for the shear diagram, while the M equations are plotted in Figure 7.7f for the bending-moment diagram.

Applied Couple

Beams are also used in situations where they support applied couples. These couples may arise from applied forces which are equal and opposite, as shown in Figure 7.8a. Here the forces are applied to a rigid bracket spaced a distance d to produce a couple of magnitude Pd. Figure 7.8b is an equivalent

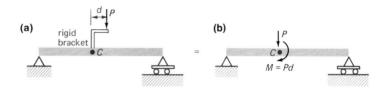

Figure 7.8

loading diagram showing the couple applied at point C of the beam. Figure 7.9a shows another loading arrangement; its equivalent loading diagram is shown in Figure 7.9b. The

Figure 7.9

following example problem shows how to draw a shear and moment diagram for the case where applied couples are present.

Example 7.3.3

Find the equations for the shear and bending moment and draw the shear and moment diagrams for the beam in Figure 7.10a.

The beam reactions are obtained using the equivalent loads at point C for the free-body diagram in Figure 7.10b. Thus

$$\Sigma M_A = 0 \qquad 5B_y - 400(2) - 200 = 0 \qquad B_y = 200 \text{ lb}$$

and

$$\Sigma F_y = 0 \qquad A_y + B_y - 400 = 0 \qquad A_y = 200 \text{ lb}$$

Referring to Figures 7.10c and d, we have the following: For $0 < x < 2$,

$$\Sigma F_y = 0 \qquad 200 - Q = 0$$

$$Q = 200 \text{ lb} \qquad \qquad \text{Answer}$$

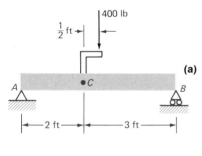

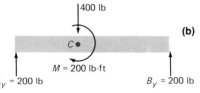

Figure 7.10

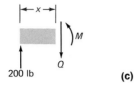

(c)

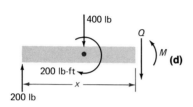

(d)

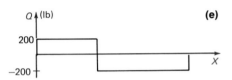

(e)

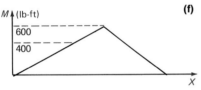

(f)

Figure 7.10

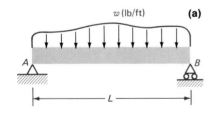

(a)

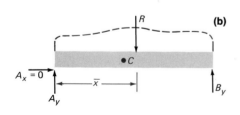

(b)

Figure 7.11

and

$$\Sigma M_x = 0 \qquad M - 200x = 0$$

$$M = 200x \text{ lb-ft} \qquad \text{Answer}$$

For $2 < x < 5$,

$$\Sigma F_y = 0 \qquad 200 - 400 - Q = 0$$

$$Q = -200 \text{ lb} \qquad \text{Answer}$$

and

$$\Sigma M_x = 0 \qquad M - 200x + 400(x - 2) - 200 = 0$$

$$M = 1000 - 200x \text{ lb-ft} \qquad \text{Answer}$$

The shear and bending-moment diagrams are shown in Figures 7.10e and f, respectively. Since we have an applied couple at point C, note the corresponding step change in the moment diagram. This is similar to a step change in the shear diagram where we have a concentrated load.

Distributed Load

Before developing the shear and bending-moment diagrams for the case of distributed loads, let us review the procedure for finding the beam reactions with distributed loads present. Figure 7.11a shows a beam supporting a distributed load. The free-body diagram of the beam is shown in Figure 7.11b, where we replace the distributed load w by R at a distance x so that

$$R = \int_0^L w \; dx \qquad (7.5)$$

$$\bar{x} = \frac{\int_0^L w \, x \; dx}{\int_0^L w \; dx} \qquad (7.6)$$

Figure 7.11c shows the free-body diagrams of the cut at point C. Now the distributed loads to either side of the section are replaced by R_1 and R_2 placed at the centroid of each portion of the distributed load. Thus,

$$R_1 = \int_0^x w \; dx \qquad R_2 = \int_x^L w \; dx \qquad (7.7)$$

$$\bar{x}_1 = \frac{\int_0^x w \, x \; dx}{\int_0^x w \; dx} \qquad \bar{x}_2 = \frac{\int_x^L w \, x \; dx}{\int_x^L w \; dx} \qquad (7.8)$$

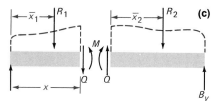

(c) Having these expressions, we can now write the expression for the shear Q and the bending moment M at the section in question.

Example 7.3.4

Find the expressions for the shear and bending moment for the beam in Figure 7.12a and draw the shear and moment diagrams.

For the free-body diagram in Figure 7.12b,

$$R = \int_0^L w\,dx = wL \qquad \text{and} \qquad \bar{x} = \frac{\int_0^L wx\,dx}{R} = \frac{L}{2}$$

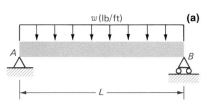

(a)

For the beam reactions,

$$\Sigma M_A = 0 \qquad B_y L - R\frac{L}{2} = 0 \qquad B_y = w\frac{L}{2}$$

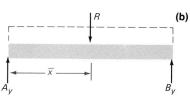

(b)

and

$$\Sigma F_y = 0 \qquad A_y - R + B_y = 0 \qquad A_y = w\frac{L}{2}$$

Figure 7.12c shows the free-body diagram of a typical section of the beam. Now

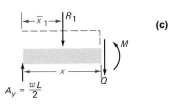

(c)

$$R_1 = \int_0^x w\,dx = wx \qquad \text{and} \qquad \bar{x}_1 = \frac{\int_0^x wx\,dx}{R_1} = \frac{x}{2}$$

For equilibrium, where $0 < x < L$, we find

$$\Sigma F_y = 0 \qquad \frac{wL}{2} - R_1 - Q = 0$$

$$Q = \frac{wL}{2} - wx \qquad\qquad \text{Answer}$$

(d)

and

$$\Sigma M_x = 0 \qquad M - \frac{wL}{2}x + R_1\frac{x}{2} = 0$$

(e)

$$M = \frac{wLx}{2} - \frac{wx^2}{2} \qquad\qquad \text{Answer}$$

Figures 7.12d and e show the shear and bending-moment diagrams.

Figure 7.12

Problems

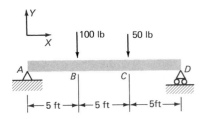

Figure 7.13

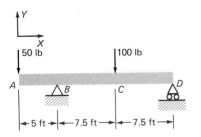

Figure 7.14

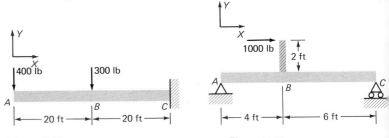

Figure 7.15   **Figure 7.16**

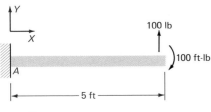

Figure 7.17

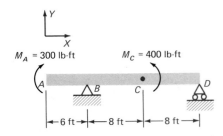

Figure 7.18

7.3.1 Write the equations for shear force and bending moment for the beam in Figure 7.13.

7.3.2 Write the equations for shear force and bending moment for the beam in Figure 7.14.

7.3.3 Obtain the shear-force and bending-moment equations for the beam in Figure 7.15.

7.3.4 Obtain the shear-force and bending-moment equations for the beam in Figure 7.16. Assume the load is applied to a rigid bracket.

7.3.5 Derive the equations for the shear force and bending moment for the beam in Figure 7.17.

7.3.6 Derive the equations for the shear force and bending moment for the beam in Figure 7.18.

7.3.7 Draw the shear and bending-moment diagrams for the beam in Figure 7.13.

7.3.8 Draw the shear and bending-moment diagrams for the beam in Figure 7.14.

7.3.9 Obtain the shear and bending-moment diagrams for the beam in Figure 7.15.

Obtain the shear and bending-moment diagrams for the beam in Figure 7.16.

7.3.11 Draw the shear and bending-moment diagrams for the beam in Figure 7.17.

7.3.12 Draw the shear and bending-moment diagrams for the beam in Figure 7.18.

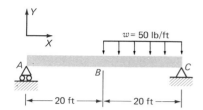

Figure 7.19

7.3.13 Obtain the shear and bending-moment equations for the beam with a distributed load shown in Figure 7.19.

7.3.14 Obtain the shear and bending-moment equations for the beam with a distributed load shown in Figure 7.20.

7.3.15 For the beam in Figure 7.21, obtain the shear-force and bending-moment equations.

7.3.16 For the beam in Figure 7.22, obtain the shear-force and bending-moment equations.

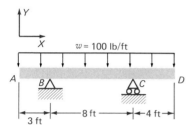

Figure 7.20

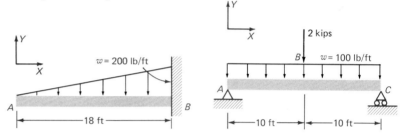

Figure 7.21   **Figure 7.22**

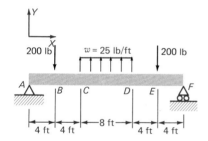

Figure 7.23

7.3.17 What are the shear-force and bending-moment equations for the beam shown in Figure 7.23?

7.3.18 What are the shear-force and bending-moment equations for the beam shown in Figure 7.24?

7.3.19 For the beam in Figure 7.25, obtain the shear-force and bending-moment equations.

7.3.20 For the beam in Figure 7.26, obtain the shear-force and bending-moment equations.

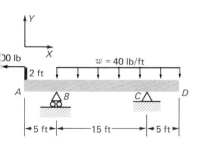

Figure 7.24   **Figure 7.25**   **Figure 7.26**

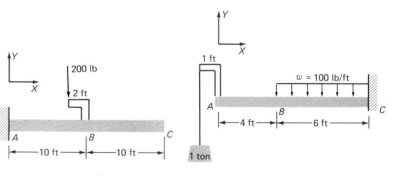

7.4 Load, Shear, and Bending-Moment Relations

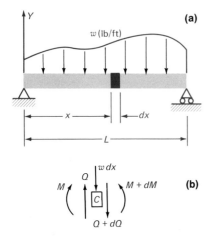

Figure 7.27

(a) Consider the beam in Figure 7.27a subject to a distributed load w (lb/ft). Let us isolate a differential length of beam dx and draw the free-body diagram as shown in Figure 7.27b. The magnitude of the shear Q and the bending moment M on the left side of the element increases by the amount $(Q + dQ)$ and $(M + dM)$, respectively, on the right side. Positive directions for the shear and bending moment are assumed. For equilibrium, we write

$$\Sigma F_y = 0 \qquad Q - (Q + dQ) - w\,dx = 0 \qquad dQ = -w\,dx$$

(b) or

$$\frac{dQ}{dx} = -w \tag{7.9}$$

Integrating equation (7.9) between x_1 and x_2 gives us

$$\int_{Q_1}^{Q_2} dQ = -\int_{x_1}^{x_2} w\,dx$$

so that

$$Q_2 - Q_1 = -\int_{x_1}^{x_2} w\,dx \tag{7.10}$$

Equation (7.10) indicates that the difference of the shear between two points of the beam equals the negative of the area under the load curve. Note that this expression holds only for distributed loads, and that the positive direction of w is downward. By way of example, consider the beam in Figure 7.28. The shear between A and B is a constant 500 lb since the free-body diagram of this part shows that the shear magnitude is equal to the reaction A_y. The change in shear between B and C equals the area under the load diagram. Thus,

$$Q_2 = Q_1 - \int_{x_1}^{x_2} w\,dx$$

$$= 500 - \int_{10}^{20} 100\,dx = 500 - 1000 = -500 \text{ lb}$$

Between C and D the shear remains -500 lb until point D is reached, which satisfies the boundary condition.

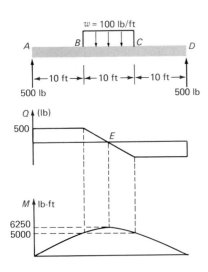

Figure 7.28

Returning to Figure 7.27b for the beam element, we also have equilibrium. Thus, summing moments about the left edge,

$$\Sigma M_C = 0 \qquad (M + dM) - M - w\ dx\ \frac{dx}{2} - (Q + dQ)\ dx = 0$$

$$dM - \frac{w}{2}\ (dx)^2 - Q\ dx - dQ\ (dx) = 0$$

Since dM, dQ, and dx are differentials and, therefore, are small quantities, their products may be neglected so that

$$dM - Q\ dx = 0$$

or

$$\frac{dM}{dx} = Q \tag{7.11}$$

We integrate as before to get

$$\int_{M_1}^{M_2} dM = \int_{x_1}^{x_2} Q\ dx$$

so that

$$M_2 - M_1 = \int_{x_1}^{x_2} Q\ dx \tag{7.12}$$

that is, the difference between the bending moments at two points on the beam equals the area under the shear curve between these same two points. Returning to Figure 7.28, at A the moment must be zero. Thus, between A and B,

$$M_B = M_A + \int_0^{10} Q\ dx = 0 + 500(10) = 5000 \text{ lb-ft}$$

Between B and E,

$$M_E = M_B + \int_{10}^{15} Q\ dx = 5000 + \frac{1}{2}\ (500)(5) = 6250 \text{ lb-ft}$$

Between E and C,

$$M_C = M_E + \int_{15}^{20} Q\ dx = 6250 - \frac{1}{2}\ (500)(5) = 5000 \text{ lb-ft}$$

Between C and D,

$$M_D = M_C + \int_{20}^{30} Q\ dx = 5000 - 500(10) = 0$$

(Checks)

Consequently, when we have the shear diagram, we can locate the coordinates of the bending-moment diagram fairly rapidly. In the above example, we note that the shear is constant between points A and B and the corresponding curve between A and B is termed a zero-order curve. The integral of this curve is a straight line (first-order curve) as shown by the bending-moment curve between A and B. Similarly, the integral of the straight line between points B and C of the shear curve is represented by a parabola (second-order curve) on the bending-moment curve.

Example 7.4.1

Draw the shear and bending-moment diagrams for the beam in Figure 7.29.

Beam Reactions:

$$\Sigma M_A = 0 \qquad 20D_y - 2000(5) - 1000(15) = 0 \qquad D_y = 1250 \text{ lb}$$

and

$$\Sigma F_y = 0 \qquad A_y - 2000 - 1000 + D_y = 0 \qquad A_y = 1750 \text{ lb}$$

Shear Diagram:

Having the reaction A_y, we begin construction of the shear diagram at point A. Between A and B, the area under the load diagram is 2000 lb, so that

$$Q_B = Q_A - \int_A^B w \, dx$$
$$= 1750 - 2000 = -250 \text{ lb}$$

Since the load diagram is of zero order, the shear diagram is first order, and hence the straight line between A and B. Between B and C the shear is constant, and at C it experiences a step change in value of 1000 lb. Between C and D it remains constant at -1250 lb and checks at D with a reaction of $+1250$ lb.

Moment Diagram:

We now construct the bending-moment diagram directly from the shear diagram. First we locate point E from the geometry. At point A, $M = 0$, so that

$$M_E = \text{area under } Q \text{ curve between } A \text{ and } E$$
$$= \tfrac{1}{2}(1750)(8.75) = 7650 \text{ lb-ft}$$

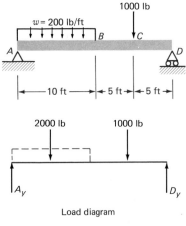

Load diagram

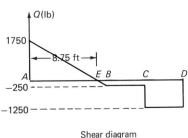

Shear diagram

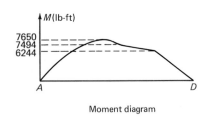

Moment diagram

Figure 7.29

Between E and B,

$$M_B = M_E + \text{area under } Q \text{ curve between } E \text{ and } B$$
$$= 7650 - \tfrac{1}{2}(250)(1.25) = 7494 \text{ lb-ft}$$

Between B and C,

$$M_C = M_B + \text{area under } Q \text{ curve between } B \text{ and } C$$
$$= 7494 - 250(5) = 6244 \text{ lb-ft}$$

Between C and D,

$$M_D = M_C + \text{area under } Q \text{ curve between } C \text{ and } D$$
$$= 6244 - 1250(5) = -6 \text{ lb-ft} \qquad \text{(close enough)}$$

Notice that M_D should be zero, but due to errors from the slide rule we have a value of -6 lb-ft, which is close enough to the exact value.

Example 7.4.2

Draw the shear and bending-moment diagrams for the beam in Figure 7.30.

Beam Reactions:

$$\Sigma M_A = 0 \qquad M_O - 240(6) + 800 = 0 \qquad M_O = 640 \text{ lb-ft}$$

and

$$\Sigma F_y = 0 \qquad A_y - 240 = 0 \qquad A_y = 240 \text{ lb}$$

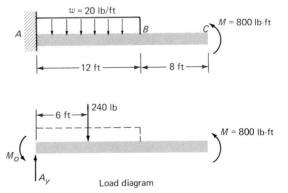

Figure 7.30

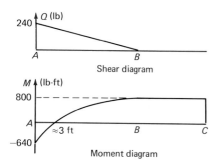

Figure 7.30

Shear Diagram:

Starting at point A with a value of 240 lb, the shear changes linearly between A and B. Thus,

$$Q_B = Q_A - \int_A^B w \, dx$$
$$= 240 - 240 = 0$$

The shear remains zero for the remainder of the beam since there are no other loads present.

Moment Diagram:

At A, $M_0 = -640$, where the negative sign is used due to our sign convention for bending moments. Thus,

$$M_B = M_A + \text{area under the } Q \text{ curve between } A \text{ and } B$$
$$= -640 + \tfrac{1}{2}(240)(12) = 800 \text{ lb-ft}$$

The moment between B and C remains 800 lb-ft and agrees with the couple at point C.

Example 7.4.3

Draw the shear and bending-moment diagrams for the beam in Figure 7.31.

Beam Reactions:

$$\Sigma M_B = 0 \qquad 20D_y - 200(5) - 200(10) - 200(30) = 0$$
$$D_y = 450 \text{ lb}$$

and

$$\Sigma F_y = 0 \qquad 200 + B_y - 200 + 450 - 200 = 0 \qquad B_y = -250 \text{ lb}$$
$$B_y = 250 \text{ lb} \downarrow$$

Shear Diagram:

Starting at A the shear $Q = 0$ and increases linearly between A and B. Thus, at B

$$Q_B = Q_A - \int_A^B w \, dx$$

Since w acts *upward* it is negative by the sign convention in equation (7.10). Thus,

$$Q_B = 0 + 20(10) = 200 \text{ lb}$$

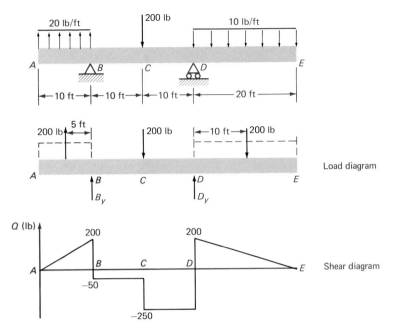

Figure 7.31

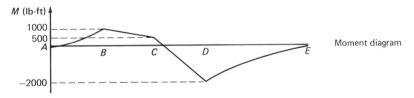

At B, there is a step change in shear due to the downward reaction at B. Between B and C, the shear is constant and undergoes a step change in shear at C and at D. From D to E, load is uniform so that

$$Q_E = Q_D - \int_D^E w\, dx$$

$$= 200 - 10(20) = 0 \qquad \text{(Checks)}$$

Moment Diagram:
Between A and B,

$$M_B = M_A + \int_A^B Q\, dx$$

$$= 0 + \tfrac{1}{2}(200)(10) = 1000 \text{ lb-ft}$$

Between B and C,

$$M_C = M_B + \int_B^C Q \, dx$$

$$= 1000 + (-50)(10) = 500 \text{ lb-ft}$$

Between C and D,

$$M_D = M_C + \int_C^D Q \, dx$$

$$= 500 + (-250)(10) = -2000 \text{ lb-ft}$$

Between D and E,

$$M_E = M_D + \int_D^E Q \, dx$$

$$= -2000 + \tfrac{1}{2}(200)(20) = 0 \quad \text{(Checks)}$$

Example 7.4.4

Draw the shear and bending-moment diagram for the beam in Figure 7.32.

Beam Reactions:

$$\Sigma M_A = 0 \qquad M_O - 300(8) - 100(20) = 0 \qquad M_O = 4400 \text{ lb-ft}$$

and

$$\Sigma F_y = 0 \qquad A_y - 300 - 100 = 0 \qquad A_y = 400 \text{ lb}$$

Shear Diagram:

Starting at A, $Q_A = 400$ lb. Thus,

$$Q_B = Q_A - \int_A^B w \, dx$$

$$= 400 - \tfrac{1}{2}(50)(12) = 100 \text{ lb}$$

The shape of the curve connecting Q_A and Q_B is second order (parabola) since the loading curve between A and B is first order (straight line). From B to C the shear remains constant at 100 lb and checks with the shear at C.

Moment Diagram:

Between A and B,

$$M_B = M_A + \int_A^B Q \, dx$$

To find the area under the shear curve between A and B, divide

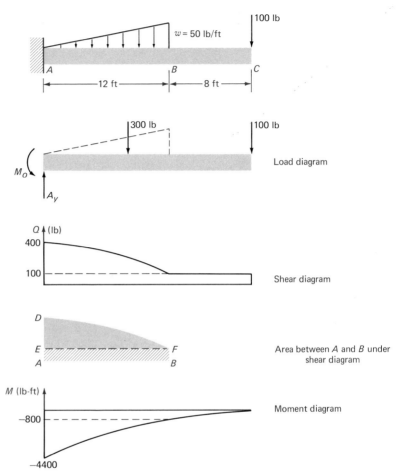

Figure 7.32

the area into area *DEF* and area *ABFE* as shown in Figure 7.32.

$$\text{Area of } DEF = \tfrac{2}{3}\,(DE)(EF) = \tfrac{2}{3}\,(400 - 100)(12) = 2400$$

$$\text{Area of } ABFE = 100(12) = 1200$$

$$\text{Total area} = 2400 + 1200 = 3600 \text{ lb-ft}$$

$$M_B = -4400 + 3600 = -800 \text{ lb-ft}$$

Between *B* and *C*,

$$M_C = M_B + \int_B^C Q\,dx$$

$$= -800 + 100(8) = 0 \qquad \text{(Checks)}$$

Problems

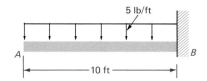

Figure 7.33

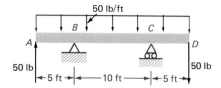

Figure 7.34

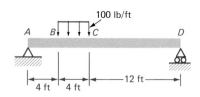

Figure 7.35

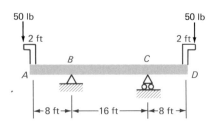

Figure 7.36

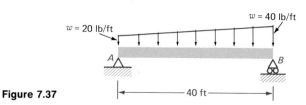

Figure 7.37

7.4.1 Draw the shear and bending-moment diagrams for the beam in Figure 7.19 (p. 233).

7.4.2 Draw the shear and bending-moment diagrams for the beam in Figure 7.20 (p. 233).

7.4.3 Draw the shear and bending-moment diagrams for the beam in Figure 7.21 (p. 233).

7.4.4 Draw the shear and bending-moment diagrams for the beam in Figure 7.22 (p. 233).

7.4.5 Obtain the shear and bending-moment diagrams for the beam in Figure 7.23 (p. 233).

7.4.6 Obtain the shear and bending-moment diagrams for the beam in Figure 7.24 (p. 233).

7.4.7 Draw the shear and bending-moment diagrams for the beam in Figure 7.25 (p. 233).

7.4.8 Draw the shear and bending-moment diagrams for the beam in Figure 7.26 (p. 233).

7.4.9 Using the integral approach obtain the shear and bending-moment diagrams for the beam in Figure 7.33.

7.4.10 Draw the shear and bending-moment diagrams for the beam in Figure 7.34.

7.4.11 By using the integral approach, obtain the shear and bending-moment diagrams for the beam in Figure 7.35.

7.4.12 Sketch the shear and bending-moment diagrams for Figure 7.36.

7.4.13 Find the magnitude and location of the maximum bending moment in the beam shown in Figure 7.37. Sketch the shear and bending-moment diagram.

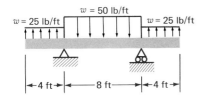

Figure 7.38

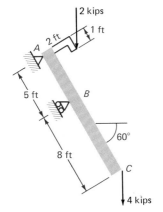

Figure 7.39

7.4.14 Sketch the shear and bending-moment diagrams for the beam in Figure 7.38.

7.4.15 A mathematical model of a fin stabilizer for surface ships is shown in Figure 7.39 subjected to two concentrated loads. Sketch the shear and bending-moment diagrams.

7.4.16 A trench 18 ft deep is supported on each side by sheet piling and braces as shown in Figure 7.40. Let $\gamma = 120$ lb/ft³ for the soil and consider a 5-ft section between the braces. Derive the shear and bending moment equations and draw the shear diagrams of the piling assuming it behaves as a cantilever beam.

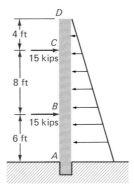

Figure 7.40

7.5 Summary

A   The important *ideas:*

1. A beam develops axial forces, shear forces, and bending moments throughout its span.

2. The shear diagram is the integral of the loading diagram.

3. The bending-moment diagram is the integral of the shear diagram.

B   The important *equations:*

$$Q_2 - Q_1 = -\int_{x_1}^{x_2} w\,dx \qquad (7.10)$$

$$M_2 - M_1 = \int_{x_1}^{x_2} Q\,dx \qquad (7.12)$$

Chapter 8
Friction

When one body moves relative to another with which it is in contact, a tangent frictional force tends to impede motion. In many cases, this frictional force helps to maintain equilibrium. In writing the equations of equilibrium we must therefore include this force. The particular type of frictional force that will concern us in this chapter is called dry or Coulomb friction.

8.1 Introduction

When a surface slides or rolls along another surface with which it is in contact, a force is developed that tends to oppose the motion of one body in relation to the other. This force is tangential to the plane of the surfaces and is referred to as friction. Fluid friction develops between layers of fluids, dry friction between rigid bodies in contact. If there is to be motion of one surface or body relative to another with which it is in contact, frictional force must be overcome by externally applied forces. Although in ideal systems friction is normally ignored, in *real* systems it must be accounted for and included in their analysis. While the occurence of friction has many advantages, as in wedges, brakes, clutches, belt drives, and even walking, in some cases it is more detrimental than useful. In the reentry of space capsules, for example, friction is a serious problem; and the results of friction on gears, bearings, and the like are certainly undesirable.

Friction results in the dissipation of energy in the form of heat. The real nature of friction is very complex and not entirely understood. It is known to be a function of surface roughness and of microscopic phenomena at the interface. We shall be concerned here with the macroscopic aspects of friction. Specifically, we will deal with dry, or Coulomb, friction as it occurs between the surfaces of two rigid bodies.

8.2 Coulomb or Dry Friction

A simple example of dry friction involves the sliding of a block along a rough surface. Assume a block to be at rest on the floor. Figure 8.1a shows the free-body diagram under this condition. Now assume a small force P applied as shown in Figure 8.1b. Although the block does not move, a force f appears which balances the applied force P. The force f is due to friction between the two contacting surfaces. As P is increased until the block begins to *just* move, f increases to its maximum value f_m. This is the instant of *impending motion* and is represented by Figure 8.1c. Once the block does move as shown in Figure 8.1d, f_m decreases to f_k, so that the force P necessary to sustain the motion of the block is less than that necessary to begin the motion. The maximum force f_m is known as the *static-friction force*, while f_k is the *kinetic-* or

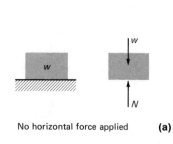

No horizontal force applied **(a)**

Figure 8.1

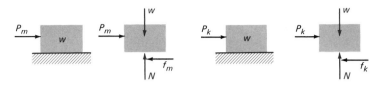

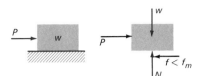

(b)   Horizontal force less than f_{max}

(c)   Horizontal force equal to f_{max}
Impending motion.

(d)   Horizontal force larger than f_{max}
Block moves.

sliding-friction force. These forces are shown in Figure 8.2.
From experimentation, it has been found that the static-friction force is proportional to the normal force N; thus,

$$f_m = \mu_0 N \qquad (8.1)$$

where μ_0 is the *coefficient of static friction.* The kinetic-friction force, also, is proportional to the normal force. That is,

$$f_k = \mu N \qquad (8.2)$$

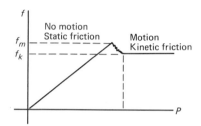

Figure 8.2

where μ is the *coefficient of kinetic* or *sliding friction.* Notice that both these forces are in a direction *opposite* to P, and therefore tend to oppose motion. Some commonly used values of μ_0 and μ appear in Table 8.1. The wide range of values given is due mainly to the difficulty of measuring the coefficient accurately and the great variability of surfaces.

Table 8.1
Values of μ_0 and μ

	μ_0	μ
Metal on stone	0.30–0.70	0.20–0.45
Metal on metal	0.15–0.60	0.10–0.40
Wood on wood	0.25–0.50	0.15–0.35
Wood on metal	0.20–0.60	0.15–0.40
Rubber on asphalt	0.70–0.90	0.50–0.60

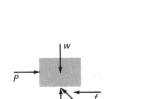

(a)

Figure 8.3

In the presence of frictional forces, the resultant reaction force R is a combination of N and f_m as shown in Figure 8.3a. If the motion is impending, then

$$R = \sqrt{N^2 + f_m^2} = N\sqrt{1 + \mu_0^2} \qquad (8.3a)$$

$$\tan \varphi_0 = \frac{f_m}{N} = \mu_0 \qquad (8.3b)$$

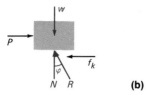

(b)

Figure 8.3

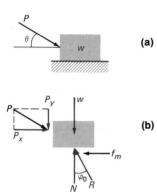

(a)

(b)

Figure 8.4

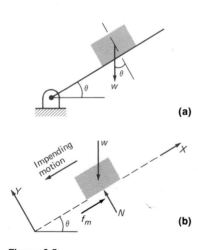

(a)

(b)

Figure 8.5

The angle φ_0 is called the *angle of static friction* or angle of *repose*. As soon as motion occurs, the forces are as shown in Figure 8.3b, so that

$$R = \sqrt{N^2 + f_k^2} = N\sqrt{1 + \mu^2} \qquad (8.4a)$$

$$\tan \varphi = \frac{f_k}{N} = \mu \qquad (8.4b)$$

where φ is the *angle of kinetic friction*. We note that $\varphi \le \varphi_0$. The normal force N can be computed by summing the forces in the vertical direction, and in this case, $N = w$.

The externally applied force P need not be a horizontal force. The block in Figure 8.4a is subjected to a force P which makes an angle θ with the horizontal. For the case of impending motion, a free-body diagram is drawn in Figure 8.4b. Summing the vertical forces gives us

$$N = w + P_y$$

and since

$$f_m = \mu_0 N$$

we have

$$f_m = \mu_0(w + P_y)$$

The magnitude of the reaction R is

$$R = \sqrt{N^2 + f_m^2} = (w + P_y)\sqrt{1 + \mu_0^2}$$

and the angle of repose is

$$\tan \varphi_0 = \frac{f_m}{N} = \mu_0$$

We note that although the magnitude of R changes for this case, its direction is the same as in the case where P is applied horizontally.

Static friction and its associated angle of repose may be viewed with the aid of an inclined plane. Assume that a block is resting on a plane that is at an angle θ with the horizontal as shown in Figure 8.5a. Allow the plane to be tilted slowly upward. We would now like to establish the maximum angle θ before the block begins to slide. First, a free-body diagram is drawn as shown in Figure 8.5b. We then assume that the plane has been tilted so that there exists impending motion. Summing the forces in the X and Y direction gives us

$$N = w \cos \theta$$

$$f_m = w \sin \theta$$

But we already know that

$$f_m = \mu_0 N$$

$$= \mu_0 w \cos \theta$$

so that

$$f_m = w \sin \theta = \mu_0 w \cos \theta$$

which yields

$$\tan \theta = \mu_0$$

Problems involving dry friction can be conveniently divided into three categories as follows:

1. The condition of impending motion exists so that the frictional force is static and $f_m = \mu_0 N$. This force must be included when drawing the free-body diagram.
2. The frictional force f is less than the static-frictional force f_m. The frictional force is assumed to exist in the free-body diagram and then computed from the conditions of equilibrium. It is often of interest to know whether f is sufficient to maintain the body at rest.
3. Motion is not impending but has occurred, so that the frictional force is kinetic and $f = f_k = \mu N$.

Our concern in this text shall be limited to the first two cases.

Example 8.2.1

A block weighing 100 lb is pulled by a rope as shown in Figure 8.6a. The coefficient of static friction is 0.6. (a) Determine the tension needed in the rope to start the block moving. (b) If $T = 50$ lb what is the frictional force?

(a) The force T must overcome the friction force f_m as shown in Figure 8.6b. Thus,

$$T = f_m = \mu_0 N$$

The normal force is $N = w$ so that

$$T = \mu_0 w = 0.6(100)$$

$$= 60 \text{ lb} \qquad\qquad \text{Answer}$$

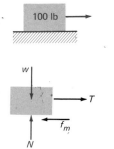

(a)

(b)

Figure 8.6

(b) In this case,

$$f = T = 50 \text{ lb} \qquad \text{Answer}$$

Example 8.2.2

In the previous example, assume that the rope makes an angle of 45° with the horizontal as shown in Figure 8.7a. What is the tension T that will move the block?

(a)

The force is again that which must overcome the static-friction force as shown in Figure 8.7b. Thus,

$$T \cos 45° = f_m = \mu_0 N$$

Summing vertical forces gives

$$N = w - T \sin 45°$$

(b)

so that

$$T \cos 45° = \mu_0 N = \mu_0 (w - T \sin 45°)$$

$$T = \frac{\mu_0 w}{\cos 45° + \mu_0 \sin 45°}$$

$$= \frac{(0.6)(100)}{0.707 + (0.6)(0.707)}$$

$$= 53.1 \text{ lb} \qquad \text{Answer}$$

Figure 8.7

Example 8.2.3

In an experiment, a 100-lb weight is placed on an inclined plane. When the angle of the plane is 30°, the weight begins to slide away. What magnitude of the force P is necessary to prevent the weight in Figure 8.8a from sliding away when the angle is 45°? What is the normal reaction force?

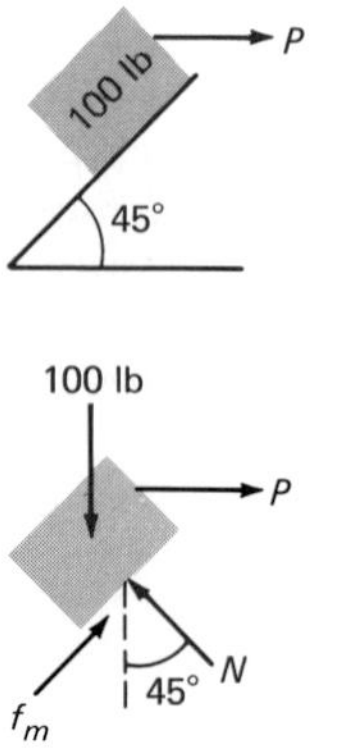

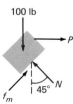

(a)

The free-body diagram of the weight on the inclined plane is shown in Figure 8.8b. Summing the forces in the vertical and horizontal directions gives us

$$\Sigma F_y = N \cos 45° + f_m \sin 45° - 100 = 0$$

$$\Sigma F_x = f_m \cos 45° + P - N \sin 45° = 0$$

(b) We also know that $\tan 30° = \mu_0 = 0.577$ and

$$f_m = 0.577 N$$

Figure 8.8

so that substituting in the two equations yields

$$N(\cos 45° + 0.577 \sin 45°) - 100 = 0$$

$$N(0.577 \cos 45° - \sin 45°) + P = 0$$

Solving the first equation gives

$$N = \frac{100}{\cos 45° + 0.577 \sin 45°}$$

$$= 89.7 \text{ lb} \qquad\qquad \text{Answer}$$

From the second equation we get

$$P = 89.7(\sin 45° - 0.577 \cos 45°)$$

$$= 26.8 \text{ lb} \qquad\qquad \text{Answer}$$

Problems

Figure 8.9

8.2.1 What force P must be applied so that block A in Figure 8.9 just begins to move?

8.2.2 Determine the force P necessary to begin moving the 100-lb block up the incline shown in Figure 8.10.

8.2.3 Determine the force P necessary to hold the 100-lb block on the incline shown in Figure 8.10.

8.2.4 The 200-lb block shown in Figure 8.11 is to be pulled up the slope. Determine the angle and magnitude of the minimum force necessary to achieve this. The coefficient of static friction is 0.3.

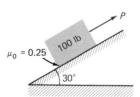

Figure 8.10

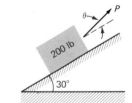

Figure 8.11

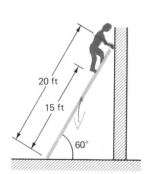

Figure 8.12

8.2.5 For the block in problem 8.2.4, determine the minimum force necessary to hold it in the position shown if θ is zero.

8.2.6 A 150-lb man has climbed 15 ft up a ladder weighing 50 lb when the ladder begins to slide as shown in Figure 8.12. What is the coefficient of friction between the ladder and the wall as well as the floor assuming they are equal?

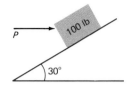

Figure 8.13

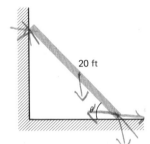

Figure 8.14

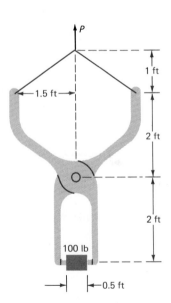

Figure 8.18

8.2.7 Determine the value of P in Figure 8.13 necessary to (a) hold the block and (b) move the block up the incline. Assume $\mu_0 = 0.25$.

8.2.8 A 50-lb beam, shown in Figure 8.14, is placed against a wall. If $\mu_0 = 0.2$ for all contacting surface, determine the minimum value of θ when the beam just begins to slide.

8.2.9 In another experiment, the beam of Figure 8.14 is put against a different wall. The beam then slides when $\theta = 30°$. If μ_0 is assumed zero between wall and beam, what is μ_0 between the floor and beam?

8.2.10 A pair of tongs is used to hold a small steel cylinder as shown in Figure 8.15. Determine the μ_0 that is necessary for the cylinder not to slip. Neglect the weight of the cylinder.

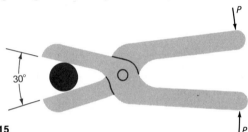

Figure 8.15

8.2.11 A 200-lb crate is pushed by a man as shown in Figure 8.16. Determine the direction and the magnitude of the force P with which the man must push in order to start the crate moving but without tipping about point A. Let $\mu_0 = 0.25$.

8.2.12 If the force P for problem 8.2.11 is applied 5 ft from the floor, determine values for θ and P that allow the crate to be pushed without tipping.

8.2.13 A 100-lb roller is supported as shown in Figure 8.17. Determine the coefficient of static friction and the tension T necessary for equilibrium.

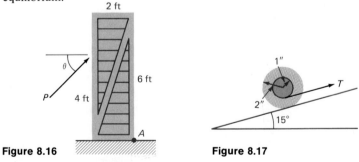

Figure 8.16   **Figure 8.17**

8.2.14 A 100-lb block is to be lifted by a pair of tongs as shown in Figure 8.18. What must be the coefficient of static friction in order to prevent the block from slipping?

8.3 Wedges and Screws

Machines, as mentioned in Chapter 4, are structures used for transmitting forces. A wedge, perhaps the simplest of machines, is useful for transmitting large forces. Screws can also be considered as machines, since they can be used for transmitting power, e.g., in the case of a jack or press. The following development makes clear the importance of friction to these two machines.

Wedges

Consider the wedge A, weighing w_A lb, that is to be used for lifting the block weighing w lb as shown in Figure 8.19a. We assume μ_0 to be the coefficient of static friction between all surfaces. This need not be the case actually, but the assumption simplifies our discussion. The free-body diagrams of the block and wedge are shown in Figures 8.19b and c. Since we are assuming impending motion, the resultant force on the surface of the wedge will be in a direction opposing the motion of the wedge. From the free-body diagrams the various forces are

$$f_B = \mu_0 N_B \qquad f_A = \mu_0 N_A \qquad f_C = \mu_0 N_C$$

We would now like to obtain the force P that is necessary to move the block. The total number of unknowns are N_A, N_B, N_C, and P. These unknown forces can be obtained from the conditions of equilibrium applied to the block and wedge separately so that we obtain a total of four independent equations. Notice that we are using f_A, f_B, and f_C to denote the frictional force f_m at surfaces A, B, and C.

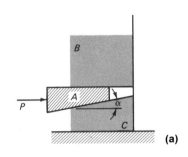

(a)

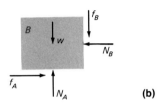

(b)

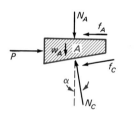

(c)

Figure 8.19

Screws

The screw can be analyzed by applying the method developed earlier for the case of a block sliding on an inclined plane. Consider the screw shown in Figure 8.20a, where an axial force w (which includes the weight of the screw) is applied. We isolate a small element of the screw and draw its free-body diagram as shown in Figure 8.20b. We note that this small element of the screw will slide on the nut strip which is stationary. The screw, when turned relative to the nut, will be subjected to a friction force f. Moving the screw up or down is analogous to raising or lowering the load w along an

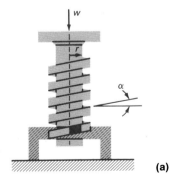

(a)

Figure 8.20

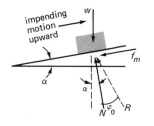

(b)

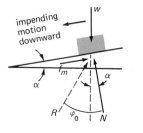

(c)

Figure 8.20

inclined plane as shown in Figures 8.20b and c. For the case of raising the load w, sum the forces in the vertical direction thus,

$$\Sigma F_y = -f_m \sin \alpha + N \cos \alpha - w = 0$$

Assuming that the motion is impending, $f_m = \mu_0 N$, so that the above equation becomes

$$N(\cos \alpha - \mu_0 \sin \alpha) - w = 0$$

and therefore

$$N = \frac{w}{\cos \alpha - \mu_0 \sin \alpha} \qquad (8.5)$$

The net horizontal force is obtained by summing the forces in Figure 8.20b in the X direction, that is,

$$-f_m \cos \alpha - N \sin \alpha = -N(\mu_0 \cos \alpha + \sin \alpha)$$

and this force gives rise to a moment about the axis of the screw. Since the moment arm is r, the moment involved in raising the load is

$$M_U = Nr(\mu_0 \cos \alpha + \sin \alpha)$$

Substituting for N from equation (8.5) we obtain

$$M_U = wr \frac{\mu_0 \cos \alpha + \sin \alpha}{\cos \alpha - \mu_0 \sin \alpha} \qquad (8.6)$$

and since $\tan \varphi_0 = \mu_0$ we have

$$M_U = wr \frac{\tan \varphi_0 \cos \alpha + \sin \alpha}{\cos \alpha - \tan \varphi_0 \sin \alpha}$$

$$= wr \tan (\varphi_0 + \alpha) \qquad (8.7)$$

Figure 8.20c shows the free-body diagram of the screw element for impending downward motion. If no moment is applied to the screw, and $\varphi_0 > \alpha$, the screw remains in place and is self-locking. In order to lower the screw, the lowering moment is given by

$$M_L = wr \tan (\varphi_0 - \alpha) \qquad (8.8)$$

Example 8.3.1

A 5-lb wedge is to be driven between two 50-lb plates as shown in Figure 8.21a. What force P must be applied to move the

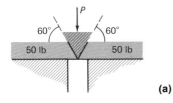

(a)

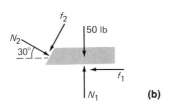

(b)

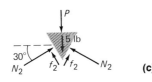

(c)

Figure 8.21

plates? Assume that $\mu_0 = 0.5$ between all the surfaces.

First, a free-body diagram of the right plate is drawn as shown in Figure 8.21b. Summing the forces in the vertical and horizontal directions gives us

$$\Sigma F_y = N_1 - 50 - N_2 \cos 60° - f_2 \cos 30° = 0$$

$$\Sigma F_x = N_2 \cos 30° - f_2 \cos 60° - f_1 = 0$$

Since $f_1 = 0.5 N_1$ and $f_2 = 0.5 N_2$,

$$N_1 - N_2(\cos 60° + 0.5 \cos 30°) = 50$$

$$0.5 N_1 + N_2(0.5 \cos 60° - \cos 30°) = 0$$

Solving for N_1 and N_2, we obtain

$$N_1 = 206 \text{ lb} \qquad N_2 = 167.2 \text{ lb}$$

Now we can draw the free-body diagram of the wedge as shown in Figure 8.21c. Summing the forces in the vertical direction gives us

$$\Sigma F_y = -P - 5 + 2N_2 \cos 60° + 2\mu_0 N_2 \cos 30° = 0$$

and substituting for N_2, we obtain

$$P + 5 - 2(167.2)0.5 - 2(0.5)(167.2)(0.866) = 0$$

$$P = 307 \text{ lb} \qquad\qquad \text{Answer}$$

Example 8.3.2

The jackscrew having 5 threads/in. shown in Figure 8.22a is to be used to lift a weight. The maximum magnitude of force P which produces the uplifting moment is 500 lb. If $\mu_0 = 0.3$, what weight w can be lifted?

Since the screw moves through 5 turns and travels 1 in., it moves 0.2 in. per turn. Having this information, we can determine the angle α. Therefore, as shown in Figure 8.22b,

$$\ell = 0.2 \text{ in.}$$

which is the pitch of the thread. The pitch ℓ is related to α by $\tan \alpha = \ell/2\pi r$ so that

$$\tan \alpha = \frac{0.2}{(0.5)2\pi} = 0.0637$$

$$\alpha = 3.6°$$

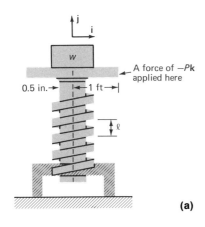

(a)

(b)

Figure 8.22

Also

$$\varphi = \tan^{-1} 0.3 = 16.7°$$

Now we use equation (8.7),

$$(500)(1) = w \frac{(0.5)}{12} \tan (16.7 + 3.6)°$$

$$w = 32,400 \text{ lb} \qquad \text{Answer}$$

Problems

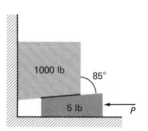

Figure 8.23

8.3.1 Determine the horizontal force P necessary to move the 1000-lb block shown in Figure 8.23. The coefficient of static friction is 0.3 between all surfaces.

8.3.2 A 10-lb wedge is used to lift the 5000-lb block shown in Figure 8.24. The coefficient of static friction is 0.2 between all surfaces. Determine the value of P.

8.3.3 Determine the value of P required for moving the block of problem 8.3.1 if $\mu_0 = 0.1$ between all surfaces.

8.3.4 A wedge is used to move the two 200-lb blocks shown in Figure 8.25. Determine the value of P if $\mu_0 = 0.3$ between all surfaces shown.

8.3.5 A wedge is used to split wood as shown in Figure 8.26. Determine the value of θ if it is desired that the wedge should not slip out once inserted. Assume $\mu_0 = 0.7$.

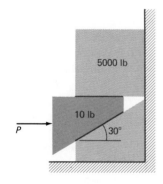

Figure 8.24

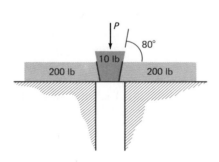

Figure 8.25

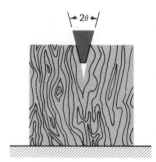

Figure 8.26

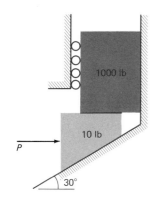

Figure 8.27

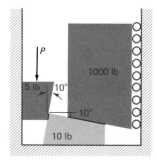

Figure 8.28

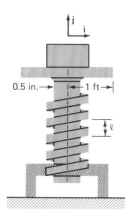

Figure 8.29

8.3.6 A 1000-lb block is moved up by a wedge as shown in Figure 8.27. If $\mu_0 = 0.3$ for all surfaces, determine the necessary force P.

8.3.7 Two wedges are used, in the arrangement shown in Figure 8.28, for raising a 1000-lb block. When a downward force P is applied to the 5-lb wedge it causes the block to rise. Determine the necessary force P. Let $\mu = 0.1$ between all forces.

8.3.8 A jackscrew having 4 threads/in. is to be used to lift a weight. If a 10,000-lb weight must be lifted and $\mu_0 = 0.4$, what force P must be applied to the end of the lever shown in Figure 8.29.

8.3.9 If a 100 lb-ft moment is applied to a jackscrew of the type illustrated in Figure 8.29 in order to lift 10,000 lb, what is the coefficient of static friction?

8.3.10 One end of a car is to be lifted by the jackscrew shown in Figure 8.30. The jackscrew is single-square-threaded, the pitch is 0.18 in., the radius is 0.75 in., and $\mu_0 = 0.3$. If the weight to be lifted is 750 lb, what moment must be applied to the jackscrew?

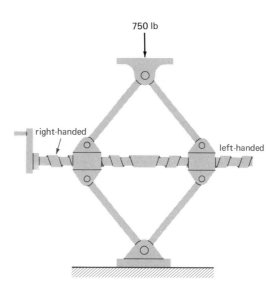

Figure 8.30

8.3.11 The jackscrew in problem 8.3.10 is slightly greased so that the coefficient of static friction is decreased by 20%. What is the moment required to lift the 750 lb weight?

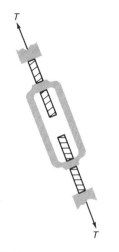

Figure 8.31

Figure 8.32

8.3.12 The turnbuckle shown in Figure 8.31 supports a tension of 500 lb. The screws are square-threaded, pitch is 0.18 in., mean radius is 0.75 in., and $\mu_0 = 0.25$. Determine the moment that must be applied on the turnbuckle to loosen it.

8.3.13 For the turnbuckle of problem 8.3.12, determine the moment that must be applied to loosen it if the tension is 1000 lb and $\mu_0 = 0.3$.

8.3.14 The clamp shown in Figure 8.32 holds two pieces of angle iron. Determine the forces exerted on the pieces of iron if a 50 lb-ft moment is applied to tighten the clamp. Assume that the clamp is single-square-threaded, pitch is 0.12 in., mean radius is 0.375 in., and $\mu_0 = 0.25$.

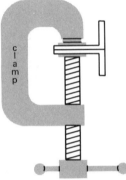

8.3.15 For the clamp of problem 8.3.14, determine the torque required to loosen the clamp if the pieces of iron are pressed with a force of 1000 lb.

8.4 Belt Friction

In designing drives and brakes, engineers make frequent use of ropes and belts. Since, when so employed, ropes and belts can slip over surfaces with which they are in contact, the phenomena of friction occurs.

Consider a belt wrapped around a drum as shown in Figure 8.33a. The drum is subjected to the two belt tensions as well as a bearing reaction R and a moment M necessary to prevent rotation. We wish to establish the relationship between the two belt tensions at the instant of impending motion. Owing to the direction of M, we note that $T_2 > T_1$. A relationship between the tensions can be derived from the free-body diagram of the differential element of the belt shown in Figure 8.33b. Summing the forces in the X direction gives us

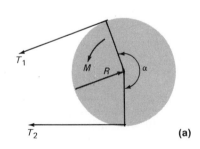

(a)

Figure 8.33

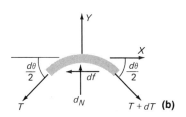

$$\Sigma F_x = -T \cos \frac{d\theta}{2} + (T + dT) \cos \frac{d\theta}{2} - df = 0$$

If $d\theta$ is small, $\cos(d\theta/2) \approx 1$, and the above equation yields

$$df = dT$$

Since

$$df = \mu_0 \, dN$$

we have

$$dN = \frac{dT}{\mu_0} \tag{8.9}$$

Now we sum the forces in the Y direction and noting that $\sin(d\theta/2) \approx d\theta/2$ for small $d\theta$, we obtain

$$\Sigma F_y = dN - T \sin \frac{d\theta}{2} - (T + dT) \sin \frac{d\theta}{2} = 0$$

$$dN = T \, d\theta \tag{8.10}$$

where the term $dT \, d\theta$ is negligible, and therefore set equal to zero. Equating the right sides of equations (8.9) and (8.10) gives us

$$\frac{dT}{\mu_0} = T \, d\theta \quad \text{or} \quad \frac{dT}{T} = \mu_0 \, d\theta$$

Integrating this expression over the length of belt in contact with the drum,

$$\int_{T_1}^{T_2} \frac{dT}{T} = \int_0^{\alpha} \mu_0 \, d\theta$$

$$\log \frac{T_2}{T_1} = \mu_0 \alpha$$

or

$$\frac{T_2}{T_1} = e^{\mu_0 \alpha} \tag{8.11}$$

This gives the ratio of the two tensions when the rope or belt is about to slip. Note that α is expressed in radians and represents the contact angle. If the rope or belt is wrapped around n times, then $\alpha = 2\pi n$ radians. Another observation to be made is that the equation for tension is independent of the drum radius. For this reason the equation may be applied

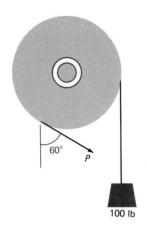

60°

P

100 lb

Figure 8.34

to noncircular cross sections as long as the correct angle is used. The analysis of vee belts is carried out in much the same way and is illustrated in an example problem.

Example 8.4.1

A rope is used to lift a 100-lb weight using the locked pulley shown in Figure 8.34. If $\mu = 0.2$, determine the P necessary to begin lifting the weight.

The tension force P must be greater than the weight since frictional forces have to be overcome. The angle of contact is

$$\alpha = 240 \left(\frac{\pi}{180} \right) = 4.19 \text{ radians}$$

From equation (8.11) we get

$$\frac{P}{100} = e^{(4.19)(0.2)} = e^{0.84} = 2.31$$

$$P = 231 \text{ lb} \qquad \text{Answer}$$

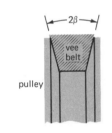

2β

vee belt

pulley

(a)

Example 8.4.2

If, in example 8.4.1, a vee belt is used instead of a rope, as shown in Figure 8.35a, what force is necessary to lift the weight?

A free-body diagram of a differential element of the vee belt is shown in Figure 8.35b. Summing the forces in the X and Y directions gives us

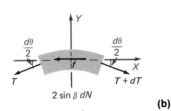

$\frac{d\theta}{2}$ Y $\frac{d\theta}{2}$

f X

T $T + dT$

$2 \sin \beta \, dN$

(b)

$$\Sigma F_x = -T \cos \frac{d\theta}{2} + (T + dT) \cos \frac{d\theta}{2} - 2 \, \mu_0 \, dN = 0$$

$$\Sigma F_y = T \sin \frac{d\theta}{2} + (T + dT) \sin \frac{d\theta}{2} - 2 \sin \beta \, dN = 0$$

Since $d\theta$ is small, we set $\cos (d\theta/2) \approx 1$, $\sin d\theta/2 \approx d\theta/2$, and we neglect terms like $dT \, d\theta$ to obtain,

$$dT = 2\mu_0 \, dN$$

$$T \, d\theta = 2 \, dN \sin \beta$$

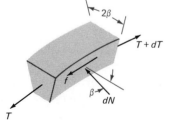

2β

$T + dT$

f

β dN

T

Figure 8.35

Solving these equations for dN and equating, we obtain

$$\frac{dT}{2\mu_0} = \frac{T \, d\theta}{2 \sin \beta} \qquad \text{or} \qquad \frac{dT}{T} = \left(\frac{\mu_0}{\sin \beta} \right) d\theta$$

We now define the effective friction as

$$\mu_{0v} = \frac{\mu_0}{\sin \beta}$$

so that

$$\frac{dT}{T} = \mu_{0v} d\theta$$

Integrating this differential equation,

$$\int_{T_1}^{T_2} \frac{dT}{T} = \int_0^{\alpha} \mu_{0v} \, d\theta$$

so that

$$\frac{T_2}{T_1} = e^{\mu_{0v}\alpha}$$

This result is similar to the flat-belt example except that we now use the effective friction μ_{0v}. For the values in example 8.4.1 and assuming that $2\beta = 60°$, we have

$$\mu_{0v} = \frac{\mu_0}{\sin \beta} = \frac{0.2}{\sin 30°} = 0.4$$

and

$$\frac{P}{100} = e^{(4.19)(0.4)} = e^{1.675} = 5.34$$

$$P = 534 \text{ lb} \qquad\qquad \text{Answer}$$

Problems

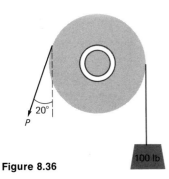

Figure 8.36

8.4.1 Determine the force P necessary to hold the 100-lb weight shown in Figure 8.36. The coefficient of static friction is 0.4.

8.4.2 In problem 8.4.1, determine the P necessary to raise the weight.

8.4.3 A flat belt is used to transmit the 50 lb-ft torque developed by the motor shown in Figure 8.37. Determine the tensions in the belt. Assume that there is no slippage. The coefficient of static friction is 0.4.

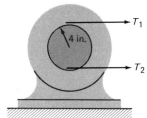

Figure 8.37

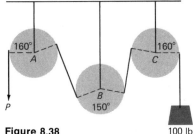

Figure 8.38

100 lb

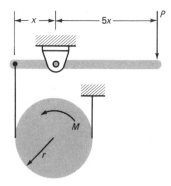

Figure 8.41

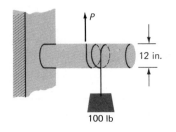

100 lb

Figure 8.42

8.4.4 In problem 8.4.3, if the maximum tension the belt can withstand is 1000 lb, determine the largest torque that can be transmitted.

8.4.5 Determine the force P necessary to (a) hold and (b) raise the 100-lb weight shown in Figure 8.38. Let the coefficient of static friction be 0.2 between the rope and each pulley.

8.4.6 The motor shown in Figure 8.39 is used to transmit 100 lb-ft of torque. If $\mu_0 = 0.2$, determine the tensions in the belt. Assume that there is no belt slippage and that the belt is flat. Let $\theta = 0°$.

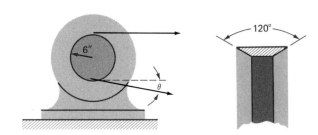

Figure 8.39   **Figure 8.40**

8.4.7 Determine the tensions in the belt for $\theta = 30°$ in problem 8.4.6.

8.4.8 Verify the equation for vee belts derived in example 8.4.2.

8.4.9 If the vee belt shown in Figure 8.40 is used in place of the flat belt of problem 8.4.3, determine the tensions in the belt.

8.4.10 If the vee belt shown in Figure 8.40 is used in place of the flat belt of problem 8.4.6, determine the tension in the belt for $\theta = 0$.

8.4.11 For the brake drum shown in Figure 8.41, derive a relation between the applied force P and the moment M due to the frictional force applied to the drum. Let $\mu_0 = 0.5$.

8.4.12 For problem 8.4.11, compute M if $P = 20$ lb, $r = 6$ in., and $\mu = 0.5$.

8.4.13 A 100-lb weight is suspended by a rod whose cross section is circular of radius 6 in. as shown in Figure 8.42. If $\mu_0 = 0.25$, determine the P necessary to (a) hold the weight and (b) raise the weight.

8.4.14 In problem 8.4.13, if 500 lb is necessary to raise the weight, determine the coefficient of friction.

8.5 Bearings

Bearings are commonly used to support rotating machinery consisting of shafts and axles. Although a small amount of lubricant is often used, analyses using the methods developed for cases of dry friction provide satisfactory approximations. Bearings can be classified into journal bearings and thrust bearings. Journal bearings give lateral support to shafts; thrust bearings supply axial or thrust support.

Journal Bearings

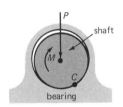

(a)

Consider the journal bearing, shown in Figure 8.43a, that supports a shaft which is rotating uniformly. This shaft requires a torque or moment to maintain its rotation. A radial load P causes the shaft to touch the bearing at C and thereby gives rise to a reaction force consisting of the normal force N and the friction force f_k. From the free-body diagram in Figure 8.43b, we have, for equilibrium,

$$R = P$$

where the force R is tangent to the circle with radius r_f. This circle is called the *friction circle*. Summing the moments about O gives us

$$\Sigma M_O = M - f_k r = 0$$

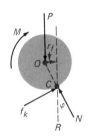

(b)

and since $f_k = \mu R$

$$M = \mu R r$$

Figure 8.43

where the kinetic-friction force is used owing to the existence of rotational motion. The moment necessary to maintain uniform motion of the shaft is, therefore,

$$M = \mu P r \qquad (8.12)$$

Thrust Bearings

Thrust bearings are used for providing axial support to shafts and axles. In general, there are two types of thrust bearings— end bearings and collar bearings. In the former, the shaft end rotates in a collar which is stationary so that friction is produced primarily between the shaft end and the collar. In collar bearings, friction occurs between two ring-shaped areas

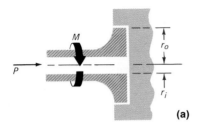

(a)

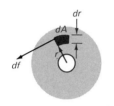

(b)

Figure 8.44

that are in contact. It is worth noting that friction developed in thrust bearings is also found in clutch plates and disk brakes.

By way of example of a thrust bearing, consider a hollow rotating shaft whose end is in contact with a fixed bearing as shown in Figure 8.44a. Let us assume that the hollow shaft is cylindrical with outer radius r_o and inner radius r_i. The force P keeps the surfaces in contact, while M is the torque necessary to sustain uniform rotation. The area in contact is

$$A = \pi(r_o^2 - r_i^2)$$

and, therefore, the pressure p between the surfaces is

$$p = \frac{P}{A} = \frac{P}{\pi(r_o^2 - r_i^2)}$$

The normal force on a small area dA is $p\,dA$, so that the friction force df, as shown in Figure 8.44b, is

$$df = \mu p\,dA$$

and the moment produced by this frictional force is

$$dM = r\,df = r\mu p\,dA$$

We recall that the differential area $dA = r\,d\theta\,dr$ so that the total moment becomes

$$M = \int_0^{2\pi} \int_{r_i}^{r_o} \mu p r^2\,d\theta\,dr$$

Integrating this yields

$$M = \frac{2}{3}\mu P \frac{r_o^3 - r_i^3}{r_o^2 - r_i^2} \tag{8.13}$$

which is the moment necessary to sustain the rotation. If the contact area is the entire disk, then

$$M = \tfrac{2}{3}\,\mu P r_o \tag{8.14}$$

Problems

8.5.1 The shaft of a motor is fitted in a bearing as shown in Figure 8.45. If the motor shaft exerts a moment of 1 lb-ft to start rotation, determine μ_0 between the shaft and bearing at each of two supports. Assume that the motor and shaft weighs 30 lb.

8.5.2 Verify equation (8.13) by performing the double integration on the previous equation.

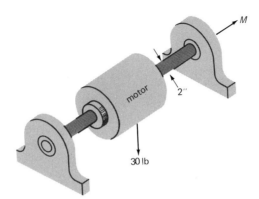

Figure 8.45

8.5.3 Determine an expression for the moment M necessary to begin turning a sander, shown in Figure 8.46, under an axial load of P lb. Assume that the pressure p between the sander and floor is constant and the coefficient of friction is μ_0.

8.5.4 In problem 8.5.3, obtain the moment necessary to begin turning the sander if $P = 75$ lb, $\mu_0 = 0.3$, $r = 6$ in.

8.5.5 The drum of 1-ft radius shown in Figure 8.47 is used to hoist a 500-lb block. The drum and shaft weigh 100 lb and $\mu = 0.3$. Determine the moment that must be applied to the drum shaft in order to raise the weight at uniform speed.

8.5.6 In problem 8.5.5, if $\mu = 0.25$, what is the moment necessary to overcome friction at each of the two bearings?

8.5.7 The thrust P is supported by the flat collar bearing shown in Figure 8.48. The thrust is 100 lb and $\mu = 0.1$. Determine the moment necessary to maintain constant speed of rotation.

8.5.8 If the maximum moment is 56 lb-in. in problem 8.5.7 and $\mu = 0.1$, what is the maximum thrust that can be supported?

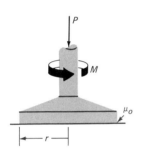

Figure 8.46

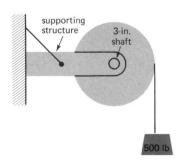

Figure 8.47

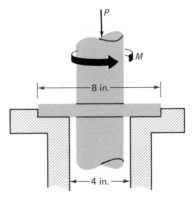

Figure 8.48

8.6 Summary

A   The important *ideas:*

1. Dry frictional force is proportional to the normal force. The proportionality constant is the coefficient of friction.

2. The coefficient of static friction is greater than the coefficient of kinetic friction.

3. Use μ_0 as the coefficient of friction for impending motion.

4. The angle of repose is the maximum angle to which a plane can be tilted before a block on the plane will begin to slide.

B   The important *equations:*

$$f_m = \mu_0 N \tag{8.1}$$

$$R = N\sqrt{1 + \mu_0^2} \tag{8.3a}$$

$$\tan \varphi_0 = \mu_0 \tag{8.3b}$$

$$M_U = wr \tan (\varphi_0 + \alpha) \tag{8.7}$$

$$M_L = wr \tan (\varphi_0 - \alpha) \tag{8.8}$$

$$\frac{T_2}{T_1} = e^{\mu_0 \alpha} \tag{8.11}$$

$$M = \mu P r \tag{8.12}$$

$$M = \frac{2}{3} \mu P \frac{r_o^3 - r_i^3}{r_o^2 - r_i^2} \tag{8.13}$$

Chapter 9
Special
Topics

The principle of virtual work, discussed in this chapter, is another method for obtaining the equations of equilibrium of rigid bodies and structures. Once the equilibrium of the structure is established, the stability of equilibrium is ascertained by considering the potential energy of the body.

9.1 Introduction

To this point, we have studied static equilibrium by means of the basic equations of statics, from which we have computed the forces and couples required to maintain the equilibrium of a body. The principle of virtual work is another method for studying static equilibrium. Its major advantage is found in treating complicated problems. As an introduction to this principle, we shall define what we mean by the concepts of work, virtual displacements, and virtual work.

Once the equilibrium of a body is established, it is often necessary to know whether the body is in a stable or unstable equilibrium position. We will treat this special topic by considering the behavior of the potential energy of the body in the neighborhood of its static equilibrium positions.

The topics covered in this chapter are very useful when applied to problems in statics. However, it is worth noting that they are especially important in the study of dynamics and, consequently, form the foundation for the development of some advanced techniques in dynamics.

9.2 The Concept of Work

Forces

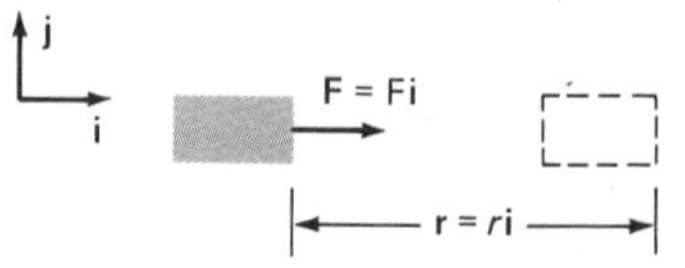

Consider a block, such as that in Figure 9.1, that moves through a displacement $\mathbf{r} = r\mathbf{i}$ due to a constant force $\mathbf{F} = F\mathbf{i}$. The *work* done by the force $\mathbf{F}$ on the block is

$$\text{Work} = W = \mathbf{F} \cdot \mathbf{r}$$

$$= F\mathbf{i} \cdot r\mathbf{i} = Fr \qquad (9.1)$$

We see that the work is a scalar quantity and the usual units are ft-lb.

Let us now consider a particle P moving along some path under the action of a force $\mathbf{F}$ as shown in Figure 9.2. The figure shows the particle P at some instant along its path and its differential displacement $d\mathbf{r}$. The work done by $\mathbf{F}$ in this differential displacement is

$$dW = \mathbf{F} \cdot d\mathbf{r} \qquad (9.2)$$

This differential element of work is, therefore, the projection of $\mathbf{F}$ on the differential displacement $d\mathbf{r}$. This agrees with our

Figure 9.1

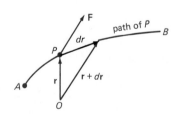

Figure 9.2

earlier discussion of a dot product. Consequently, the total work done by the force **F** as *P* moves from position *A* to position *B* is:

$$W = \int_A^B \mathbf{F} \cdot d\mathbf{r} \tag{9.3}$$

Equation (9.3) is an example of a line integral and is the general form of the expression for the work done by a force **F**. We see that it reduces to equation (9.1) when the force is of constant magnitude and acts in the same direction as the displacement of the particle.

If there is more than one force acting on the body, the total work is the summation of the work done by each force. Thus, if there are *n* forces acting on the body,

$$\mathbf{F} = \mathbf{F}_1 + \mathbf{F}_2 + \cdots + \mathbf{F}_n$$

then the total work is given by

$$W = \int_A^B \mathbf{F} \cdot d\mathbf{r} = \int_A^B (\mathbf{F}_1 + \mathbf{F}_2 + \cdots + \mathbf{F}_n) \cdot d\mathbf{r} \tag{9.4}$$

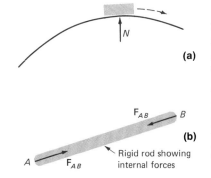

(a)

(b)

Rigid rod showing internal forces

Figure 9.3

The weight of a body, friction, and externally applied forces are examples of forces that do work when a body moves from one position to another. On the other hand, there are forces that, because of physical constraints, do no work. These forces are associated with what we call "workless constraints." Two examples of workless constraints are shown in Figure 9.3. In Figure 9.3a, the normal force **N** is always perpendicular to the path of the body, so that this force does no work. In the case of the rigid rod *AB* with the internal force F_{AB} acting at each joint, as seen in Figure 9.3b, it can be shown that since the rod does not deform, the net work done by these forces is zero even though the rod itself may move through a displacement.

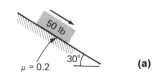

(a)

Figure 9.4

Example 9.2.1

A 50-lb block is sliding down an inclined plane as shown in Figure 9.4a. The coefficient of kinetic friction between the block and the plane is 0.20. Find the work done on the block as it slides a distance of 10 ft.

Figure 9.4

(b)

The free-body diagram of the block is shown in Figure 9.4b. The total force acting on the particle is written as

$$\mathbf{F} = w(\sin 30°\,\mathbf{i} - \cos 30°\,\mathbf{j}) + N\mathbf{j} - \mu N\mathbf{i} \qquad d\mathbf{r} = dx\,\mathbf{i}$$

therefore

$$W = \int_0^{10} [w(\sin 30°\,\mathbf{i} - \cos 30°\,\mathbf{j}) + N\mathbf{j} - \mu N\mathbf{i}] \cdot (dx\,\mathbf{i})$$

$$= \int_0^{10} (w\,\sin 30° - \mu N)\,dx$$

Note that the force $N\mathbf{j}$, which is a workless constraint, does not contribute to the work. Since the block does not leave the inclined plane,

$$\Sigma F_y = 0 \qquad N - w\,\cos 30° = 0$$

and

$$N = w\,\cos 30°$$

therefore

$$W = \int_0^{10} (w\,\sin 30° - \mu N)\,dx$$

$$= \int_0^{10} (w\,\sin 30° - \mu w\,\cos 30°)\,dx$$

$$= \int_0^{10} [50(0.5) - 0.2(50)(0.866)]\,dx$$

$$= \int_0^{10} (16.34)\,dx = 163.4\ \text{ft-lb} \qquad \text{Answer}$$

Couples

In addition to the work done by forces, we also define the work done by couples. For example, consider the disk in Figure 9.5a, which rotates from position A to position B under the action of two equal and opposite forces of magnitude F. Figure 9.5b shows the plane of the disk as it rotates through the angle θ. During this motion, each force travels a distance $(a\theta)$, so that the work done by these forces is

$$W = F(a\theta) + F(a\theta) = F(2a)\theta$$

$$= M\theta \tag{9.5}$$

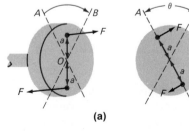

(a)   **(b)**

Figure 9.5

where $M = F(2a)$ = couple formed by the forces. Thus, the work done by the couple is the product of the couple and the angle through which the body rotates (in radians).

As in the case of forces, the expression for the work done by a series of couples can be written as vectors in integral form, that is,

$$W = \int_A^B \mathbf{M} \cdot d\boldsymbol{\theta} \tag{9.6}$$

where $\mathbf{M}$ is the sum of all applied couples acting on the body as it changes from position A to position B. Since θ is expressed in radians, the units for work done by a couple are still ft-lb.

Problems

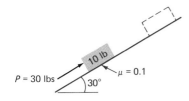

Figure 9.6

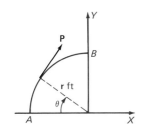

Figure 9.7

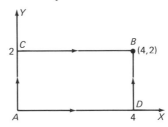

Figure 9.8

9.2.1 The 10-lb block shown in Figure 9.6 moves up the inclined plane under the action of a 30-lb force. If the coefficient of friction between the block and the plane is $\mu = 0.1$, find the work done on the block in moving it 5 ft.

9.2.2 A particle weighing w lb is moved from A to B over a smooth surface as in Figure 9.7 by the applied force $\mathbf{P} = C(\sin\theta\,\mathbf{i} + \cos\theta\,\mathbf{j})$ lb where C is a constant. What is the work done on the particle for this change in position?

9.2.3 Repeat problem 9.2.2 to include a coefficient of friction μ between the particle and the surface.

9.2.4 A particle travels along the curve $y = x^2$ from $x = 1$ ft to $x = 3$ ft. If $\mathbf{F} = 2\mathbf{i} - 4\mathbf{j}$ lb, find the work done on the particle.

9.2.5 Repeat problem 9.2.4 for $\mathbf{F} = 10x\mathbf{i} + 4y\mathbf{j}$ lb.

9.2.6 A particle is to move from position A to position B over two possible paths, ACB or ADB as shown in Figure 9.8. If $\mathbf{F} = 20\mathbf{i} + 20\mathbf{j}$ lb, find the work over each path.

9.2.7 If the particle in problem 9.2.6 travels around the path $ACBDA$, find the total work done on the particle.

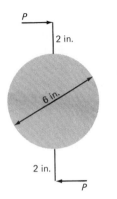

Figure 9.9

9.2.8 The cylinder in Figure 9.9 turns through 90° under the action of the applied forces of magnitude $P = 6$ lb. What work is done on the cylinder for this change in position if the forces remain perpendicular to the 2-in. rods?

9.2.9 What is the total work done by the force **F** and the couple **M** shown in Figure 9.10 as the body moves from position A to position B while it rotates 2 revolutions clockwise?

9.2.10 A brake AB is applied to the spinning drum shown in Figure 9.11. If the kinetic coefficient of friction is 0.1 between the brake and the drum, what work is done on the drum for 20 revolutions?

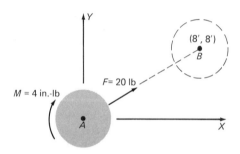

Figure 9.10

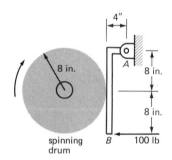

Figure 9.11

9.3 The Concept of Virtual Work

If a particle moves through a displacement $d\mathbf{r}$ under the action of a force **F** as described in the last section, the particle is not in a state of equilibrium. However, in studying the equilibrium of bodies, we sometimes find it useful to introduce fictitious displacements which we call *virtual displacements*. Virtual displacements are small displacements which occur without the passage of time and which do not violate the constraints on the body. A virtual displacement is represented as $\delta\mathbf{r}$ rather than $d\mathbf{r}$ since the latter connotes a time differential dt. Consequently, the *virtual work* done by the net force **F** acting on a particle which experiences the virtual displacement $\delta\mathbf{r}$ is

$$\delta W = \mathbf{F} \cdot \delta\mathbf{r} \tag{9.7}$$

Likewise, the virtual work for a rigid body which may translate an amount $\delta\mathbf{r}$ and rotate an amount $\delta\boldsymbol{\theta}$ is

$$\delta W = \mathbf{F} \cdot \delta\mathbf{r} + \mathbf{M} \cdot \delta\boldsymbol{\theta} \qquad (9.8)$$

The *principle of virtual work* says that if a body is in equilibrium, the virtual work is zero. Thus, for the case of a particle in equilibrium,

$$\delta W = \mathbf{F} \cdot \delta\mathbf{r} = 0 \qquad (9.9)$$

and for a rigid body in equilibrium,

$$\delta W = \mathbf{F} \cdot \delta\mathbf{r} + \mathbf{M} \cdot \delta\boldsymbol{\theta} = 0 \qquad (9.10)$$

We can summarize the principle of virtual work as follows:

1. A particle is in equilibrium if the virtual work of all applied forces is zero for all virtual displacements.
2. A rigid body is in equilibrium if the virtual work due to all forces and couples is zero for all virtual displacements.

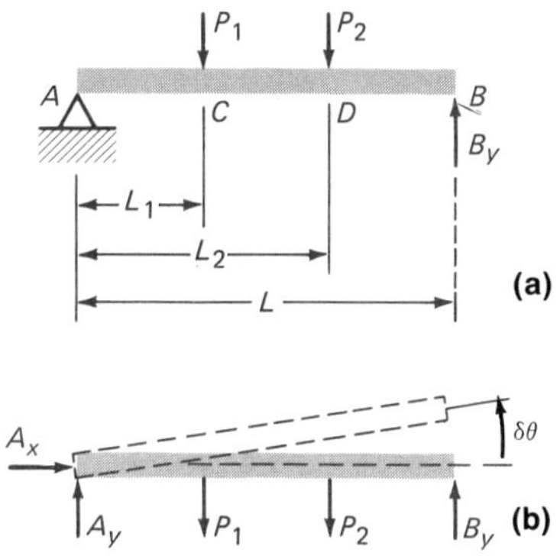

We can demonstrate the principle of virtual work, by finding the force B_y required to keep the rigid rod AB in Figure 9.12a in a state of equilibrium. Since the bar is pinned at A, we allow it to rotate an amount $\delta\theta$ as shown in Figure 9.12b. Keep in mind that $\delta\theta$ is very small. The virtual work is therefore,

$$\delta W = -P_1(L_1 \; \delta\theta) - P_2(L_2 \; \delta\theta) + B_y(L \; \delta\theta)$$

For equilibrium, $\delta W = 0$ and

$$(-P_1L_1 - P_2L_2 + B_yL) \; \delta\theta = 0$$

Since $\delta\theta$ is very small, but not zero,

$$-P_1L_1 - P_2L_2 + B_yL = 0 \qquad B_y = \frac{P_1L_1 + P_2L_2}{L}$$

It should be apparent that the above result could have been obtained using the equilibrium equation $\Sigma M_A = 0$. However, as we shall discover in the next section, the principle of virtual work is a useful tool in studying the equilibrium of more complex systems.

Example 9.3.1

Use the principle of virtual work to find the force $\mathbf{F}$ required to keep the rigid bar in Figure 9.13a in static equilibrium if the magnitude of $M = 400$ lb-ft and (a) $P = 200$ lb, (b) $P = 100$ lb, and (c) $P = 50$ lb.

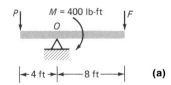

Figure 9.12

Figure 9.13

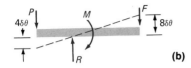

(b)

Figure 9.13

Allow the rod which is pivoted at O to rotate by a small amount $\delta\theta$ as shown in Figure 9.13b. Thus, by the principle of virtual work,

$$\delta W = P(4\ \delta\theta) - M\ \delta\theta - F(8\ \delta\theta) = (4P - M - 8F)\ \delta\theta = 0$$

so that

$$F = \frac{4P - M}{8} = \frac{4P - 400}{8}$$

(a) If $P = 200$ lb, $F = 50$ lb   Answer

(b) If $P = 100$ lb, $F = 0$ Answer

(c) If $P = 50$ lb, $F = -25$ lb $F = 25$ lb ↑   Answer

Example 9.3.2

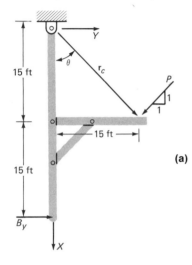

(a)

Use the principle of virtual work to find the force B_y to keep the frame shown in Figure 9.14a in static equilibrium.

Figure 9.14b shows the frame rotated by a small amount $\delta\theta$. In this case,

$$\mathbf{r}_c = r_c(\cos\theta\,\mathbf{i} + \sin\theta\,\mathbf{j})$$

where

$$r_c = \sqrt{15^2 + 15^2} = 21.2 \text{ ft}$$

therefore

$$\delta\mathbf{r}_c = r_c(-\sin\theta\,\mathbf{i} + \cos\theta\,\mathbf{j})\ \delta\theta$$

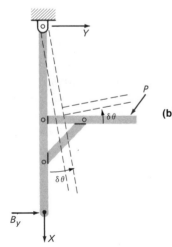

(b)

Note that we differentiate in the usual way except that we use the symbol δ instead of the familiar d since we are interested in virtual displacements.

From the figure we see that $\delta\mathbf{r}_B = 30\ \delta\theta\,\mathbf{j}$. For equilibrium,

$$\delta W = (B_y\mathbf{j}) \cdot (30\ \delta\theta\,\mathbf{j}) + \mathbf{P} \cdot \delta\mathbf{r}_c = 0$$

$$30\ \delta\theta\ B_y + (0.707P\mathbf{i} - 0.707P\mathbf{j}) \cdot (-\sin\theta\,\mathbf{i} + \cos\theta\,\mathbf{j})r_c\ \delta\theta = 0$$

therefore

$$B_y = 0.707P \qquad\qquad \text{Answer}$$

Figure 9.14

Problems

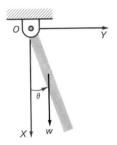

Figure 9.15

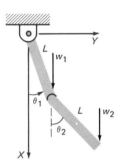

Figure 9.16

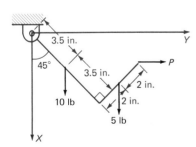

Figure 9.18

9.3.1 Figure 9.15 shows a rod of length L and weight w at the position θ. What is the virtual work done on the rod for $\delta\theta$?

9.3.2 Repeat problem 9.3.1 for a resisting couple M acting clockwise on the rod.

9.3.3 Two rods are connected to form a double pendulum as shown in Figure 9.16. For the forces shown, what is the virtual work (a) if θ_1 varies by $\delta\theta_1$ holding θ_2 fixed, and (b) if θ_2 varies by $\delta\theta_2$ holding θ_1 fixed?

9.3.4 What is the virtual work for problem 9.3.3 if θ_1 and θ_2 are both allowed to vary?

9.3.5 The rod of length L shown in Figure 9.17 has a force $\mathbf{F}$ and couple $\mathbf{M}$ applied to it as shown. What is the virtual work due to $\mathbf{F}$ and $\mathbf{M}$?

9.3.6 Use the principle of virtual work to find the unknown force $\mathbf{P}$ to maintain static equilibrium for the system shown in Figure 9.18.

9.3.7 Use the principle of virtual work to find the unknown couple $\mathbf{M}$ to maintain static equilibrium for the system shown in Figure 9.19.

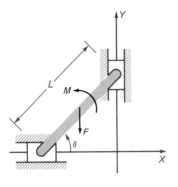

Figure 9.17

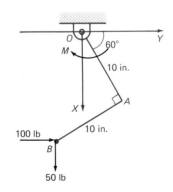

Figure 9.19

9.4 Connected Systems

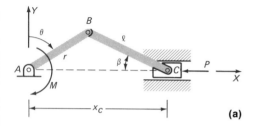

(a)

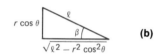

(b)

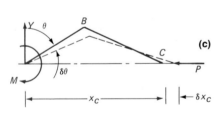

(c)

Figure 9.20

In applying the principle of virtual work to bodies that are connected to each other, we shall treat those cases where we have ideal connectors, that is, where there is no friction at the joints. By way of example, consider the slider-crank mechanism in Figure 9.20a which has a force P acting on the cylinder at C. Assuming that no friction is present, let us use the principle of virtual work to find the torque M required to maintain the system in equilibrium.

Our first step in dealing with connected systems is to establish the number of ways the system is free to move, that is, its number of degrees of freedom. From the figure we see that there is only one degree of freedom which is described by the coordinate x_C or the angle θ. It is important then to establish the relationship between these two coordinates since only one degree of freedom is present. Such a relationship we call an equation of constraint. In this example, we see from Figure 9.20a that

$$x_C = r \sin \theta + \ell \cos \beta \qquad (9.11)$$

where

$$\ell \sin \beta = r \cos \theta$$

From Figure 9.20b we see that

$$\cos \beta = \frac{\sqrt{\ell^2 - r^2 \cos^2 \theta}}{\ell} \qquad (9.12)$$

Substituting equation (9.12) into (9.11), we obtain the desired relationship between x_C and θ:

$$x_C = r \sin \theta + \sqrt{\ell^2 - r^2 \cos^2 \theta} \qquad (9.13)$$

so that

$$\delta x_C = r \cos \theta \, \delta\theta + \tfrac{1}{2} [\ell^2 - r^2 \cos^2 \theta]^{-1/2} [-2r^2 \cos \theta (-\sin \theta) \, \delta\theta]$$

$$= \left(r \cos \theta + \frac{r^2 \sin \theta \cos \theta}{\sqrt{\ell^2 - r^2 \cos^2 \theta}} \right) \delta\theta \qquad (9.14)$$

To investigate the equilibrium requirement, we see in Figure 9.20c that the mechanism is given a virtual displacement which we can view as a result of $\delta\theta$ or δx_C. The virtual work is

$$\delta W = M \, \delta\theta - P \, \delta x_C = 0$$

$$M \, \delta\theta = P \, \delta x_C \qquad (9.15)$$

Using equation (9.14), we get

$$M = P\left(r \cos \theta + \frac{r^2 \sin \theta \cos \theta}{\sqrt{\ell^2 - r^2 \cos^2 \theta}}\right) \qquad (9.16)$$

Note that when $\theta = 90°$, $M = 0$ and the system is locked so that no moment is required for equilibrium. If $\theta = 0$, $M = Pr$ for equilibrium which should be obvious after sketching the mechanism in this configuration.

The above example demonstrates the value of the principle of virtual work when we study involved mechanisms. Note that it is not necessary to draw a free-body diagram of each member of the system if each member is joined by frictionless pin connections. This is one of the advantages of the method.

Example 9.4.1

Find the value of P necessary to keep the mechanism in Figure 9.21a in equilibrium, defined by the angle θ.

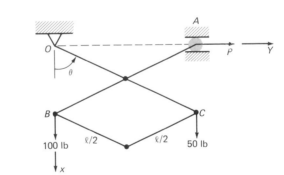

(a)

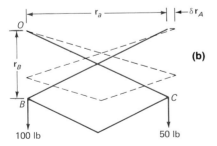

(b)

Figure 9.21

Since the mechanism has one degree of freedom described by the angle θ, Figure 9.21b shows the mechanism deformed due to $\delta\theta$. Now

$\mathbf{r}_A = \ell \sin \theta \mathbf{j}$ $\delta\mathbf{r}_A = \ell \cos \theta \, \delta\theta \mathbf{j}$

$\mathbf{r}_B = \ell \cos \theta \mathbf{i}$ $\delta\mathbf{r}_B = -\ell \sin \theta \, \delta\theta \mathbf{i}$

$\mathbf{r}_C = \ell \cos \theta \mathbf{i} + \ell \sin \theta \mathbf{j}$ $\delta\mathbf{r}_C = -\ell \sin \theta \, \delta\theta \mathbf{i} + \ell \cos \theta \, \delta\theta \mathbf{j}$

The virtual work is

$$\delta W = P\mathbf{j} \cdot \delta\mathbf{r}_A + 100\mathbf{i} \cdot \delta\mathbf{r}_B + 50\mathbf{i} \cdot \delta\mathbf{r}_C = 0$$

$$P\mathbf{j} \cdot (\ell \cos\theta\,\delta\theta\mathbf{j}) + 100\mathbf{i} \cdot (-\ell \sin\theta\,\delta\theta\mathbf{i})$$
$$+ 50\mathbf{i} \cdot (-\ell \sin\theta\,\delta\theta\mathbf{i} + \ell \cos\theta\,\delta\theta\mathbf{j}) = 0$$

$$P\,\ell\,\cos\theta - 100\,\ell\,\sin\theta - 50\,\ell\,\sin\theta = 0$$

therefore

$$P = 150 \tan\theta \text{ lb} \qquad\qquad \text{Answer}$$

Problems

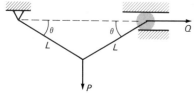

Figure 9.22

9.4.1 Obtain a relationship between P and Q for the equilibrium of the mechanism shown in Figure 9.22.

9.4.2 What is the relationship between P and Q for equilibrium of the structure shown in Figure 9.23?

9.4.3 What is the relationship between P and Q for the equilibrium of the mechanism shown in Figure 9.24?

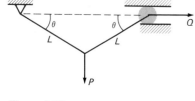

Figure 9.23

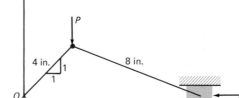

Figure 9.24

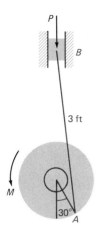

3 ft

M

30°

A

P

B

Figure 9.25

9.4.4 Obtain the relationship between *P* and *M* for equilibrium of the system shown in Figure 9.25.

9.4.5 Determine *P* for the equilibrium of the bar shown in Figure 9.26.

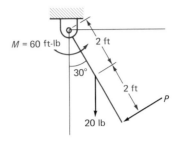

M = 60 ft-lb   2 ft

30°

2 ft

P

20 lb

Figure 9.26

9.5 Potential Energy

On occasion, the elastic members with which bodies are connected to each other are idealized as springs. The resistance to the force we apply, experienced when we pull or push on a spring, is called the spring modulus k, whose units are usually in lb/in. For example, if $k = 100$ lb/in., it takes 50 lb to stretch or compress the spring $\frac{1}{2}$ in., while it takes 200 lb to deform it 2 in. When a spring is deformed, we say that the spring has energy stored in it, this energy being called *potential energy*. Thus, we say that the amount of work required to deform a spring is equal to the change in the potential energy stored in the elastic member.

Consider, for example, a linear spring of unstretched length L, as shown in Figure 9.27a. Gradually apply a force **F** to the end of the spring so that it stretches by an amount $x - L$, as shown in Figure 9.27b. Figure 9.27c shows the free-body diagram of the spring; and, for static equilibrium,

$$\Sigma F_x = 0 \qquad F - k(x - L) = 0$$

therefore

$$F = k(x - L) \tag{9.17}$$

Let us now calculate the work done in stretching the spring from x_A to x_B. Referring to equation (9.3), i.e.,

$$W = \int_A^B \mathbf{F} \cdot d\mathbf{r} \tag{9.3}$$

(a)

L

k

x

(b)

x

F

B

(c)

$k(x-L)$ *F*

B

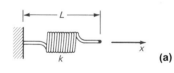

Figure 9.27

For the spring force shown in Figure 9.27c,

$$\mathbf{F} = -k(x - L)\mathbf{i} \qquad d\mathbf{r} = dx\, \mathbf{i}$$

and therefore,

$$W = -\int_{x_A}^{x_B} k(x - L)\mathbf{i} \cdot dx\, \mathbf{i}$$

$$= -\left[\frac{k(x_B - L)^2}{2} - \frac{k(x_A - L)^2}{2}\right] \tag{9.18}$$

This expression for work represents the negative change in potential energy V, that is,

$$W = -(V_B - V_A) \tag{9.19}$$

where

$$V_B = \tfrac{1}{2}k(x_B - L)^2 \qquad V_A = \tfrac{1}{2}k(x_A - L)^2$$

In general, we may say that the potential energy of a spring stretched or compressed by an amount $(x - L)$ is

$$V = \tfrac{1}{2}k(x - L)^2 \tag{9.20}$$

If x is measured from the unstretched position, then

$$V = \tfrac{1}{2}kx^2 \tag{9.21}$$

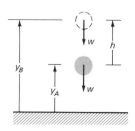

Figure 9.28

There is also said to be a change in potential energy when a body changes its position relative to the surface of the earth. Consider, for example, a particle, shown in Figure 9.28, which weighs w lb. The work done on the particle by the weight is

$$W = \int_A^B \mathbf{F} \cdot d\mathbf{r}$$

where

$$\mathbf{F} = -w\mathbf{j} \qquad d\mathbf{r} = dy\, \mathbf{j}$$

so that,

$$W = -\int_{y_A}^{y_B} w\mathbf{j} \cdot dy\, \mathbf{j} = -(wy_B - wy_A) \tag{9.22}$$

Referring to equation (9.19), we see that

$$-(V_B - V_A) = -w(y_B - y_A) = -wh \tag{9.23}$$

By convention, we let $V_A = 0$, so that $V_B = wh$. Consequently, if a particle is a vertical distance h above a given reference point, its potential energy relative to the reference point is

$$V = wh \qquad (9.24)$$

Note that if the body is a vertical distance below the reference point, $V = -wh$ relative to the reference point.

Example 9.5.1

What is the potential energy of a 2-lb particle in positions A, B, and C, respectively, relative to lines 1, 2, and 3 in Figure 9.29?

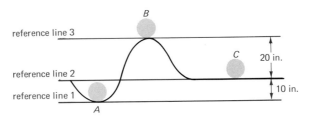

Figure 9.29

Line 1: at A, $V = 0$

at B, $V = 2(30) = 60$ in.-lb

at C, $V = 2(10) = 20$ in.-lb

Line 2: at A, $V = 2(-10) = -20$ in.-lb

at B, $V = 2(20) = 40$ in.-lb

at C, $V = 0$

Line 3: at A, $V = 2(-30) = -60$ in.-lb

at B, $V = 0$

at C, $V = 2(-20) = -40$ in.-lb

Note that for each reference line, ΔV is the same between two points, for example, between points A and C,

$$\Delta V = V_C - V_A = 20 \text{ in.-lb}$$

no matter which reference line is chosen. Thus, since in mechanics we are always interested in *changes* in potential energy, we choose the most convenient reference line.

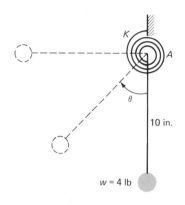

w = 4 lb

Figure 9.30

Example 9.5.2

A simple pendulum weighs 4 lb and has a torsional spring with modulus $k = 100$ lb-in./rad as shown in Figure 9.30. When $\theta = 0$, the torsional spring is undeformed. Find the potential energy of the system for (a) $\theta = 0$, (b) $\theta = 45°$, and (c) $\theta = 90°$.

It can be shown that the torsional spring behaves in a manner similar to the linear spring, so that $V = \frac{1}{2} k\theta^2$.

Choose point A as the reference point for the potential energy of the weight.

(a) $\theta = 0$, $V = 4(-10) = -40$ in.-lb   Answer

(b) $\theta = \dfrac{\pi}{4}$, $V = 4(-10 \cos 45°) + \dfrac{1}{2}(100)\left(\dfrac{\pi}{4}\right)^2$

$$= -28.3 + 30.8 = 2.5 \text{ in.-lb}$$ Answer

(c) $\theta = \dfrac{\pi}{2}$, $V = \dfrac{1}{2}(100)\left(\dfrac{\pi}{2}\right)^2 = 123$ in.-lb   Answer

Problems

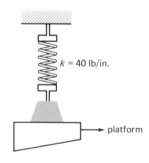

k = 40 lb/in.

platform

Figure 9.31

9.5.1 A linear spring, attached to a 20-lb weight as shown in Figure 9.31, is unstretched as the weight rests on a platform. If the platform is slowly removed, find (a) the potential energy stored in the spring, and (b) the change in the total potential energy of the system.

9.5.2 Consider a linear spring, shown in Figure 9.32, of modulus $k = 50$ lb/in. and unstretched length $L = 10$ in. What is the potential energy if $\mathbf{x}_A = -2\mathbf{i}$ in. and $\mathbf{x}_B = 12\mathbf{i}$ in.?

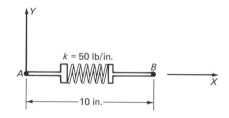

Figure 9.32

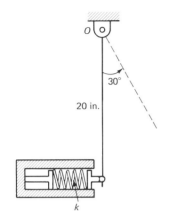

Figure 9.33

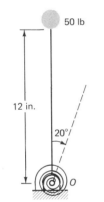

Figure 9.34

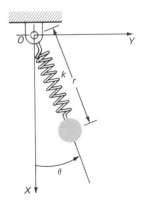

Figure 9.37

9.5.3 What is the potential energy stored in the spring shown in Figure 9.33 when the rod rotates $30°$ counterclockwise if $k=20\,\text{lb/in.}$? The spring is in its unstretched position when the rod is vertical.

9.5.4 An inverted pendulum supports a 50-lb weight as shown in Figure 9.34. The attached helical spring of modulus $k = 50$ lb-ft/rad is unstretched for the position shown. What is the change in the potential energy of the system if the pendulum rotates $20°$ clockwise?

9.5.5 A 100-lb rod is held in its position of static equilibrium by a torsional spring of modulus $k = 50$ lb-ft/rad as shown in Figure 9.35. If the rod rotates $30°$ clockwise, what is the change in the potential energy of the system?

9.5.6 A 200-lb beam, supported by springs, is shown in its static equilibrium position in Figure 9.36. If point C deflects 2 in. downward and the beam rotates $8°$ counterclockwise, what is the change in the potential energy?

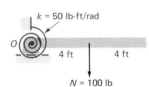

Figure 9.35

9.5.7 Repeat problem 9.5.6 for point C moving 2 in. upward and the beam rotating $8°$ clockwise.

9.5.8 A 5-lb particle rides along a frictionless rod and is restrained by a linear spring of modulus $k = 10$ lb/in., as shown in Figure 9.37. The unstretched length of the spring is 8 in. What is the change in the potential energy as the system moves from A to B if $r_A = 6$ in., $\theta_A = 0°$, and $r_B = 10$ in., $\theta_B = 45°$?

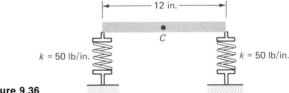

Figure 9.36

9.6 Stability of Equilibrium

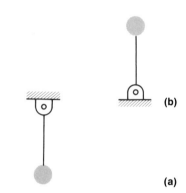

(b)

(a)

Figure 9.38

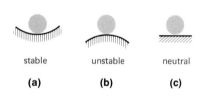

stable   unstable   neutral

(a)   **(b)**   **(c)**

Figure 9.39

Figure 9.38 shows a pendulum in static equilibrium in two different positions. Given a slight disturbance, the rod in Figure 9.38a will oscillate back and forth about its position of static equilibrium, never moving far away. On the other hand, if we disturb, no matter how slightly, the inverted pendulum in Figure 9.38b, it will "take off" on us, that is, it will deviate an appreciable distance from its position of static equilibrium. Thus, we say that the pendulum in the first position is in a *stable* equilibrium position, while in the second position it is in an *unstable* equilibrium position.

The concept of stability is also demonstrated by the ball shown in Figure 9.39. Again, a slight disturbance of the ball as shown in Figure 9.39a would increase its potential energy and the ball would exhibit a tendency to return to its original position. Consequently, this is a position of stable equilibrium. On the other hand, the ball in Figure 9.39b is in a position of unstable equilibrium because, given a slight disturbance, its potential energy would decrease. Figure 9.39c shows the ball in a position of neutral equilibrium. That is, a slight disturbance would neither increase nor decrease its potential energy. In Figures 9.39a and b we note that the potential energy is at an extremum in each case. That is, it is at a local minimum in Figure 9.39a and at a local maximum in Figure 9.39b.

Suppose we assume that the potential energy is a function of one variable, say x. Thus,

$$V = V(x)$$

We wish to investigate the question of stability about the point of equilibrium, which we will assume is at $x = x_0$. Let us expand the potential energy function V about this equilibrium point in a Taylor series expansion. Thus,

$$V = V(x_0) + (x - x_0)\left[\frac{dV}{dx}\right]_{x=x_0} + \frac{(x - x_0)^2}{2!}\left[\frac{d^2V}{dx^2}\right]_{x=x_0} + \cdots$$

For equilibrium, we know the body is at an extremum position, so that

$$\left[\frac{dV}{dx}\right]_{x=x_0} = 0$$

The change in the potential energy of the body from the

equilibrium position is:

$$\Delta V = V - V(x_0) = \frac{(x - x_0)^2}{2!}\left[\frac{d^2V}{dx^2}\right]_{x=x_0} + \cdots$$

(9.25)

Generally, the higher-order terms in the series are small and so we will delete them.

Consequently, for the potential energy to increase as the system deviates about a stable equilibrium position, we must have

$$\Delta V > 0$$

which by equation (9.25) requires that

$$\left[\frac{d^2V}{dx^2}\right]_{x=x_0} > 0$$

Likewise, for the potential energy to decrease as the system deviates about an unstable equilibrium position, we must have

$$\left[\frac{d^2V}{dx^2}\right]_{x=x_0} < 0$$

We can summarize our findings for stability about the equilibrium point as follows:

Stable equilibrium: $\quad \dfrac{dV}{dx} = 0 \quad \dfrac{d^2V}{dx^2} > 0 \quad$ (9.26)

Unstable equilibrium: $\quad \dfrac{dV}{dx} = 0 \quad \dfrac{d^2V}{dx^2} < 0 \quad$ (9.27)

A word of caution: if the second derivative of V is also zero, then we must investigate higher order derivatives. If all higher-order derivatives are zero, equilibrium will be neutral. To be stable, the higher-order derivatives must be of even order and positive. Otherwise, unstable equilibrium exists.

Example 9.6.1

A right-angle member AOB is pivoted at O as shown in Figure 9.40. Member OA weighs w_1 lb while member OB weighs w_2 lb. Find the position of static equilibrium and determine if it is stable or unstable equilibrium.

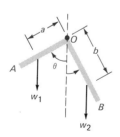

Figure 9.40

From Figure 9.40, the potential energy of the member relative to O is

$$V = -w_1 a \cos \theta - w_2 b \cos (90° - \theta)$$

$$= -w_1 a \cos \theta - w_2 b \sin \theta$$

Now

$$\frac{dV}{d\theta} = w_1 a \sin \theta - w_2 b \cos \theta = 0 \qquad \tan \theta = \frac{w_2 b}{w_1 a}$$

and therefore

$$\theta = \tan^{-1} \left(\frac{w_2 b}{w_1 a} \right) = \theta_0$$

is the position of static equilibrium.

To study the question of stability we use,

$$\left[\frac{d^2 V}{d\theta^2} \right]_{\theta = \theta_0} = \left[\frac{(w_1 a)^2 + (w_2 b)^2}{w_1 a} \right] \cos \theta_0$$

Since $(dV/d\theta^2) > 0$ for all θ, the position shown in Figure 9.40 is a stable equilibrium position. What conclusions can you draw for the same member rotated as shown in Figure 9.41?

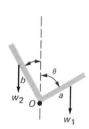

Figure 9.41

Problems

9.6.1 Show that the position of the inverted pendulum in Figure 9.42 is that of unstable equilibrium.

9.6.2 Obtain the value of k for the equilibrium of the pendulum in Figure 9.43. The spring is unstretched for the position shown. Assume θ is small.

Figure 9.42

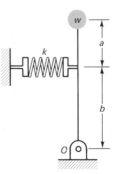

Figure 9.43

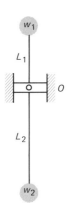

Figure 9.44

9.6.3 Find the condition for equilibrium of the member pinned at O in Figure 9.44. Determine the type of equilibrium.

9.6.4 Find (a) the position for equilibrium and (b) the type of stability for the member in Figure 9.45.

9.6.5 Find the position of equilibrium for the system in Figure 9.46 and determine the type of stability. Assume small θ and no friction at the pulley B.

9.6.6 A bar weighing w lb is restrained by a spring of modulus $k = 4w/L$ and unstretched length $s = L/2$ as shown in Figure 9.47. What is the position of equilibrium?

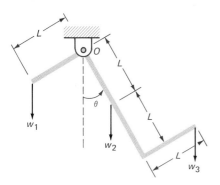

Figure 9.45

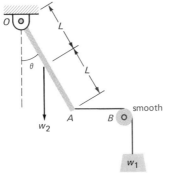

Figure 9.46

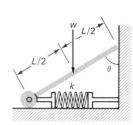

Figure 9.47

9.7 Summary

A   The important *ideas:*

1. Work is done on a body as it moves from one position to another under the action of forces and couples applied to it.

2. Virtual displacement are fictitious displacements which are very small in magnitude and do not violate the constraints of a system.

3. The principle of virtual work provides another technique for studying the equilibrium of single bodies as well as connected bodies.

4. Potential energy is energy stored in a body.

5. Static equilibrium may be stable or unstable, depending on the change in the potential energy of a system about the equilibrium position.

B   The important *equations:*

$$W = \int_A^B \mathbf{F} \cdot d\mathbf{r} \tag{9.3}$$

$$W = \int_A^B \mathbf{M} \cdot d\boldsymbol{\theta} \tag{9.6}$$

Principle of Virtual Work

Particle Equilibrium: $\delta W = \mathbf{F} \cdot \delta \mathbf{r} = 0$ (9.9)
Rigid Body Equilibrium:

$$\delta W = \mathbf{F} \cdot \delta \mathbf{r} + \mathbf{M} \cdot \delta \theta = 0 \quad (9.10)$$

Potential Energy
Spring: $V = \frac{1}{2}k(x - L)^2$ (9.20)
Weight: $V = wh$ (9.24)

Stable equilibrium: $\dfrac{dV}{dx} = 0$ $\dfrac{d^2V}{dx^2} > 0$ (9.26)

Unstable equilibrium: $\dfrac{dV}{dx} = 0$ $\dfrac{d^2V}{dx^2} < 0$ (9.27)

Answers to Even-Numbered Problems

Chapter 1

1.9.4 $\mathbf{A} + \mathbf{B} = 11\mathbf{i} + 2\mathbf{k}, \mathbf{A} - \mathbf{B} = -\mathbf{i} + 16\mathbf{j} - 2\mathbf{k}$

1.9.8 Magnitude of the projection is 5.52.

1.9.10 $\mathbf{C} \cdot \mathbf{D} = 0$

1.9.12 $\mathbf{e}_c = -0.535\mathbf{i} + 9.267\mathbf{j} + 0.802\mathbf{k}$

1.9.14 $\mathbf{A} \times \mathbf{B} = 20\mathbf{i} - 18\mathbf{j} - 10\mathbf{k}$

1.9.18 $|\mathbf{V}_2 - \mathbf{V}_1| = 0.548, \mathbf{e} = \dfrac{1}{0.548}(-0.1\mathbf{i} - 0.2\mathbf{j} + 0.5\mathbf{k})$

1.9.20 $|\mathbf{r} \times \mathbf{w}| = 13.4$

1.9.24 $z = 2$

1.9.26 $\theta = 71.8°$

1.9.28 $\mathbf{r}_{AB} = 20\mathbf{j}$

1.9.30 $\mathbf{V} = (-v_r \cos\theta - v_\theta \sin\theta)\mathbf{i} + (v_r \sin\theta + v_\theta \cos\theta)\mathbf{j}$

1.9.32 $\mathbf{MW} = 15.1(0.735\mathbf{i} - 0.655\mathbf{j})$

Chapter 2

2.2.2 $R = 642$ lb, $\theta = -98.8°$

2.2.4 $R = 232$ lb, $\theta = 6.2°$

2.2.6 $R = 203$ lb, $\theta = 16.2°$

2.2.8 $R = 239$ lb, $\theta = -94.3°$

2.2.10 a) $F_2 = 410$ lb, $\theta = -7.0°$, b) $F_2 = 414$ lb, $\theta = -7.0°$

2.2.12 $\mathbf{T} = -946\mathbf{i} - 316\mathbf{j}$ lb

2.2.14 $R = 67$ lb, $\theta = 26°$

2.2.16	$0.775, 0.465, 0.438$
2.2.18	$\mathbf{F} = -254\mathbf{i} - 424\mathbf{j} + 84.8\mathbf{k}$
2.2.20	$\mathbf{R} = 1430(0.28\mathbf{i} + 0.728\mathbf{j} + 0.627\mathbf{k})$ lb
2.3.2	$T_1 = 109$ lb, $T_2 = 29$ lb
2.3.4	$T_{CA} = 57$ lb, $T_{CB} = 152$ lb
2.3.6	$T_2 = 28.6$ lb, $T_1 = 108.7$ lb
2.3.8	$T_2 = 151$ lb, $T_1 = 57.7$ lb
2.3.10	$T_{BA} = 110$ lb, $T_{BC} = 135$ lb
2.3.12	$\theta = 27.9°$
2.3.14	$\mathbf{R} = 484\mathbf{i} + 630\mathbf{j}$
2.3.16	$T_{BA} = 101.5$ lb, $T_{BC} = 5000$ lb
2.3.18	$T_{DC} = 0, T_{DB} = T_{DA} = 528$ lb
2.3.20	$T_{AB} = T_{AC} = 715$ lb, $T_{AD} = 0$
2.5.2	$\mathbf{M}_A = -1915\mathbf{k}$ lb-in., $\mathbf{M}_B = -1091\mathbf{k}$ lb-in.
2.5.4	$\mathbf{M}_A = \mathbf{M}_B = 994\mathbf{k}$ lb-in.
2.5.6	$\mathbf{M}_A = 120\mathbf{k}$ lb-in.
2.5.8	$\mathbf{M}_O = 624\mathbf{k}$ lb-in.
2.5.10	$\mathbf{M}_A = -2492\mathbf{k}$ lb-in.
2.5.12	$\mathbf{M}_P = -176.5\mathbf{k}$ lb-in.
2.5.14	$\mathbf{M}_A = 585 \curvearrowright$ lb-in.
2.5.16	$\mathbf{M} = 994\mathbf{k}$ lb-in.
2.5.18	$\mathbf{M} = 585 \curvearrowright$ lb-in., $\mathbf{R} = 4.25\mathbf{i} - 1.1\mathbf{j}$ lb
2.5.20	$\mathbf{M} = 347 \curvearrowright$ lb-in.
2.5.22	$\mathbf{M}_A = 277(0.544\mathbf{i} + 0.654\mathbf{j} + 0.525\mathbf{k})$lb-ft
2.5.24	$\mathbf{M}_O = -131.5(0.0607\mathbf{i} + 0.995\mathbf{k})$lb-ft
2.5.26	$\mathbf{M} \cdot \mathbf{e}_{AB} = 798$ lb-ft
2.5.28	$\mathbf{M} = -226\mathbf{i} - 226\mathbf{j} - 2030\mathbf{k}$ lb-ft
2.6.2	$\mathbf{M} = -1915\mathbf{k}$ lb-in., $\mathbf{R} = 136.7\mathbf{i} + 136.7\mathbf{j}$ lb
2.6.4	$\mathbf{R} = 0, \mathbf{M} = 994\mathbf{k}$ lb-in.
2.6.6	$\mathbf{R} = 0, \mathbf{M} = 120\mathbf{k}$ lb-in.
2.6.8	$\mathbf{R} = 141\mathbf{i}$ lb, $\mathbf{M}_P = 424 \curvearrowright$ lb-in.
2.6.10	$\mathbf{R} = 10\mathbf{i} - 10\mathbf{j}$ lb, $\mathbf{M}_A = -130\mathbf{k}$ lb-in.
2.6.12	$\mathbf{M}_A = 0, \mathbf{R} = -32.6\mathbf{i} - 185.2\mathbf{j}$ lb
2.6.14	$\mathbf{R} = 50\mathbf{i} - 136.6\mathbf{j}$ lb, $\mathbf{M}_A = 862 \curvearrowright$ lb-ft
2.6.16	$\mathbf{M}_A = -163\mathbf{i} + 81.6\mathbf{j}$ lb-ft, $\mathbf{R} = 100(0.408\mathbf{i} + 0.816\mathbf{j} + 0.408\mathbf{k})$lb

2.6.18 $\mathbf{R} = 143.3\mathbf{i} + 75\mathbf{j}$ lb, $\mathbf{M}_A = 265\,\overset{\curvearrowright}{}$ lb-in.

2.6.20 $\mathbf{F}_A = 200\mathbf{i}$ lb, $\mathbf{F}_O = -200\mathbf{i} + 150\mathbf{j}$ lb

Chapter 3

3.3.2 $\mathbf{A} = (49.7\mathbf{i} + 49.7\mathbf{j})$ lb, $\mathbf{B} = 121\mathbf{j}$ lb

3.3.4 $\mathbf{A} = -5\mathbf{j}$ lb, $\mathbf{B} = 5\mathbf{j}$ lb

3.3.6 $\mathbf{A} = -5\mathbf{j}$ lb, $\mathbf{B} = 5\mathbf{j}$ lb

3.3.8 a) $\mathbf{T} = 322\mathbf{i}$ lb, b) $\mathbf{N}_A = \mathbf{N}_B = 191.5\mathbf{j}$ lb

3.3.10 $\mathbf{T} = 250\mathbf{j}$ lb

3.3.12 $\mathbf{T} = -125\mathbf{j}$ lb

3.3.14 a) $T = 172.5$ lb, b) $\mathbf{O}_x = 30\mathbf{i}$ lb, $\mathbf{O}_y = -70\mathbf{j}$ lb

3.3.16 a) $T = 125$ lb, b) $\mathbf{A} = (108.2\mathbf{i} + 37.5\mathbf{j})$ lb

3.3.18 $\mathbf{M}_A = 1000\mathbf{k}$ lb-ft, $\mathbf{A} = 200\mathbf{j}$ lb

3.3.22 a) $T = 400$ lb, b) $\mathbf{A} = (346\mathbf{i} - 100\mathbf{j})$ lb

3.3.24 $P = 5.17$ kips

3.3.26 $\mathbf{A} = 50\mathbf{i}$ lb, $\mathbf{B} = -100\mathbf{i}$ lb

3.3.28 $\mathbf{A}_y = 10\mathbf{j}$ lb

3.3.30 $M = 391\,\overset{\curvearrowright}{}$ lb-in., $\mathbf{A} = (8.7\mathbf{i} + 149\mathbf{j})$ lb

3.3.32 $\mathbf{A} = (-1\mathbf{i} - 2.25\mathbf{j})$ kips, $\mathbf{B} = 3.75\mathbf{j}$ kips

3.3.34 $\mathbf{A} = 1360\mathbf{j}$ lb, $\mathbf{B} = 1640\mathbf{j}$ lb

3.3.36 $T = 2280$ lb, $\mathbf{A} = (1975\mathbf{i} + 360\mathbf{j})$ lb

3.3.38 $\mathbf{A} = (53.4\mathbf{i} + 58.4\mathbf{j})$ kips, $T_C = 41.8$ kips, error $= 0.374\%$ and is acceptable

3.3.40 a) $T = 173$ lb, b) $\mathbf{C} = (50\mathbf{i} - 173\mathbf{j})$ lb

3.3.42 $\theta = 11.3°$

3.3.44 $T = 25 \cos \theta$ lb, $\mathbf{A}_x = -25 \cos \theta \sin \theta\,\mathbf{i}$ lb
$\mathbf{A}_y = 25(\mathbf{j} - 2 \cos^2 \theta\,\mathbf{j})$ lb

3.3.46 $\mathbf{A} = (106\mathbf{i} - 102\mathbf{j})$ lb, $\mathbf{M}_A = -1880\mathbf{k}$ lb-in.

3.3.48 $\mathbf{M}_A = 107\mathbf{k}$ lb-in., $\mathbf{A} = (-31.6\mathbf{i} - 4\mathbf{j})$ lb

3.4.2 a) $T_{DA} = T_{DC} = 112$ lb, $T_{DC} = 200$ lb, b) $\mathbf{O} = -483.7\mathbf{i} - 42.8\mathbf{j} + 432.2\mathbf{k}$ lb

3.4.4 $A_x = A_y = 0, A_z = 50\mathbf{k}$ lb, $\mathbf{M}_A = (35\mathbf{i} + 90\mathbf{j})$ lb-in.

3.4.6 a) $T = 423$ lb, b) $\mathbf{A} = 291.5\mathbf{i} + 37.5\mathbf{j}$ lb, $M_x = 0$

3.4.8 $\mathbf{M}_A = (-100\mathbf{j} - 300\mathbf{k})$ lb-in., $\mathbf{A} = (-50\mathbf{i} - 50\mathbf{j})$ lb

3.4.10 $M = 138\mathbf{k}$ lb-ft, $\mathbf{A} = (8.7\mathbf{i} + 59.3\mathbf{j})$ lb

Chapter 4

4.3.2 $A_x = 895\mathbf{i}$ lb, $A_y = 560\mathbf{j}$ lb, $E_y = 1230\mathbf{j}$ lb

4.3.4 $F_{DE} = 1755$ lb C, $F_{CD} = 2255$ lb C, $F_{EF} = 1347$ lb T,
       $F_{DF} = 1117$ lb C

4.3.6 $F_{DE} = 283$ lb C, $F_{BE} = 142$ lb C, $F_{CD} = 200$ lb T,
       $F_{CE} = 141$ lb C

4.3.8 $F_{EF} = 2000$ lb C, $F_{DE} = 1410$ lb C, $F_{CE} = 1000$ lb C,
       $F_{AE} = 0$, $F_{BE} = 1000$ lb C

4.3.10 $F_{BC} = 18.1$ kips T

4.3.12 $F_{CE} = 2000$ lb C

4.3.14 $F_{CG} = 0$

4.3.16 $F_{AC} = 960$ lb T, $F_{AD} = 0$

4.3.18 $F_{AB} = F_{BC} = 1250$ lb C, $F_{AH} = F_{HG} = F_{GF} = 230$ lb T,
       $F_{FC} = 1578$ lb T

4.4.8 $F_{BC} = 1500$ lb T

4.5.2 $F_{BF} = 1000$ lb C, $F_{BC} = 1700$ lb C

4.5.4 $F_{FG} = F_{BG} = 706$ lb T

4.5.6 $F_{JI} = 14.1$ kips T, $F_{DI} = 0.9$ kips C

4.5.8 $F_{CE} = 14000$ lb C, $F_{CF} = 7500$ lb C, $F_{DE} = 7500$ lb C

4.5.10 $F_{JM} = 2.62$ kips C

4.5.12 $F_{BD} = -3.23$ kips C

4.5.14 $MN, NK, JI, JK, KL, JL, HJ$

4.6.2 $\mathbf{A} = (267\mathbf{i} + 84.7\mathbf{k})$ lb, $\mathbf{B} = (-400\mathbf{j} + 561\mathbf{k})$ lb,
       $\mathbf{D} = (-267\mathbf{i} - 345.7\mathbf{k})$ lb, $F_{AC} = 87.5$ lb C, $F_{AB} = 467$ lb C

4.6.4 $\mathbf{A} = -125\mathbf{k}$ lb, $\mathbf{B} = 250\mathbf{k}$ lb, $\mathbf{C} = 375\mathbf{k}$ lb, $F_{AE} = 144$ lb T

4.7.2 $F_{AB} = 125$ lb T

4.7.4 $A_x = A_y = 75$ lb, $T_C = 106$ lb, $F_{AB} = F_{BC} = 125$ lb T

4.7.6 $G_y = 7\mathbf{j}$ kips, $\mathbf{E} = -7\mathbf{j}$ kips, $F_{DF} = 0$

4.7.8 $\mathbf{A} = (-106.7\mathbf{i} + 40\mathbf{j})$ lb, $T_C = 106.7$ lb

4.7.10 $\mathbf{A} = 22\mathbf{j}$ kips, $\mathbf{D} = (13.53\mathbf{i} - 9.9\mathbf{j})$ kips, $T_E = 2$ kips,
       $F_{CB} = 16.4$ kips T

4.7.12 $\mathbf{B} = (100\mathbf{i} + 200\mathbf{j})$ lb, $\mathbf{E} = (-100\mathbf{i} - 100\mathbf{j})$ lb, $\mathbf{W} = -100\mathbf{j}$ lb

4.7.14 $P = 960$ lb

4.7.16 $P = 20.5$ lb

4.7.18 $M = 85$ lb-in.

4.7.20 $\mathbf{M}_R = 37.5\mathbf{i}$ lb-in.

Chapter 5

5.2.2	$A = 1.51$ in.^{2}
5.2.4	1.51
5.2.6	0.69
5.2.8	1
5.4.2	$\bar{x} = 0,\ \bar{y} = 2r/\pi$
5.4.4	$\bar{x} = 3'',\ \bar{y} = 2''$
5.4.6	$\bar{x} = 1'',\ \bar{y} = 5/3''$
5.4.8	$\bar{x} = 0,\ \bar{y} = (4r/3\pi)$
5.4.10	$\bar{x} = 8/3'',\ \bar{y} = 4/3''$
5.4.12	$\bar{x} = 2.25'',\ \bar{y} = 0.66''$
5.4.14	$\bar{x} = \bar{y} = 0,\ \bar{z} = 3r/8$
5.4.16	$\bar{x} = 2.2'',\ \bar{y} = 1.14''$
5.4.18	$\bar{x} = 3.2'',\ \bar{y} = 0.335''$
5.4.20	$\bar{x} = 2.26'',\ \bar{y} = 0.78''$
5.4.22	$\bar{x} = 3.3'',\ \bar{y} = 0.337''$
5.4.24	$\bar{x} = 5.74'',\ \bar{y} = 1.92''$
5.4.26	$\bar{x} = \bar{y} = 1.08''$
5.4.28	$\bar{x} = 0,\ \bar{y} = -2.19''$
5.4.30	$\bar{x} = \bar{z} = 0,\ \bar{y} = 0.186''$
5.4.32	$\bar{x} = 1.5'',\ \bar{y} = 6.05'',\ \bar{z} = 2.5''$
5.5.2	$A = 134.5$ in.^{2}
5.5.4	a) $A = 50.4$ in.^{2}, b) $A = 79$ in.^{2}
5.5.6	$V = 38.85$ in.^{3}
5.5.8	$V = 1071$ in.^{3}
5.5.10	$V = 78.5$ in.^{3}
5.6.2	a) $\mathbf{A} = 183.3\mathbf{j}$ lb, $\mathbf{B} = 116.7\mathbf{j}$ lb, b) $\mathbf{R} = 300\mathbf{j}$ lb, $\bar{x} = 4.67$ ft
5.6.4	a) $\mathbf{A} = 26.8\mathbf{j}$ lb, $\mathbf{B} = 33.2\mathbf{j}$ lb, b) $\mathbf{R} = -60\mathbf{j}$ lb, $\bar{x} = 6.09$ ft
5.6.6	a) $\mathbf{A} = 140\mathbf{j}$ lb, $\mathbf{B} = 2360\mathbf{j}$ lb, b) $\mathbf{R} = 2500\mathbf{j}$ lb, $\bar{x} = 28.3$ ft
5.6.8	a) $\mathbf{A} = \mathbf{B} = 300\mathbf{j}$ lb, b) $\mathbf{R} = 600\mathbf{j}$, $\bar{x} = 10$ ft
5.6.10	$\mathbf{R} = -1310\mathbf{j}$ lb, $\bar{y} = 12.3$ ft

5.6.12 $T = 281$ lb

5.6.14 $\mathbf{D} = (10160\mathbf{i} + 12000\mathbf{j})$lb, $\mathbf{M} = -46960\mathbf{k}$ lb-ft

5.6.16 $\mathbf{A} = (18\mathbf{i} + 12.3\mathbf{j})$kips, $\mathbf{M} = -147.7\mathbf{k}$ kip-ft

5.6.18 $F = 5.26$ lb

5.6.20 $F = 15.51$ lb

5.6.22 $h = 3.18$ ft

5.7.2 $\mathbf{A} = (-2.69\mathbf{i} + 10.22\mathbf{j})$kips, $\mathbf{D} = (2.69\mathbf{i} + 9.78\mathbf{j})$kips

5.7.4 $\mathbf{A} = -9\mathbf{i} + 2\mathbf{j}$ lb, $h = 10.65$ ft

5.7.6 $L = 346$ ft

5.7.8 $h = 30.4$ ft

Chapter 6

6.2.2 $I_x = \dfrac{a^{10}}{30}$

6.2.4 $I_x = 2/9a$

6.2.6 $I_y = a^6$

6.2.8 $I_y = a^6/6$

6.2.10 $I_y = 1.14/a^3$

6.2.12 $J = \dfrac{\pi a^4}{4}$, $k = 0.707a$

6.2.14 $I_x = \dfrac{\pi ab^3}{4}$

6.3.2 $I_u = \dfrac{14}{6}bh^3$, $I_v = \dfrac{14}{6}hb^3$

6.3.4 $I_x = 3a^4$

6.3.6 $I_x = 119.4$ in.^{4}

6.3.8 $I_x = 340.8$ in.^{4}

6.3.10 $I_x = 843$ in.^{4}

6.3.12 $I_x = 330$ in.^{4}

6.3.14 $J = 6a^4$

6.3.16 $I_y = 9.1$ in.^{4}

6.3.18 $I_y = 44.6$ in.^{4}

6.3.20 $I_y = 442$ in.^{4}

6.4.2 $I_{xy} = 162$ in.^{4}

6.4.4 $I_{xy} = 10$ in.^{4}

6.4.6 $I_{xy} = 1152$ in.^{4}

6.4.8 $I_{xy} = 580$ in.^{4}

6.4.10 $I_{xy} = 880$ in.^{4}

6.5.4 a) $\bar{I}_x = \bar{I}_y = 2640$ in.^{4}, $\bar{I}_{xy} = -68$ in.^{4}, b) $\theta_m = 135°, 45°$

6.5.6 a) $\bar{I}_x = 650$ in.^{4}, $\bar{I}_y = 229$ in.^{4}, $\bar{I}_{xy} = -127$ in.^{4},
b) $\theta_m = 15.5°, 105.5°$

6.5.8 $I_{min} = 194$ in.^{4}, $I_{max} = 686$ in.^{4}

6.5.10 $I_{min} = 195$ in.^{4}, $I_{max} = 685$ in.^{4}

6.5.12 $I_u = 117$ in.^{4}, $I_v = 20$ in.^{4}, $I_{uv} = 48$ in.^{4}

6.6.6 $I_O = 1.75$ slug-ft^2

6.6.8 $I_{AA'} = 0.78$ slug-ft^2

6.6.10 $I_{AA'} = 209$ slug-ft^2

6.6.12 $I = 3.38$ slug-ft^2

Chapter 7

7.3.2 $0 < x < 5 : Q = -50$ lb, $M = 50x$ lb-ft
$5 < x < 12.5 : Q = 66.8$ lb, $M = 66.8x - 250$ lb-ft
$12.5 < x < 20 : Q = -33.2$ lb, $M = -33.2x + 666$ lb-ft

7.3.4 $0 < x < 4 : Q = -200$ lb, $M = -200x$ lb-ft
$4 < x < 10 : Q = -200$ lb, $M = -200x + 200$ lb-ft

7.3.6 $0 < x < 6 : Q = 0$, $M = 300$ kip-ft
$6 < x < 14 : Q = 6.25$ kips, $M = 262.5 - 6.25x$ kip-ft
$14 < x < 22 : Q = 6.25$ kips, $M = 6.25x - 137.5$ kip-ft

7.3.14 $0 < x < 3 : Q = -100x$ lb, $M = 50x^2$ lb-ft
$3 < x < 11 : Q = 656 - 100x$ lb,
$M = -50x^2 + 656x - 1968$ lb-ft
$11 < x < 14 : Q = 1500 - 100x$ lb,
$M = -50x^2 + 1500x - 11248$ lb-ft

7.3.16 $0 < x < 10 : Q = 2 - 0.1x$ kips, $M = -0.05x^2 + 2x$ kip-ft
$10 < x < 20 : Q = -0.1x$ kips, $M = -0.05x^2 + 20$ kip-ft

7.3.18 $0 < x < 5 : Q = 0$, $M = -600$ lb-ft
$5 < x < 20: Q = 106 - 40x$ lb,
$M = -20(x - 5)^2 + 306(x - 5) - 600$ lb-ft
$20 < x < 25 : Q = 800 - 40(x - 5)$ lb
$M = -20(x - 5)^2 + 800x - 12000$ lb-ft

7.3.20 $0 < x < 4 : Q = -2000$ lb, $M = -2000x - 2000$ lb-ft
$4 < x < 10 : Q = -100(x - 4) - 2000$ lb
$M = -50(x - 4)^2 - 2000x - 2000$ lb-ft

Chapter 8

8.2.2	$P = 71.6$ lb
8.2.4	$P = 107.5$ lb, $\theta = 45°$
8.2.6	$\mu_o = 0.41$
8.2.8	$\theta = 67.4°$
8.2.10	$\mu_o = 0.268$
8.2.12	$P = 94.3$ lb, $\theta = 45°$
8.2.14	$\mu = 0.445$
8.3.2	$P = 4690$ lb
8.3.4	$P = 61.2$ lb
8.3.6	$P = 310$ lb
8.3.8	$P = 208$ lb
8.3.10	$M_\mu = 32.1$ lb-ft
8.3.12	$M = 13.1$ lb-ft
8.3.14	$W = 5170$ lb
8.4.2	$P = 305$ lb
8.4.4	$M = 237.7$ lb-ft
8.4.6	$T_1 = 230$ lb, $T_2 = 430$ lb
8.4.10	$T_1 = 189$ lb, $T_2 = 389$ lb
8.4.12	$M = 39.6$ lb-ft
8.4.14	$\mu_o = 0.128$
8.5.4	$M = 7.5$ lb-ft
8.5.6	$M = 9.37$ lb-ft
8.5.8	$P = 180$ lb

Chapter 9

9.2.2	$W = \left(\dfrac{\pi}{2}C - w\right)r$ ft-lb
9.2.4	$W = -28$ ft-lb
9.2.6	$W = 120$ ft-lb for both paths
9.2.8	$W = 94.2$ in.-lb
9.2.10	$W = 1600$ ft-lb
9.3.2	$\delta W = -\left(\dfrac{w}{2}L \sin \theta + M\right)\delta\theta$

9.3.4 $\delta W = -(w_1 + w_2)L \sin \theta_1 \, \delta\theta_1 - (w_2 L \sin \theta_2) \, \delta\theta_2$

9.3.6 $P = 26.6$ lb

9.4.2 $Q = 2.5(P \cot \theta)$

9.4.4 $M = 0.39$ P

9.5.2 $V = 34$ ft-lb

9.5.4 $\Delta V = 0.34$ ft-lb

9.5.6 $\Delta V = -166$ in.-lb

9.5.8 $\Delta V = -5.3$ in.-lb

9.6.2 For stable equilibrium, $k > \dfrac{w(a + b)}{b^2}$.

9.6.4 a) $\theta = \tan^{-1}\left(\dfrac{w_1 + w_3}{w_2 - 2w_3}\right)$, b) stable equilibrium

9.6.6 $\theta = 75°$

Photo Credits

Index